Minerals
for the
Genetic
Code

An Exposition and Analysis of the Dr. Olree
Standard Genetic Periodic Chart and the Physical,
Chemical and Biological Connection

Minerals
for the Genetic Code

An Exposition and Analysis of the Dr. Olree
Standard Genetic Periodic Chart and the Physical,
Chemical and Biological Connection

Charles Walters

Acres U.S.A.
Greeley, Colorado

Minerals for the Genetic Code

Acres U.S.A.
P.O. Box 1690
Greeley, Colorado 80632 U.S.A.
1-800-355-5313
info@acresusa.com • www.acresusa.com

Printed in the United States of America

Publisher's Cataloging-in-Publication

Walters, Charles, 1926-2009

Minerals for the Genetic Code / Charles Walters. Greeley, Colorado
    ACRES U.S.A., 2006.
    xxii, 306 pp., 23 cm., charts, tables.
    Includes index.
    ISBN: 978-0-911311-85-3

1. Trace elements. 2. Trace elements in nutrition.
3. Trace elements — therapeutic use. 4. Nutrition; nutritional requirements. I. Walters, Charles, 1926-   II. Olree, Richard. III. Title.

RB113.W35 2006   612/.0152

Dr. Richard Olree, chiropractic physician,
for over 25 years a student of genetics,
author of the Olree Standard Genetic Chart.

Dedicated to the memory of Walter Russell,
physicist, philosopher, interdisciplinary giant,
who first postulated the existence
of 22 subatomic particles.

Contents

Foreword xi

Part 1: The Tyranny of Pharmaceuticals
Chapter 1: Dust Thou Art 1
Chapter 2: Two False Premises 11
Chapter 3: The Deadly Potential. 23
Chapter 4: The Beginning: The Gene. 31
Chapter 5: The GMO Fallacy. 43
Chapter 6: The Trace Mineral 61
Chapter 7: Atomic Suicide. 73

Part 2: The Olree Standard Chart
Understanding the Olree Standard Chart 89
Chapter 8: The Olree Standard Chart. 93
Chapter 9: I Ching 173
Chapter 10: A Pantheon of Minerals 175

Part 3: Sourcing the Elements
Chapter 11: Sourcing the Elements. 185
Chapter 12: The Terminal Word 289

Acknowledgments 295
Index 297

Foreword

The date is late in the 1930s. I was pulled in off the farm and landed in a small Kansas town with a Carnegie library. It was there that I encountered an article by Paul de Kruif entitled "Banting: Who Found Insulin." The story he told in understandable terms took the reader into science, experiments, the sacrifice of test animals, and finally, an answer of sorts to a scourge that heretofore had no answer. It was science-writing so perfect that a whole generation of journalists held it up as a norm to be equaled, if not conquered. Very young people do not ask: Where did it come from, this diabetes? The disease was virtually unknown before it identified itself as a disease of civilization.

A very wise old physician told me — sometime in the middle of World War II — that I should look at fluorine. By then I had become acquainted with the Mendeleyev Periodic Chart of Elements, and I found fluorine soon enough. It held down position #9, thus: "It is one of the groups known as halogens. It trumped chlorine, bromine, and iodine. Iodine is absolutely essential for thyroid function. The thyroid gland produces thyroxin, and thyroxin is absolutely essential if you want to metabolize sugar." The old gentleman gave me a lecture about sucking on soda pop and eating sugar, in words more recalled than recorded. Fluorine damages health. How could that be? Hadn't *Reader's Digest* just published an article styled *The Town Without a Toothache?* The story had it that fluorine in the well water under Deaf Smith County, Texas — the location of the town Hereford — was loaded with fluorine. The conclusion was obvious, according to public relations spin. Fluoride must be added to the nation's drinking water with all deliberate speed.

By the time I started publishing *Acres U.S.A.*, a fair measure of skepticism and research swept away many youthful impressions. The fluoride story became the first continuing report in that youthful publication.

But there are 80 to 92 elements in the Mendeleyev chart. A scant few have been cataloged with the damning finality and the public relations clout and often finality of fluoride as a dental health factor. "All these elements will be essential," seawater specialist Don Jansen told me, "as soon as someone can certify their role and package them for sale." That might be. Henry A. Schroeder, the author of *Trace Elements and Man*, wasn't so sure. He calculated that if the present rate of discovery isn't increased, it will require 400 years to find all the answers.

Happily, Schroeder's projection has come to naught. As the pages of this book will reveal, we now have the answer to all the roles played by trace elements and sub-atomic particles in the construction of amino acids and therefore enzymes.

I started assembling some few entries that I hoped would be a book on trace elements some time ago. The details of my findings have now been published in a book entitled *Fertility from the Ocean Deep*. More recently it came to pass that a doctor of chiropractic healing from Hillman, Michigan gave me the mother lode. We were discussing fluoride, of course.

"Look," said Dr. Richard Olree, "the cells are all protein producers. Trace nutrients govern the kind of protein you will have." Accordingly, Olree set out to discover which individual amino acid was governed by which individual trace mineral. Some 25 years of work has enabled this genetic pioneer to identify all 64 codons and atomic sub-particles as they relate to the Standard Genetic Chart.

"You have to take a close look at the electron valences," Olree said. He explained that the classic example was sodium chloride. Sodium is positive, chloride is negative. The minerals that are not on the standard genetic chart have electron valences that substitute for various minerals via a complicated natural arrangement that so far has baffled the fools and fooled the wise.

According to Olree, the traces are almost always a case of genetic starvation or genetic toxicity. If deficiency labels a mineral or if there is a toxicity of a given mineral, proper genetic expression becomes impossible. The metes and bounds of this concept are so revolutionary, they stand ready to call into question the praises of all coal-tar derivative drugs and AMA medicine as practiced, trace minerals excepted.

Even without full disclosure of the seven-league strides made by physician Olree, the story had advanced to a remarkable degree.

Olree listened patiently to my recitation on fluoride findings. He confirmed the fact that fluorine trumped the iodine, "and you end up making a bunch of stupid people. The thyroid pathways keep your memory working and your brain functioning. When fluorine enters, it shuts down 72 known iodine pathways, and you end up getting hypo-thyroidism and people who can't remember their names. Add teeth-rot to the above," he said.

The anatomy of the fluorine element was well understood long before *The Town Without a Toothache* made headlines. The Nazi concentration camp killers used it to render docile the political prisoners in their camps. That knowledge was quite available to the proprietors of the aluminum and phosphate companies. In the fullness of time, that same knowledge was harnessed to the cash register of the pharmaceutical companies. Thus, Prozac came into being. Prozac is a fluoride-based pill. Its function is mind control. The scope of its mischief has been confirmed by the suicide statistics of users.

Indeed, the idea of medicine based on pharmaceuticals with side effects and reverse effects has been called into question. The generally accepted statistic counts over 150,000 deaths per annum of prescription drug users, the number one cause of preventable death.

In the pages that follow you will meet Dr. Richard Olree, physician, hockey player and referee, bush pilot, wilderness explorer, and pioneer developer of a healing system based on the nutritional demands of the human body. Fluoride was the first great impediment to human health that he encountered.

No controversy in modern life has drawn and thrown as much fire as fluoridation. Indeed, never has a single subject taken on such an air of religious fervor. It was, therefore, not surprising that an unpublished paper on the subject should turn up among the papers of Dr. William A. Albrecht. After *Fluoridation of Public Drinking Water* was circulated to a few friends in mimeo form, Albrecht's attention was drawn to a paper, *New Concepts in Bone Healing,* by Lewis B. Barnett, M.D. *(Journal of Applied Nutrition,* 1954). Dr. Barnett, as a practicing physician in Deaf Smith County, Texas, presented that paper before the Orthopedic Section of the annual meeting of the Texas Medical Association, Dallas, Texas on May 6, 1952.

It was at his suggestion, said Dr. Barnett, "that Dr. Edward Taylor of the Texas State Department of Health and his staff made an extensive survey of dental conditions in that county." The results of that survey were first reported in the *Journal of the American Dental Association* in August 1952. At that time the school children of Deaf Smith County had the lowest rate of dental decay ever reported in a civilized country. Following the report, the U.S. Public Health Service did an extensive survey on water in the high plains area. From their findings, it was deduced that this unusually low rate of tooth decay was due to fluorine in the drinking water. It was considered that the Deaf Smith County area had the optimum fluorine for good dental health. It is on the basis of this study that the American Medical Association, the U.S. Department of Public Health, and other similar groups and agencies approved the fluoridation of all drinking water in the United States. "To some of us it was apparent that factors other than fluorine were, at least partially, responsible for these findings," said Dr. Barnett.

Albrecht's comment was equally to the point. "That such a highly tenuous correlation of fluorine at one part-per-million in the drinking water and the low dental caries per child should be considered cause and prescription of the former for the latter, would certainly be hesitatingly taken as the universal logic among members of a professional society, according to which alone we can be born, or can die, legally. Yet it seems that it is on the basis of such fallacious logic, considering no other factors affecting dental health, that the fluoridation of public drinking waters is premised, and legally enforced."

The profitable truth that the inorganic chemical element, fluorine, in well waters was responsible for good teeth in Deaf Smith County, Texas was embraced by the aluminum and phosphate industries. "For a time, *The Town Without a Toothache* became copybook maxim, but it was a fallacy," said Albrecht. It was not the first time that Albrecht had annihilated a commonly accepted truth. He, of course, had reported to the farm community that limestone to remove soil acidity was simply supposed science, that the real role of this dust on the fields was to nourish crops with calcium and magnesium. Bordeaux mixture as a plant spray was not a poison, really, but copper for the crop so that it could grow its own antibiotic. Blue vitriol for stomach worms in sheep did the same thing. Epsom salts as a purge functioned by exchanging magnesium for calcium in the intestinal wall and bloodstream until the latter was restored to established intestinal conditions.

"We make the mistake in reasoning that the fluorine in the water is the cause of the better teeth, when we should look to the presence of liberal amounts of the calcium-bearing and phosphorus-bearing apatite putting more calcium and more phosphorus in the foods at the same time that by decomposition it is putting fluorine into the water percolating down through the soil."

What Albrecht was saying was transparently obvious. Fluorine was the most soluble of the three elements. It had a single valence, or combining power. It was highly soluble. As a consequence, it departed from the soil's surface easily and percolated into wells and underground water supplies. Calcium represents a double valence, phosphorus a triple valence. As fluorine left the apatite rock, it left behind the calcium and phosphorus to combine with each other to be both more readily available to crop plants than these two essential elements were in the original apatite. By draining away the fluorine, calcium and phosphorus remained to nurture mineral-rich, high-protein crops by which healthier bodies were built (with better teeth as exposed parts of better skeletons). It was the presence of calcium and phosphate in the soil that was the logical reason for good teeth rather than fluorine in the drinking water.

Albrecht's science was brushed aside, just as has been the science of thousands of others in the literature.

One of the finest reports on fluoride I have ever seen was written by John R. Lee, M.D., a California physician.

Lee had joined the fluoride fray because of an upcoming debate in his local medical society. In researching his role, he discovered that both those for and against fluoridation of the water supply used the same technical data, each reading science in a different way. This caught his attention. It did not seem likely that science — the arbiter of such controversies — could not furnish an answer.

Lee found that fluoride was a uniquely potent enzyme poisoner, in fact the most powerful one of all the elements. There are several reasons for this. In the Table of Elements, fluorine shares chemical properties with its close relatives: chlorine, bromine, and iodine.

As ions, reacting with other particles, they all carry one negative charge. As the halogen having the smallest atomic weight, fluorine is naturally the most active. It is extremely active in combining with any element or molecule having a positive valence, such as the mineral ions (enzyme cofactors). It decomposes water to form hydrogen fluoride, which readily attacks glass. It actively replaces its sibling halogen, chlorine, in any solution, including the hydrochloric acid within our stomachs, or any chlorine-containing molecule within our blood or our intracellular fluid.

Fluoride's negative charge and atomic weight of 19 is almost identical to the negative charge and weight of the hydroxyl group (OH) 17.008, which is vitally important to the chemical composition of innumerable substances throughout the human organism. It is, in fact, such interchangeability with the hydroxyl group that is cited as the reason for increased hardness of the apatite crystal of tooth enamel when fluoride is involved.

Unfortunately, and all too obviously, this structural change is not confined to teeth, but occurs elsewhere in the body as well. Fluoride poisons enzymes. The book *Fluorides*, published by the National Academy of Sciences, 1971, lists nine enzymes involved in the breakdown of sugar (glycolysis process) that are fluoride-sensitive. The halogen inhibits many enzymes by tenaciously binding with the metal ions they require in order to function. It inhibits others by a direct poisoning action of their protein content.

But the ultimate shocker is the toxic effect that fluoride has on genes and gene function. Painstaking research at the International Institute for the Study of Human Reproduction, Columbia University College of Physicians and Surgeons, as well as at the University of Missouri, has proved beyond doubt that fluoride is mutagenic, *i.e.,* it damages genes in mammals at doses approximating those we humans receive from artificial fluoridation exposure.

Such a statement ought to clear the air, but this has not happened. In-depth research by Gladys Caldwell, Dean Burk, and John Yiamouyiannis — the last two being Ph.D.s — and George L. Waldbott, M.D., in collaboration with Albert W. Burgstahler, Ph.D., and H. Lewis McKinney, Ph.D., the authors of *Fluoridation: the Great Dilemma*, all support these reports.

In covering the fluoride story, I have tapped many of the 50,000+ articles on the subject that have been parked in the scientific literature. Included was a statement by retired U.S. Army Colonel Lindegren that has ever caused radio and television announcers to chortle. Lindegren told me that in the early 1930s, "Hitler had his scientists hunt out an odorless drug that could be unobtrusively administered to the German people to make them more docile and open to suggestion." Accordingly, chemists at I.G. Farben came up with sodium fluoride. Lindegren said "In the rear occipital of the left lobe of the brain, there is a small area of tissue responsible for the individual's power to resist domination. Repeated doses of infinitesimal amounts of sodium fluoride will in time gradually reduce the individual's power to resist domination by slowly poisoning and narcotizing this area of brain tissue. In large doses, sodium fluoride causes paralysis and death. The drug allows a muscle to move one way, but blocks it from a corresponding reaction or contraction. But when an individual continually receives minute doses of it, the next effect is a marked weakening of the will."

Colonel Lindegren went on to accuse the shadow government of the United States of pushing fluoridation for the same reason Hitler did. I.G. Farben's record was partially revealed at Nuremburg, and its interlock with Standard Oil of New Jersey, David Rockefeller, and Exxon is too well known to merit discussion. More important is the fact that the first U.S. Secretary of Defense, James Forrestal, strongly opposed fluoridation of water supplies on military posts. He died on May 22, 1949, ostensibly of self-defenestration. Many informed observers believed, however, that he was thrown from his hospital-room window. One of them was Wesley C. Trollope, an FBI agent. According to Trollope, Forrestal was very much opposed to the dociling of servicemen. He said reports revealing this effect were available from the House Committee on Un-American Activities, volumes 7 and 9, *Reports of the Special House Committee on Un-American Activities in the Armed Forces, Hearings of the 77th Congress.*

Unfortunately, these proceedings have all but disappeared off the face of the earth. No art of journalism, no Freedom of Information request, and no intervention by Congressman or Senator can free up these hearings, and therefore the cited information becomes available via testimony only. The fluoride story has continued to pile up biographical entries. Dr. Paul Connett of St. Lawrence University, Canton, New York, put the notes that follow in perspective as these pages were finalized. In 2005 the Centers for Disease Control staged a three-day public relations session in Chicago chest-thumping the 60-year record of water supply fluoridation. Connett's offer to the seminar to supply the rest of the story was rejected the way Fido rejects a mock hamburger. Current news has provided the revelation that a Ph.D. thesis at Harvard has indicted fluoridation for its correlation between osteosarcoma in young boys and fluoride in water mains. This study does not stand alone. In the Harvard case, the writer, Elise Bassin, found when the children were exposed during their sixth, seventh, and eighth year, during their mid-growth spurt, they were most vulnerable. Previous studies seemingly overlooked this nuance. Connett reaffirmed the proposition that America is being medicated without a single data base in support of this drastic program, or even a defensible rationale refuting the damning evidence arrayed against it. That evidence added to everything stated above now exhibits some 30 new studies revealing damage to animal brains, Chinese studies indicating a lowering of IQ, studies showing bone damage, and a Loma Linda-inspired Chinese study revealing the dose-related consequence of fluoridation. At 1.5 ppm, hip fractures doubled. At 4-4.3 ppm, hip fractures tripled. "Science is being absconded by the powerful," Connett said. At stake are reputations and bibliographies, not children's teeth or health. Before I close out these few paragraphs, mention must be made of Dr. John Collqhuon of New Zealand. The standard fluoridation issue began to fall apart in 1980. It was then that John Collqhuon, a dental official for Auckland, tripped around the world to study fluoridation. On five continents he found the evidence to support fluoridation was not there. He found the same results in New Zealand. Collqhuon had the courage and decency to reverse the position he had previously accepted.

Over the years I have interviewed most of the great names in the fluoride debate. None laid it on the line like Richard Olree.

"Sodium fluoride! It's basically a poison . . . added to the drinking water during World War II in German concentration camps. They soaked up all the lithium and made all the prisoners more depressed and easy to manage. Yet sodium fluoride is a key ingredient in toothpaste! This has proved lethal in Africa where children often do not have the nutritional support necessary to endure the assault."

The fluoride debate has become so extensive, it has spawned a Fluoride Action Network run by Paul Connett. *Fluoride Action Newsletter* deals with the toxin in all its ramifications. Paul Connett travels widely taking on the water fluoridation challenge, foreign and domestic. The fluoride issue emerged from the underworld of science the day the president of the Canadian Dental Association reversed the society's position, one held during his entire professional lifetime. This was Hardy Limeback, Ph.D., D.D.S., head of the Department of Preventive Dentistry at the University of Toronto and head of the Canadian Association for Dental Research. It turned out that the settled science being invoked was far from settled.

The lore buttressing the accuracy of the Olree Standard Genetic Chart is so extensive it could fill volumes. I will not detain the reader except to note that the Nazi findings have now been turned into a pharmaceutical pill called Prozac. It is fluorine-based, eternally fries the brain, and has been implicated in countless suicides. The Columbine shooters were on a sister antidepressant drug. The suicide rate of such drug users is so high that Great Britain has banned Prozac for anyone under the age of 18.

"Fluoride is used by the body in a desperate attempt to replace iodine if the body is deficient in iodine. As a consequence, thyroid medicine usually has to be doubled in 60 days when a medical physician orders up Prozac," Olree said. "Low levels of perfluorooctanic, a chemical used to make Teflon, poses a potential risk of retarded development and other adverse effects. It's known as PFOA or C-8, and its presence can cause cancer in test animals, but the FDA hasn't nailed down the cancer threat in humans. It shows up in breast milk."

Agronomists will see the disconnect between professed aims and scientific reality. Toronto citizens were told to avoid tap water for infant formulas while on vacation because errant science has been dumping tons of toxins from Tampa Bay, Florida scrubbers into water for fluoridation. Products of the phosphate industry smokestack scrubbers are also rich in fluoride, lead, arsenic, and radium.

Probably the best book ever written on fluoride is titled *The Fluoride Deception,* by Christopher Bryson. Its searing report on neurotoxologist Phyllis Mullenix terrifies those who believe in the integrity of science. Mullenix lost her career when she told Forsyth Dental the politically incorrect, albeit scientifically valid truth, that fluoride is a serious neurotoxin.

We talk of elements as though the cute little boxes in the Mendeleyev Table were collector's items for a glass shelf, not the makings for life and death. I have even heard a type of fast verbalizer saying the names of all the elements non-stop without a pause for a comma. Those elements — trace or sub-atomic particles — are real, and their roles have been smoked out with the zeal of Sherlock Holmes. Go to Chapter 1, page 1. Then walk with me through several chapters that will take you to the most profound overlay of nature's reality since the Russian Mendeleyev constructed the Periodic Table of Elements. It is this insight that has evolved the modeling of the DNA and compilation of the Genome Project. And now the Olree genetic connection paired with the genome codon stands ready to assist the healing arts to free themselves from the tyranny of pharmaceuticals.

Part 1
The Tyranny
of Pharmaceuticals

Dust Thou Art

It has been well over half a century since Dean John B. Saunders of the California School of Medicine made the point that the absence of elements from the diet of a mother during pregnancy was the cause of physical and mental problems in youngsters. He emphasized that almost all of the malfunctions in humankind have indeed been produced in test animals by altering the diet of the mother during gestation to create either a shortage of select nutrients or a marked imbalance. Dean Saunders was early in his profession in nailing the thesis of balanced nutrition to the medical protocol used. His words, pregnant with reason and science, ask to be quoted and memorized. "A diet deficient in folic acid produced virtually all known types of abnormality in the hearts, arteries, and veins of baby rats." He went on to note the near universal failure to appreciate that almost all defects and malfunctions in the young are not the consequence of mutation resulting from damage to the genes as a prime cause, but are due to the disconnect between nature's design of the human form and the nutritional support our agriculture and food processing allows. This deficiency enlarges itself soon enough into endocrine and toxic disorders.

For the better part of a century, millions of dollars have been poured into a hunt for causes of metabolic disorders that probably could not have existed under conditions of good nutrition constructed on the basis of the knowledge centered in the chart that is the backbone for the content of this book.

"This matter of nutritional shortages," notes Richard Olree, "or complete absence of nutrients, and a failure to understand the roles of almost unpronounceable elements, stands between the acceptance of a new concept of the healing arts and a system of coal-tar pharmacology often found wanting."

Dean Saunders called the elements of nutrition "dusts of the soil." They are all a part of the beautiful planet upon which we live. They leave their mark on a human being much as stated in the opinion of ancient churchmen — original sin implanted its permanent moral mark. "This particular original sin," wrote Dean Saunders, "I have chosen to call agronomic original sin to emphasize its origin. It is an agronomic influence to which the mother has been subjected while she bore her child, and which mark the child forever through creation of defective metabolism of certain of its cells."

The influences identified above can also be exercised through the milk the newborn consumes and through the food supply used to nurture the individual through life.

During his life of scholarship, the late William A. Albrecht, Ph.D., constructed two charts. One depicted the composition of soils. The second chart detailed the makeup of the human mammal. These charts can be read only in terms of their complexity. It is this complexity that Richard Olree unravels with discerning finality in the major section of this book. For now it is enough just to hint at the great difficulty of the task.

During the mid-years of the previous century, the U.S. Department of Agriculture fielded a program that hoped to eradicate brucellosis from cattle herds. The announced goal was to make various areas brucellosis free. The common name for brucellosis is Bang's Disease. The official title is infectious *Brucella abortus.* The human variant is called undulant fever.

The physician Ira Allison of Springfield, Missouri, working with Albrecht, followed the nutritional model in conquering the disease. The protocols followed could fill a book the size of this one. Here, we can be content with the results. Allison found that brucellosis was a nutritional disease. It could be fed out of cattle, and its variant out of human beings, with measured supplementation of magnesium, manganese, cobalt, zinc, copper and iodine. Cure by slaughter was proved unnecessary. Albrecht noted, "Brucellosis is about as infectious as the stomachache."

In the trace nutrient's scheme of things, it is immunity that counts. It is axiomatic that you don't build immunity with drugs. You do this only with nutrition and immune cells. Omega fatty acids figure as do trace elements, especially selenium. Nutrients that increase enzymes build immunity. Human beings are resilient. The human body is able to correct malfunctioning genes 90% of the time, usually within 24 hours. Mice, as test animals, are able to correct only 13% of the time. Nature, in short, has given us the key, and that key can be described as elemental nutrition. That is why you will encounter an inventory of plants that order up micronutrients according to genus and species, often without a soil source, possibly as a consequence of biological transmutation, or perhaps out of the ambient air. Richard Olree's match between selenium and the valence of the opposing anion or enzyme makes suggestions that can no longer be ignored.

Take the Russian knotweed, or bindweed, and its DNA blueprint. It contains a substance that protects the plant from insects and disease. That's the short version. The long version follows. It blocks the progression of estrogen-related cancer. It inhibits metastasis, the spreading of cancer to organs. It maintains normal estrogen activity that kills cancer in all three phases: incubation, promotion, progression. It is effective against the Beta protein which causes disease. It increases nitrogen oxide to relieve the blood vessels, canceling out abnormal blood clots. It inhibits COX-2 enzymes. This weed ecology has been designed to work with a perfectly reliable ecology in the human body, and the key to healing and health maintenance is the paired valence: plus 1, 2, 3 and 4 minus 1, 2, 3 and 4. It is a pharmacology based on compliance with nature, not one antagonistic to nature.

The cancer patient who is slipping away is dying of cachexia, malnutritionally wasting away. Cancer lives on glucose. The cell takes glucose via insulin. Cancer cells have up to 15 more receptor sites. Greedy for glucose, they starve the body ergo the patient — all because somewhere in the cell replacement cycle of seven years the system ran out of selenium.

One of the signers of the Declaration of Independence was a physician named Benjamin Rush. It was his opinion and argument that no discipline in the healing arts should be given a dominant role in the new republic. He wanted freedom for medicine just like freedom for religion.

Arbitrarily, one must select the moment in time from which to proceed forward or look back. That moment, for the purposes of the exposition and analysis that follows, came during the last year of World War II. The great discovery of penicillin was released, and sulfa drugs were sidetracked. It all harked back to the debate between Louis

Pasteur and Antoine Beauchamp. It was Pasteur's vision to annihilate the bugs, Beauchamp's to serve the terrain. Beauchamp was plowed under when pasteurization swept the field, and the idea that the terrain governs the body with immunity, fungal and viral attack are still challenged under the auspices of AMA authority. Now, as we enter the 21st century, medicine seems to mean, "read a blood test" and "write a prescription."

Antibiotics seem to mean "a magic bullet," and all the art of healing from Hippocrates forward retreated into archives, esoteric disciplines, and folklore. Botanical knowledge was given second-rate status by peer review journals, with the new way of doctoring conferring on itself the title "conventional."

In effect, conventional medicine told the public . . . we now have a pill to manage your symptoms. Once symptomatology and a prescription became the norm, total management with pharmaceutical remedies was expected. The ancient arts of iridology, acupuncture, reflexology, and the relatively new art of Palmer Chiropractic Treatment came to endure both hostility and attack. The idea that nutrition ultimately governs human health was dismissed as repugnant to the scientific method.

Withal, the lore of pharmacy finally settled on the blood test as the final arbiter in defining kidney failure, prostate debilitation, organ trouble, even the presence or absence of degenerative metabolic diseases. Any reading of the blood test implied the existence of a pharmaceutical drug — usually a free sample — capable of dealing with the problem. Spin, hype, Food and Drug Administration validation, and the concept that M.D. meant superior healing art conspired to close down the insight that a few practitioners such as Dr. Olree espoused. When the American Medical Association became the strongest lobby in the world, near total eclipse of alternative healing seemed imminent.

It was not until the legal case of *Wilk vs. AMA* that the medical monopoly received a telling blow. Wilk was a chiropractor, one of a profession made to endure covert and overt hostility. The case itself was decided in the early 1980s, and a similar case brought against osteopath *Edward O. McDonagh vs. Board of Health*, with John Renner and his Quack Busters supporting the Board. The Board was drummed out of court by the Missouri State Supreme Court.

Pharmaceutical pills as now used in the practice of medicine are basically symptom alleviators. These nostrums may alleviate symptoms, but they do nothing to encourage the immune system to work better.

Geneticist Richard Olree puts it this way: "When we have various mineral deficiencies coupled with environmental toxicities, the DNA being in control of homeostasis of the cell, if one pathway doesn't work, then the human system is required to try another way."

One can imagine the level of turmoil when 71 pathways are closed down, as with fluorine's annihilation of that many enzymes. Each failure calls on a different set of amino acids and minerals to substitute. The substitute pathway required can well be multiplied 700- or 1,000-fold compared to the unimpeded natural way.

Prednisone, a commonly used drug in cases of irritable bowel syndrome, or Crohn's disease, annihilates no less than 200 amino connectors. The consequences of such great deviation from the natural design of the human system is the well-known "side effect." In some cases, the effect is "reversed," meaning that the drug does exactly the opposite of what it is supposed to do.

This observation brings into focus a phenomenon of our times: GMOs, or genetically modified organisms. Taking a pharmaceutical pill is like trying to live off GMO wheat or corn or soybeans or rice. Implied in the very process is an attempt to modify how genes function without all the necessary raw materials to make it work. But genetics cannot be altered that way with impunity, not with GMO food or malignant nutrition.

The problems with pharmaceutical medicines are legion. The *Physicians' Desk Reference* nails down these problems, usually in more than one page of small type. Few physicians read this disclaiming material, and fewer still remember the chemistry course work they took in medical school. Very few doctors know whether a pill is sulfur-based pill or fluorine-based. Dialysis patients are now given a lanthanum carbonate pill. On the chart in Part 2 of this volume, lanthanum is #63 (page 95).

Lanthanum has a profound effect on the human body when used in trivial amounts. It has the capacity to grab creatine and move it across the filter in dialysis cases. This is an example of a mineral now being used. Richard Olree, however, postulates that lanthanum is simply necessary for human functioning. The point here is that transport of the idea depends on the pharmaceutical salesman, not the professional training of the doctor.

Without a handle on minerals, the modern medical practitioner is relegated to an ever-contracting chamber not greatly unlike the dungeons that once housed intellectual thought in darker ages.

When Richard Olree lays out his charts of minerals, much like a deck of cards, he challenges the countervailing that should, but doesn't, rely on the mineral in question. "Someone with a known thyroid condition, someone who takes some type of thyroid supplementation, perhaps a drug like thyroxin, often goes on a fluorine-based pill like Prozac. Within a very short period of time, they have to double their thyroid medicine to compensate for fluorine toxicity."

Toxicity asks the kidneys or liver to get rid of it. That is why drugs of several stripes make whoopee with broad sugar levels and otherwise cause so much ink to be expended explaining side effects. As a matter of fact, the human condition cannot handle any of the pharmaceutical drugs except on a short-term basis. As with the LD_{50} test for toxicity, certain levels can enable one to make it to the door, albeit not without consequences. Richard Olree compares drug medicine to farming with imbalanced salt fertilizers and toxic rescue chemistry. In farming, as in human medicine, rescue chemistry appears to have gone out of control.

The real dimensions of the mischief involved can't be explained by those 150,000+ deaths of prescription victims. There are the on-going sufferers.

Prednisone has been implicated in altering over 200 genes. This means that it interferes with over 200 pathways. "I had the terrible misfortune of having a woman patient completely overmedicated with prednisone so she could keep on breathing with some comfort ... at the expense of her bone structure. In the course of four years, she came to a point where she had no bone structure visible on her X-ray. She had become a bundle of flesh with little or no bone structure. She died within 30 days. I don't know how she would be accounted for in the statistics," Richard Olree said.

The case reports stack up like cordwood. "An 82-year-old woman was presented with a backache, muscle aches, and extreme fatigue. X-rays were taken which exhibited only a trace of a skeletal system. Examination also revealed multiple fractures on every film. A history of five years of prednisone had been administered for the purpose of treating a lung inflammation symptom. Neither the family nor the patient was aware of what cortico-steroids would do. After her dilemma was pointed out to her, she returned to her physician and steroid treatment, and died quite early."

This failure to produce new bone under steroid therapy helps fill out that 150,000+ inventory of deceased mentioned earlier. A word of caution must attend revelation of the above.

Drugs have demerits, but sudden withdrawal can be worse. Each case demands its own analysis, and certainly exhibits its own prognosis. That is not the issue. The point here is that the state of the scientific art is such that a new paradigm in healing is called for.

On some future day, we will be called upon to wonder aloud about some of the contaminants Food and Drug allows in the foodweb. Processed foods containing aspartame come to mind. Richard Olree helps us with this assignment, as well. "I had a lady patient who drank diet pop with aspartame for years. She also chewed aspartame gum constantly. She had a condition the medical doctors call vasculitis. This was brought under control with steroids. She was given steroids by the MDs while she was in a coma, as a result of aspartame toxicity, over 61 days. A year later, she was still taking the steroids. She went from being anorectic to being morbidly obese, with no end in sight as far as steroid therapy was concerned. The first order of business had to be detoxification from the aspartame. In short, she had to have multiple vitamins and minerals to overcome the aspartame disease. So far, the medical doctors have elected to keep this person on prednisone. The drug is no longer necessary because detoxification from aspartame has proved successful, but the mystique of pharmaceutical medicine holds strong because no suitable alternative has proved runaway saleable. So far, the AMA does not relate to aspartame disease."

According to Olree, the AMA has missed the train on probiotics. It is well and good to use antibiotics to kill offending organisms, but treatment also calls for probiotics to repopulate organisms that are vital. Failure of intestinal repopulation can be said to author nutritional deficiencies. For instance, there is a pill called Flagyl. It is very powerful. It is designed to kill single-cell amoebas among other things. "I have seen a case in which one female patient took one Flagyl pill. She promptly went into anorexia and depression. She failed out of college, moved back home, and found not one medical doctor who could help her," Olree recalled. "Yet nothing but probiotics was required to treat this patient. It took only one Flagyl pill to ruin six months of this woman's life."

The father of medicine, Hippocrates, said it all and he said it well, "Let food be your medicine."

Food implies digestion. If digestion is not successful, then fermentation takes over. Fermentation liberates gases, hydrogen sulfide, methane and carbon dioxide. The type of gas depends on acidity and type of organisms. To say probiotics will shift the balance of microorganisms in the digestive tract is to leave unanswered the central question of the findings published herein. That answer may or may not be serendipitous.

"I was on a quest to try to find out what was causing multiple sclerosis. I spent two years thinking about why yttrium was being used in the human genetic makeup, yet not found in the body. I finally arrived at the answer in the intestinal tract. Yttrium is so rare that not one person in 1,000 seems to have heard of it. It appears near the bottom of a list of ocean minerals, and is found only rarely in mines or plants. Yet some plants pick it up even though this rare earth is usually absent in soils. Whether or not plants inhale it from particulate matter in the air is open to question," summed up Richard Olree.

Yttrium will be discussed in detail at position 55 of Richard Olree's Standard Genetic Chart. Olree's discovery was anticipated by Chaim T. Horovitz, who came to the rescue with a publication so costly it might well be weighed out on a jeweler's scale. Entitled *Biochemistry of Scandium and Yttrium*, it trailed yttrium to the intestinal tract. Richard Olree picked up fast. Could it be that certain bacteria in the intestinal tract were dependent on yttrium, yet sensitive to aluminum toxicity? The pharmaceutical industry, of course, uses aluminum almost as a mainstay in most of its pills. The syllogism started building. The suppression of yttrium and boron through the administration and utilization of aluminum could trigger the suppression of probiotic microorganisms. Of all the bacteria that have been genetically sequenced, only two of the 12 decoded are dependent on yttrium. The natural balance required makes the aluminum assault look like a Mongol horde overtaking Vienna. Cancellation of the right bacteria, often with pharmaceutical drugs, often with elements hostile to yttrium's role, no doubt accounts for nutritional deficiency. The bacteria answering roll call are the *Bifidobacterium bifidus* and *Bifidobacterium longum* bacterium species. A lot of other bacteria will use aluminum in their makeup and as part of their food supply, even when such utilization is anathema to the *Bifidobacterium*.

The assault on human health is not complete with fluorine in the water supply or aluminum in the pharmaceuticals. Many municipalities also put aluminum into their water supplies, basically to clear up water turbidity with often leaving 400-600 ppm dissolved solids. The result has been dialysis deaths, a consequence of aluminum passing through the filter directly into the bloodstream.

The turnover of cells in the human body takes up to seven years. Exposure to radiation, ionized farm chemicals, starvation or toxic irritation — and a thousand other sins of chemistry and pollution, all can so deplete nutrients that the body ignites cancer. There are exposures that can eat up all the selenium, a nutrient that wards off cancer and builds amino acids which allows the body to make 20 million new cells a day, always replacing 20 million dying cells. Each cell has to copy the one being replaced. Failing this, the new cell is mutant, one capable of taking on a life of its own.

The kind of cell and its health determines the kind of its copy. The mechanism that screens for DNA damage and cell replication is called a tumor-suppressing gene. These genes are operated by the mineral element selenium. The careless eater on a deficient diet, the auto mechanic who washes his hands in gasoline, the farmer who rescues different crops with chemistry or battles weeds with herbicides, might not be rescued from cancer when selenium runs out. Toluene or benzene pollution might not bring a cancer to fruition for, say, five years after incubation. Just the same, every form of cancer is a child of selenium deficiency.

Obviously, coal-tar derivative drugs cannot rescue the pharmaceutical medicine now current coin. Knowledge of the Mendeleyev Table of Elements seems of academic interest only when related to health without reference to genetic pathways, amino acids, and/or enzymes.

Aspartame is now being replaced with Splenda. Splenda, however, is just as bad as aspartame due to its chlorine content, Olree holds. This halogen cripples the thymus gland. "When a white blood cell is born," explains Richard Olree, "it really doesn't know what to do. It needs programming. It has to go to the thymus gland to get its marching orders. Splenda shrinks the thymus gland between 30 and 50%. It knocks out the ability to tell your white blood cells what to do."

Withal, this business of breaking down the entire genome into minerals revealed that lanthanum is the most called-for element by DNA. Lanthanum, yttrium, a roll call of minerals and their reason for being, suggests that the Olree Chart not only pushes the envelope, it stands ready to remake the healing art. Thus lanthanum and the other traces must wait their turn pending expectation of the Olree Chart in Part 2.

Students and members of the healing arts professions will not have to await validation by peer review boards or government sanctification in order to use the knowledge so far assembled. The Internet site *www.pubmed.com* is a veritable medical Library of Congress. It has assembled all the medical knowledge used to produce the Olree key to what Dean Saunders was talking about over a half century ago.

The site *www.eurekalert.org* serves up the latest information released by medical literature worldwide. Even newspaper articles are capsulated by EurekAlert. Any publication proffering a clue sends Olree back to the drawing board to find the protein sequence that goes with the mineral that makes it tick.

The Olree genetic overlay to the table of elements is based on valence: salt (sodium chloride), positive 1; chloride, negative 1. Fluorine is a negative 1, as is the case with sister halogens: iodine and bromine. Any person without proper iodine levels invites fluorine going in and mimicking iodine. The body then attempts to utilize the fluorine as though it was iodine, always unsuccessfully. In the process, it shuts down all the clinical pathways to the thyroid. Fully 71 pathways, meaning enzymes, thus become annihilated. Enzyme construction and thyroxin utilization become the observed and measured results. Fluorine also has the capacity to bind up lithium in the brain.

The poisonous character of sodium fluoride is now recognized.

A summary note on cancer is now in order. After all, the disease is said to claim one out of three Americans, and the remedy seems elusive since more people make a living from cancer than those who die from it.

As we invoke a totally new concept, we are required to pause and reflect on the proposition that much of science seems to have rejected the scientific system. When scientists reject the laws of science, only two paths remain operative, medical tyranny and chaos. I leave it to the reader to decide which one now prevails.

Two False Premises

In order to understand the healing powers of the elements, one must learn the how and why behind our nutrient-void food supply. And to understand bad food, you must first look at bad farming practices.

The ancients saw planet Earth as an organism that operated on the basis of soil, air, fire and water. It was a concept that delivered comfort to the likes of the scholars who taught Socrates, Plato and Aristotle. But it was so basic, perhaps so simple, it couldn't stand for long, could it? But it did.

Even so, the ancients discerned that everything that eats must be eaten. Also, nature was fecund, and nature ultimately wanted balance. Circling the crystal clear Canadian lake on the shores of which Richard Olree has the lone cabin, this Michigan physician came to examine the causes for debilitating disease conditions some 30 years ago. The path he followed had to start with the ancients who postulated the atom, then wondered their way through the knowledge of what makes plants grow, what indeed enabled human beings, then identification of the plants.

Even the ancient Greeks knew that plants relied on soil nutrients, but they did not know how chemicals of the air contributed to plant bulk and food production.

Jan Baptista van Helmont, a 17th-century Flemish physician, conducted an experiment that once and for all kicked open the door to the beginning, if not the end, to understanding. He simply wanted to know how soil matter was displaced with plant life. No one could measure such a proposition in the field or forest. So van Helmont planted a little willow tree in an earthen tub. The sprig weighed only five pounds. Soil used for the experiment scaled in at 200 pounds. The tub was covered except for the plant stem and a watering hole.

Five years later the 'tree' weighed 164 pounds. The scientist figured that if the tree picked up that much matter, then the soil remaining in the tub should weigh only 41 pounds when dry. It often takes a very intelligent person to be hopelessly and articulately wrong. In fact, the soil lost only two ounces after five years of tree production. Van Helmont must have pondered the problem in deep consternation. Could all this growth have been produced by the water furnished the plant? Obviously, this was the answer.

"Not so," said a fellow scientist named Nehemiah Grew. He had used the recently developed microscope to study the pores of a plant. These tiny pores look much like the pores of a human being or an animal, used for elimination of perspiration. Grew took a second look. The pores were for the admission of air. Van Helmont had completely overlooked air. The willow tree had been out in the air all the time. Even so, he didn't pause to consider that air contained dust particles, debris from volcanoes, and pollution from forest fires and chimneys. Now van Helmont used the word "obviously" for the first time. It was one thing to postulate how nature worked, another to test it out. How, indeed, could one figure whether air contributed to the growth of a plant?

An English scientist and preacher reasoned it out when he constructed his famous peppermint plant experiment. The proposition was hellishly simple. Stephen Hale potted a peppermint plant, and then clamped a glass over the plant to shut off outside air. Water surrounded the plant. If the plant used air, he figured, water in the glass would rise or fall. He knew about atmospheric pressure, and he handled that variable. A control had 20 peppermint plants. Atmospheric pressure would treat each vessel alike. If a difference developed, well, that would be sound scientific evidence that the plant had interacted with the air. Hale watched and waited. One day the plant took on a wilt. He replaced this plant, taking care to preserve the old air in the vessel. In five days the new plant faded away. Apparently plants were taking something out of the air. Was it food? Of course it was. Once the food had been exhausted by the first plant, the second one couldn't live.

Hale concluded that his mint plants were constantly changing the air. He died without learning the answer.

The idea of creating a closed chamber under glass stayed on, however. Joseph Priestley later evaluated the properties of air by following in Hale's footsteps. Priestley used trapped bodies of air to test a theory, to measure the life expectancy of a mouse in the absence of exchangeable air. After continuing his experiments for some time, Priestley announced a serendipitous discovery. "I flatter myself that I have accidentally hit on a process of restoring the air injured by the breathing of a mouse," he wrote, "and I have discovered at least one of the elements which nature employs for its purpose."

Now came a rush of insight. Even a mouse consumes a gallon of oxygen a minute. The cow needs 25 gallons of the precious stuff a minute. People used oxygen with reckless abandon long before the automobile gulped the element and the industrial age made whoopee with the supply.

Something was renewing the air, and Priestley furnished some parts of the answer. The recorded date for the discovery was August 17, 1771. The miracle of plants inhaling carbon dioxide and giving off oxygen is so fundamental that we wonder aloud how such complete simplicity could stand as a turning point in science. The Mendeleyev Table of Elements wouldn't be published for another 100 years.

In the meantime, there was an even more profound discovery by a Hollander who stood on the shoulders of Priestley. Jan Ingenhousz brought light into the equation: plants kept in the dark wouldn't purify the air. Only leaves with green webbing seemed capable of doing the job. It all seemed to get more complicated as man's puny mind expanded itself.

First air, now green webbing-matter seemed to walk hand-in-hand with that purification task. At each step along the way, there arose an investigator with a vision, perhaps a dream. It came to the suddenly enlarged world of science that plants, quite unlike animals, actually manufactured food. If its manufacturing chore was accomplished only in light, then photo, meaning light, synthesized the process. Photosynthesis described "what," not "how!"

The food produced can be called glucose. Glucose has six atoms of carbon, 12 atoms of hydrogen, and six atoms of oxygen: $C_6H_{12}O_6$. Did the oxygen released come from the water or the carbon dioxide? The debate raged for years before the answer was found out. A great deal had to be learned about chemistry and the chemistry of life, about organic and inorganic chemistry.

Dmitri Mendeleyev, a Russian chemist, first constructed his Table of Elements a little before the beginning of the last century. His insight into nature's order was so great it prompted him to supply spaces where he believed elements should be located as soon as discovered. That table still stands, and all of the blank spots have been filled in. As a consequence, we have a simple and beautiful picture of the order of the universe in which we live. It has opened physics and chemistry, and finally human health as never before, and made it possible for lesser minds to understand the structure of the atom, the DNA, the genome, and the unequivocal answers to both human health and degrading degenerative diseases.

The inventory of information contained in that table and the extrapolation based on the great leap forward called the Genome Project has now enabled the construction of the Olree Standard Genetic Table with a common denominator: the elements.

The Table of Elements starts with hydrogen:

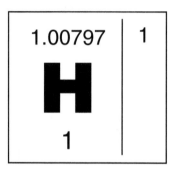

It is the lightest element. The big H is the elemental, or chemical, symbol. The bottom 1 is the atomic number. The small 1 on the right side of the vertical bar is the number of electrons in each shell. The number 1.00797 designates the atomic weight, or mass number, of the element.

As he made his rounds in northern Michigan, Olree took note of the ferns and their growth, and he saw nature in revolt.

Soil scientists knew about NPK before the 1940s, and they knew a great deal more by the 1950s when oil company technology conquered all: USDA, the colleges, the Extension workers, and farmers. How and why advanced science lost its way in favor of a primitive form of soil chemistry would remain a popular mystery, except for one development . . .

At the end of World War II, the center of gravity for the world oil industry was the Gulf of Mexico. This meant a Texas price, or in the $2.75 per barrel range. But the oil conglomerates found that oil cost no more than 4.6 cents a barrel loaded into a tanker at Ras Tanura. This proved to be more profitable than hauling slaves out of Africa and selling them in the New World at so-and-so much a pound. By the end of the 1940s, seven companies had gained a stranglehold on world oil distribution. Standard of New Jersey, Royal Dutch Shell, Gulf, Texaco, Standard Oil of California, Socony Mobil, and Anglo-Iranian (now British Petroleum) had 90% of the world markets by 1955. During this period, these companies became more powerful than most nations. They were capable of waging wars.

The public — least of all the farmers — didn't understand just what went on after World War II. They believed that there was a communist under every rock, and that there would be a post-war depression. Completely overlooked was the fact that international business was doing just what was feared of the Russians, but in a different way. Washington couldn't understand why the depression didn't develop because the politicians didn't understand what raw materials parity had to do with national stability. They still don't. Nor did Truman and Eisenhower comprehend either the thesis or the proof. Both were satisfied that economic recession could be avoided only through international trade. They ran low tariffs up the flagpole. That didn't sell because of farm price stabilization measures left over from World War II. So the great leaders went the foreign aid route to sustain exports. This was sold to the farm states because farmers, more than most, fell for the commie-under-every-stone gag. Everything was rationalized on grounds other than the ones actually figuring in the minds of the cartel managers. That's what empty-the-countryside was all about. That's what taking agriculture the fossil-fuel route was all about. Long accustomed to buying politicians like bags of popcorn, the cartel managers proceeded to buy up education. The grants — that is to say, the acceptable bribes — were so subtle even the recipients didn't understand how money influenced both the findings of science and criticism thereof. Departments in the universities needed money. It was kept coming only when results were suitable and usable. Unsuitable results didn't even rate publication. Obstinate professors were simply drummed from the corps. In order to synthesize honesty, the common denominator of the academic community became "simplify." Nothing could be simpler than magic fertilizer called nitrogen, phosphorus, and potassium (NPK). Nothing could be more easily sold than university-blessed fossil-fuel technology as long as farmers believed in the professors.

As noted earlier, the simplicity required by NPK sales manuals didn't change biology. Plants still required carbon, hydrogen, and oxygen, and these were still available as carbon dioxide and water — from the air and from soil solutions. Plants still required the positively charged (cation) elements — calcium, magnesium, potassium, manganese, iron, zinc, copper, boron and more — available only from the soil, not hydroponic tanks. Plants still required the negatively charged (anion) elements — nitrogen, phosphorus, sulfur, chloride, and so on. College people taking two anions and one cation by the nape of the neck and the seat of the pants and creating catchphrase NPK didn't exactly change biology. It just made it sound simple, and provided a sort of do-it-yourself brain surgery for the farmer and the oil company salesman. How plants are nourished and how they grow is not a complete story, even now. The story had, however, left its primer stage long before NPK laws made their grand sweep. Swept aside was a term that needs attention again: the living soil! "The term 'the living soil' is an age-old expression, but just what that connotes in the minds of different soil scientists or in our own thinking we are not sure." Yet the great scientists were sure of a few observations even children could understand. Plants are not mobile, and they do not have a stomach. "So you see the soil has to provide the anchor and the digestive apparatus for the entire crop, and the nutrition as well."

In front of the classroom, or behind their desks after they had been retired "because these professors wouldn't go along," one schoolman said, they made the living soil come alive. The soil system is the stomach. Into it are fed nutrients — whether as canal mud or manure or factory fertilizers — and these must be digested and made ready for plant use. It is the conceptualization of laboratory scientists that these nutrients become ions, cations if they are charged positively, and anions if they are negatively charged acid elements. They enter plant roots the way electricity flows, so to speak, in chemical equivalents. This has been compared to the action one gets when positive and negative poles of a battery are connected. Interactions of cations and anions dovetail with the sun's energy, carbon, hydrogen and oxygen to sustain plant life.

The first order of business for the soil colloid, then, is to hold nutrients that can be traded off as the roots of the plant demand them.

The soil laboratory measures the holding energy in the clay and the humus.

Almost all laboratories report this energy as cation exchange capacity (CEC), and they do this in terms of milliequivalents (ME). Some few farmers like to think of all this the way an electrician thinks of his payload, in terms of volts and amperes. The only difference is that the soil laboratory measures colloidal energy in terms of milliequivalents of a total exchange capacity, since soil colloids — composed of clay and humus — are negatively charged particles. They attract cations. Because anions are not attracted by negative soil colloids, they remain free to move in the soil solution or water.

A milliequivalent is the exchange capacity of 100 grams of oven-dry soil involved with 1/1,000 of a gram of hydrogen (hence, the prefix: *milli*). Each cation element has its own weight. Calcium carries 20 on the Mendeleyev Periodic Chart of the Elements. Potassium is 39. Magnesium is 12.

Fossil fuel fertilizer folk knew all this even before NPK fertilizers were turned into foo-foo dust, good for what ails a soil system regardless of low or high analysis. In fact, the old National Plant Food Institute (now The Fertilizer Institute) circulated a rather sound presentation styled *The Living Soil*. In it was revealed the intelligence that "milliequivalents can be converted to pounds per acre if you know the equivalent weight of the element involved. Multiply the equivalent weight by 20 (the computed factor) to get pounds per acre for one milliequivalent per 100 grams of soil." The atomic weight of calcium is 20: therefore, 20 x 20 = 400, or 400 pounds of calcium per acre. Cation exchange capacity of a soil depends on the type of clay and the amount of humus. This can vary widely. There are CEC figures as low as 1 and as high as 80. The clays themselves vary — kaolinite in the South often measuring 10 to 20, montmorillonite in the West measuring 40 to 80. CEC values for organic matter are higher yet — 100 to 200 ME being common. Obviously, pure sand or gravel would have a CEC of near zero. But the moment sand or gravel starts accumulating colloidal clay and humus, its CEC can go up dramatically.

Eco-farmers have long recognized that what you do to a soil system depends on the condition of that soil system in the first place. To treat a 6 ME soil the same as a 20 ME soil amounts to the same thing as powering a go-cart with an airplane engine.

Since it would take 400 pounds of calcium to fully load the top 7 inches of an acre of 1 ME soil, it would take 4,000 pounds per acre for a 10 ME tested soil. Needless to say, no farmer would want to go whole hog on one nutrient and neglect the rest. Such an outlook would come terribly close to adopting a simplistic NPK mentality.

The function of the soil audit, then, is to measure the cation exchange capacity and to determine the nutrient status a crop might rely on. Positively charged elements, of course, are potassium, magnesium, zinc, copper, sodium, etc.

An audit of the colloid's capacity for holding nutrients tells only about the inventory, not the objective. There are differing theories, and sub-schools of thought within each theory-group, on what target-figures ought to be. All except the oblivious know that only humus can be added to a soil system without some knowledge of the balance. Among eco-farmers, the Albrecht formula is both gaining strength and rolling up millions of acres of proof as a result. It works.

A few years before Professor Albrecht passed away, I taped an interview that, in effect, summarized the hundreds of scientific articles his career had accounted for. "On the basis of your research, should fertilizers be soluble?" became the routine opener. "No," said Albrecht. "Fertilizers are made soluble, but it's a damn fool idea. They should be insoluble but available. Most of our botany is solution botany. When we farm as solution botany, the first rain takes out the nutrients. There's a big difference between the laboratory and the farm."

Albrecht, in fact, worked out his "vision" in the laboratory. Because of an innate interest in medicine, he figured there had to be an optimum fertility load for soil systems just as there had to be health-giving nutrition levels for human beings. Later, this vision and the proof thereof were to find expression in an article "The Healthy Hunzas: A Climax Crop." Dr. Allen E. Banik of Kearney, Nebraska had just returned from Hunzaland, and Albrecht received from his report an understanding of why the people of Hunzaland lived so long. They managed their soils "for nearly complete conservation of them." They applied "silt-size or powdered natural rock particles in the glacial milk which they used as irrigation water," and they regularly applied organic composted materials which those same soils had grown. Glacial silt had been balanced by nature. Concluded Albrecht, "The Hunzas have been practicing soil chemistry *au natural* rather than *au science*."

The procedure for finding proof suggested itself. Since the soil colloid was the holder of cation nutrients, Albrecht prepared an experiment. He separated the finest part of the clay out of the soil by running it in a centrifuge at 32,000 rpm. The process produced thinner and thinner, smaller and smaller, clay particles. Halfway up the centrifuge sleeve the clay was as clear as Vaseline. Albrecht and his graduate students made tubs of the stuff. They put the material into an electrical field and made it acidic. They took all the cations (positively charged particles) off so that it was acid clay. This way, the researchers could titrate back given nutrients, mix them, and balance them.

Albrecht found that for best crop production, the soil colloid had to be loaded with 65% calcium, only 15% magnesium, and that the potassium cation must be in the 2-4% range. Other base elements needed to be near 5%. These, Albrecht held, were the percentage figures when nature functioned at her finest balance and was capable of producing healthy crops.

Albrecht's career became one of proving out ecological agriculture, and demonstrating how declining fertility levels brought on insect attacks for the crops and ill health for animal and man consuming them. He was well aware that even with growth stimulants and super-mining techniques, the economist's curve showed production in the U.S. had topped out, and was on a downhill slide. Ever-increasing use of NPK and toxic chemistry was being accompanied by diminished returns, with quality at the vanishing point.

One of Albrecht's great friends was E.R. Kuck of Brookside Dairy Farms in New Knoxville, Ohio. In fact, it was a case of animals telling Kuck about vanished nutrition that launched Brookside Laboratories in the first place. After plastering the walls of a new calf barn, Kuck noticed that the animals literally ate the plaster off the walls of their stalls. Calves were scouring, or experiencing rampant diarrhea, at the time.

Almost immediately, scouring stopped, and Kuck — consulting with Albrecht — determined that the hungry animals were, in fact, after the calcium carbonate and the magnesium carbonate in the plaster material. These nutrients had been mined out of the soil of the dairy operation and never replaced.

The sheer desperation of those animals emerged time and again in Albrecht's writings. "Our dietary essential minerals are taken as organo-inorganic compounds. We are not mineral eaters. Neither are the animals. When any of them take to the mineral box, isn't it an act of desperation?" Albrecht came right to the point: "Cows eat soil or chew bones when ill with acetonemia, pregnancy troubles, or deficiency ailments. Hogs root only in the immediate post-winter period after confinement to our provision for them, and their behavior suggests past deficiencies to be quickly remedied in desperate diggings of the earth."

Other observations came to the fore at Brookside Laboratories. Soil and leaf tests revealed a wide variance in crops produced on "treated vs. untreated" acres. In December, 1946, Kuck issued a report *Better Crops with Plant Food* published by The American Potash Institute (now the Potash and Phosphate Institute). This article was picked up by the farm press and given wide distribution. Feedback arrived almost immediately — 1,000+ letters from farmers telling of their own problems and asking for help. There were also 16 letters from academic folk condemning Kuck in vitriolic terms and denouncing the significance of magnesium in animal nutrition. Moreover, the college people seemed to think that no farmer had the right to make such observations and tell it the way it was without the imprimatur of credentialed people. Remember this: you'll read much of magnesium later in this book.

This was monastic scholasticism speaking. E.R. Kuck, in fact, was a qualified researcher. In 1937, with Professor Oscar Erf — then in the Animal Husbandry Department at Ohio State University — he designed a farm research program for the study of dairy animal disorders such as mastitis, bloat, milk fever, acetonemia, shy breeding, and white scours in newborn calves. George T. Christopher, the retired president and general manager of Packard Motor Car Company, put the rhubarb in focus. "It seems that Mr. Kuck, through the publication of his article, has somehow defiled the Holy of Holies so firmly established in some of our institutions of higher learning, and that while these academic powers are strong in conviction, they have failed to provide adequate services for farmers to help them solve the more important health problems on their farms."

That health problems started with the soil had long been an Albrecht contention. And now, with strong allies, Albrecht was able to balance soil on both the test plot and the farm.

On Albrecht's own farm, the exchangeable cations were tabulated ever so carefully. Once the CEC had been determined, the scientist developed desired values, added or subtracted values found, and prescribed the proper treatment: calcium, magnesium, potassium. The anion nutrient values were also determined and repaired.

Albrecht could grow healthy, clean rows and infected rows, depending on how he altered soil fertility. Balance was the one thing a farmer couldn't overdo, Albrecht observed.

Somehow, folklore became law in federal cost-sharing programs. The bureau people were always trying to erase soil acidity with liming programs, not because they understood balance, but because they loved simple answers for complex problems.

"At this moment the evolution of the technique of soil testing has not progressed far beyond what is apt to be mainly laboratory gadgetry," Albrecht told a Senate committee in 1954. Therefore, "I doubt the wisdom of a mandatory regulation on the national level for any soil treatments with applied materials, whether limestone, rock phosphate, soluble fertilizer, etc."

The farm community at large tested for soil acidity, Albrecht told the Senators, reporting results in terms of pH. This was unfortunate because pH mattered all too little when nutrient balance was correct.

Acidity is a natural condition when soil systems have enough rainfall to grow a great deal of vegetation. "They are naturally low in fertility, especially in the subsoil," when they grow mainly carbonaceous vegetation. This means that soil acidity is really a symptom of fertility deficits touching many plant nutrients. Lime and more lime cannot repair the situation. Yet the pH myth hangs on.

The pH of soil is affected and influenced by four elements: calcium, magnesium, potash, and sodium. How each figures in a soil balance must be known before either a lime or fertilization program can be designed. Pound for pound, magnesium can raise pH 1.4 times more than calcium. C.J. Fenzau, an agricultural consultant, once printed a directive that ought to be laminated and nailed to the wall of every fertilizer company in the country.

• A balanced equilibrium of calcium and magnesium creates a soil environment for bacteria and fungus activity, accounting for proper decay of organic matter into CO_2, carbonic acid, and a host of many weak and mild organic acids, all so necessary for conversion and release of mineral elements in a soil system.

• An imbalanced equilibrium of calcium and magnesium permits organic residues to decay into alcohol, a sterilant to bacteria, and into formaldehyde, a preservative of cell tissue. The symptoms of improper decay systems can be observed when previous year's stalks are plowed back up just as shiny and fresh as when they were turned down.

• Under these circumstances, larger and increasing amounts of nitrogen and fertilizer minerals will be required just to maintain normal crop yields.

• Large applications of nitrogen consume larger amounts of calcium. These applications also "burn up" crop residues and humus. Natural nitrogen fixation by bacteria on the roots of legumes, alders, Casurina trees, Elaeagnus, etc., avoids this burn-out. Farmers can get increased yields with heavy nitrogen applications for a few years because of stored-up humus, but this system wastes away the humus supply and the continued productivity of the soil. Humus is a primary carbon sink!

• Without an active organic-matter system in the soil, it is not possible to grow crops successfully, no matter how much N, P, and K is used. The soil is a living complex system that not only holds necessary minerals needed for plant life, but also is the factory that produces carbon dioxide, digests lignin into humus, provides nutrition and energy for desirable bacterial and soil-animal life, and is the container for air and water.

Albrecht was not able to convince much of the agricultural machine that eco-farming was "the" highest science, hence, his forced retirement. He spoke bitterly of the turn of events: Why were states attempting to legislate biology? Might they not just as well tell the morning fog to disappear by 10 a.m.?

". . . because what I say doesn't amount to anything in the eyes of these people," he said. "They've bought a conventional truth because there is profit in it for a few big firms." Money, in short, had come between the scientist's findings and criticism thereof. Against this giant, that handful of Cassandras was as a blade of grass in a tornado.

The tornado gobbled everything in sight. Laws, journalistic clout, and an atmosphere of intimidation in the colleges made rated NPK fertilization holy writ. Blessed by a scientific priesthood, it was swallowed hook, line, and sinker by farmers, to the delight of petro-chemical shills. Oil-company technology, after all, was an insurance policy for use of oil-company rescue chemistry. Grants created suitable findings, and two unsound concepts swept farming: partial and imbalanced fertilization, and toxic rescue chemistry. And the end result is food with compromised nutritional quality made toxic by poisons. And this is what now enters our body and is supposed to nourish our cells, our genes.

The Deadly Potential

One of the lesser avocations in academia is the study of Arthurian legends. These legends run into the hundreds beyond those preserved for us by Sir Thomas Mallory in *Le Morte de'Arthur*. One I recalled told of Arthur's long perilous trip to Nigeria, the only place on planet Earth that grows the calabar bean. As a young knight, Arthur harvested that bean and returned to England. Thus we have the calabar bean marching into history, first because legend says it stopped the black death, also because it made Sir Arthur king of the realm. That bean is of special importance as we examine the deadly potential of chemicals of organic synthesis. Joseph Campbell assures us that myths are more fact than metaphor. Arthur allegedly said "tomorrow I'll be cured or I'll be dead," this after cooking the bean for a potion even Merlin couldn't create. King Arthur didn't know it but he had stumbled upon the first of the organophosphates, physostigmine.

A few years ago Israel scientists revealed that a chemical ingested by Allied soldiers and airmen during the Gulf War in fact authored the unhappy consequences for "test animal" soldiers. The preparation dispensed as a tablet and ordered taken each day under penalty of court-martial was a synthesized physostigmine. The synthetic version has been named pyridostigmine.

The Israeli research turned out to be blockbuster stuff, not only because it identified the cause of metabolic mischief, but also because it clears up the chain of events that has led to debauchery of food and farming, the annihilation of the health profile, and the probable incubation of the modern black death about to overtake planet Earth.

The poisons that guide high science are tabun, soma, sarin and mepafax, which were first isolated from the Calabar bean in the early 1840s. The parent materials mentioned above retained their botanical properties until scientists learned how to synthesize everything from medicines to agricultural poisons. Synthesis may have unlocked a few of nature's secrets, but not all. Nevertheless, the laboratory game was off and running, leaving dying and crippled soldiers to harvest the whirlwind. One at a time the group of poisons rose like a miasma from that barrel of hydrocarbons, the so-called substitute for biodegradable botanicals.

One class came to include paraoxon, also known as mitasol, also employed as an active metabolic of parathion (metabolic means active ingredient).

The next class includes parathion, EPM (a widely employed agricultural insecticide) and malathion. This class was perceived to be safer because of rapid metabolism by higher organisms.

Another class starts out as TEPP (tetraethyl pyrophosphate). This insecticide was tested in treating glaucoma, Lou Gehrig's disease, Alzheimer's disease, etc. This preparation seemed to work until the pharmacological industry learned how to synthesize it. An insecticide OMPA proved to be inactive in the test tube, but could be metabolized by plants and animals into potent anti-CHE agents. This means that when animals metabolize it, it becomes a potent anti-CHE agent. That's what they were trying to do when they pushed pills down the throats of GIs in Desert Storm. The problem is, they did it with a synthetic rather than with a natural product of the calabar bean.

A final group is styled echothiophate, an extremely potent choline derivative employed in the treatment of eye pressure, *i.e.* glaucoma, relatively stable in an aqueous solution. Except for a few witch doctors in Nigeria, the world of science embraced synthetics. If we read the Israel tests correctly, the physostigmines of the botanical world were amended and/or shortchanged as modern Merlins subtracted hydrogen atoms from God's formula. All the products mentioned as well as a ponderous inventory flowed from the original discovery. With human vision somewhat short of deity status, the alchemists created all kinds of monsters and Dante's Hell as well. GIs who escaped the holocaust it seems, were the ones who threw away the pyridostigmines military experts figured would defend servicemen against chemical warfare. There is a perception afloat that botanicals that biodegrade are dangerous, and that traceable chemistry forever clues the police.

This misses the point that it would take a tractor-trailer load of botanicals to disturb, say, a water main, whereas a quart of paraquat would do maximum damage. Also, there is great profit. The cash register has now rung, leaving behind soldiers with disturbed central nervous systems and riddled with degenerative metabolic diseases. So far no one has revealed by what stretch of the imagination scientists came to believe a pyridostigmine could confer immunity to chemical warfare.

Sir Albert Howard said modern agriculture was operating on two false premises, partial and imbalanced fertilization and toxic rescue chemistry. That anti-nature devices could produce bins and bushels became the supreme justification for fossil-fuel technology in the early 1950s. That nature revolts against man's mistakes was less emphasized. Farmers were seldom told that plants without balanced hormone and enzyme systems summon the predators of the biotic pyramid so that misfits can be removed. But to save the crop from the penalty of agriculture's original sin, an almost unmentionable alchemy arrived on the scene, one that enlarged the crude groupings of alchemists from as far back as Homer and as far forward as King Arthur himself. These were the "synthetic poisons."

There have always been poisons in nature, frequently those associated with elements of heavy specific gravity, such as lead and mercury. Every child who reads about Alice in Wonderland knows of the Mad Hatter's disease, that unhappy condition brought on when fumes from the mercury used in the hatter's trade attacked the central nervous system, splitting amino acids, thereby creating proteins of a pathological nature. Farmers have used compounds of arsenic, copper, lead, manganese, zinc. They have also used pyrethrum from dried chrysanthemums, nicotine sulphate from plants related to tobacco, and rotenone from legumes in the East Indies. These natural poisons kill quickly or slowly, but they lack the deadly potential of man's inventions.

DDT was invented by a German chemist in 1874. Indeed, many of the miracle poisons of today can be found in some form in old German compendiums. At the end of World War I, many of the patents were handed to the world. At the end of World War II, Dr. Paul Müller of Switzerland won the Nobel Prize for discovering the insecticidal properties of DDT. At war's end, with many newsreels hailing the event, DDT was touted for stamping out insect-borne diseases and winning the farmer's war against crop destroyers.

Just what is DDT? What are the chlorinated hydrocarbons?

What are organic and inorganic chemistry, for that matter?

It was Dmitri Mendeleyev who first constructed a table of known elements in the natural order, and supplied the periodicity of property and weight. All the elements needed for life were listed as the first 53 of the 92 natural elements on planet Earth. Of these, all except one fell in order among the first 42, and all except two were listed among the first 34. There is also a natural order for abundance of elements, according to atomic weight and number. The heaviest elements are the rarest. With the exception of hydrogen, elements with even atomic numbers are more abundant than those with odd numbers. We don't know why, nor can we even guess.

The table itself is a veritable encyclopedia. There are series with missing electrons. As the eye moves from titanium to zinc, unfilled orbits change, an electron at a time. These transitions take place in natural order, moving across the table. There is also a vertical order to the table, weight increasing as each element is listed under the one above. There are groups that figure in biology and signal the entrance or exit of disease. Henry A. Schroeder, M.D., possibly the world's foremost authority on trace elements, tells us that "a heavier metal can displace a lighter one in the same group in biological tissues and alter the reaction of the lighter one." He goes on to say that tissues with an affinity for a certain element have an affinity for all other elements of the same group. Some elements are bone-seekers. Some are thyroid-seekers. All elements in two groups are liver- and kidney-seekers.

These few data only hint at the vast complexity of nature's life-plan. They also hint at how little of this vast knowledge has so far been uncovered, even though nature has been revealing herself for a long time.

A landmark event, in fact, took place in Berlin in 1828 when Friedrich Wöhler discovered that ammonium cyanate could be transformed into urea by heat alone. The consternation of Justus von Liebig can be imagined. Here was a simple agent, heat that could rearrange the atoms of a molecule into a different compound, yet still remain in possession of all the original atoms.

Hardly 30 years later, Friedrich Kekulé, in Ghent, conceptualized methane (CH_4) as a basis for organic compounds. Here was a hypothesis that explained the structural formulas for chain, or aliphatic, compounds — common to fats and oils and petroleum. Benzene, however, remained unexplained. Benzene had been isolated from oil-gas and from coal tar. Why didn't it fit the pattern? It belonged to a class known as hydrocarbons — compounds made up entirely of hydrogen and carbon, and characterized by a deficiency in hydrogen per carbon atom, to wit: C_6H_6. The story has been told that Kekulé sat before his fireplace one day and saw in the curling smoke a 'vision' of gamboling carbon compounds, one figure of which grabbed its own tail — the hexagon. And so the riddle of benzene came clear. So did the riddle of hydrocarbons in general.

High school chemistry texts often use an illustration reproduced below.

Students are asked to picture the basic element of the universe, carbon, aligned with hydrogen and/or chlorine.

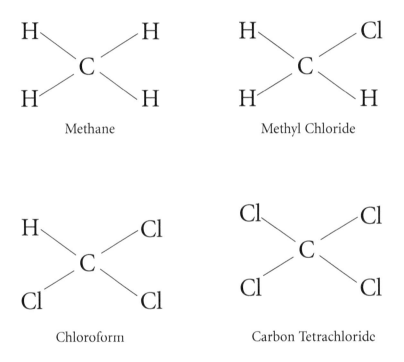

Methane   Methyl Chloride

Chloroform   Carbon Tetrachloride

The basic element of the universe is carbon. Surround one atom of carbon with four atoms of hydrogen. This is the chemical structure for methane, the common gas of swamps, the "original" hydrocarbon, having atoms of "only" carbon and hydrogen. Now take away one of those hydrogen atoms, and substitute a chlorine atom, so that the one atom of carbon is surrounded by three hydrogen atoms and one chlorine atom. This is methyl chloride. Now take away three atoms of hydrogen and replace them with chlorine, and you have chloroform. Take away all the atoms of hydrogen, and replace them all with chlorine, and you have carbon tetrachloride — the stuff formerly used in cleaning fluid and fire extinguishers.

These simple formulas advanced chemistry by leaps and bounds. Yet they accounted for mere child's play compared to the benzene ring. When Kekulé realized that a fourth valence could be absorbed intramolecularly, the door flew open. Aromatic hydrocarbons (so called because they have an odor) filled the compendiums and caused man-made compounds to proliferate.

These simple illustrations, therefore, give only the mildest hint of combinations possible and of the true complexity of the chemical world. There are rings and chains and branches, and figures grabbing their own arms and tails. A seemingly slight change in nature's formula can change the entire character of a substance. Many changes via heat and cold and pressure and mixes have developed poisons of fantastic scope. It may be an oversimplification, but it is nevertheless a fact that nature's poisons tend to wash away, and that man's poisons threaten to consume him. Nature's poisons do not easily pass through the placental wall. They obey Bertrand's Law. Some are essential. When man or animal intake high concentrations that exceed the ability to repel or excrete the excess, these elements become toxic and lethal. They therefore range from being deficient to sufficient to toxic to lethal. They are governed by a principle known as homeostasis, and are said to be under homeostatic control. The man-made poisons are of a different stripe.

The role of the placental wall illustrates something about the natural order. Indeed, the work of George A. Young, D.V.M., University of Nebraska, merits consideration at this point. In the mid-1950s Dr. Young was working SPF hogs at the University. He found that newborn pigs are disease-free, that they are protected by the mother's womb from the many diseases that hamper swine production. Once born, pigs become infected and usually they have not developed enough antibodies to survive in a swine producer's environment. Hence, the high death rate of one- and two-week-old pigs. Dr. Young broke the disease barrier by taking piglets a couple of days before normal birth by hysterectomy. This classical work became the origin of specific pathogen-free hogs. The placental wall protected the young, and broke the disease cycle.

The placental wall cannot stop DDT and the chlorinated hydrocarbons. These synthetic poisons build up in fatty tissues and ultimately overwhelm the system. They break the amino-acid chain and cause mutations. Many of the world's greatest scientists believe that these poisons have no safe level and no tolerance level. By offending the chromosomes, these substances tamper with the gene pool and the origin of life itself. All evidence says that the effects of these toxic genetic chemicals will be visited to the 20th and 30th generations.

Here Richard Olree was prompted to pause and reflect. A signal event happened during the end of World War II, one that forever changed the life and health of all those on planet Earth. It referred us all back to the support of all life, the Sun, the only safe place for atomic energy.

The Beginning: The Gene

The story of the gene, the cell, and Richard Olree's Standard Genetic Chart can look back before it proceeds ahead. A moment in time that must be remembered was the one that saw two B-29 bombers visit the crowded cities of Hiroshima and Nagasaki in Japan. There is a connection between that moment, most of the medicine being practiced today, and the development of what may turn out to be a signal leap forward in the fight to have marked progress against degenerative metabolic disease.

Radiation has been a disturbing scientific fact ever since Madame Marie Curie found an ore giving up energy without destruction of its mass. After the desolation of Hiroshima and Nagasaki, suddenly funds were forthcoming to research the genetic effects of radiation. As a consequence, the date to denote our times is not August 14, 1945, which is the date that the first atomic bomb was dropped, but April 25, 1953, which is the date that James Watson and Francis Crick published their model of the DNA and RNA in *Nature* magazine. The DNA molecule had been photographed by Rosalind Franklin using X-ray photography with the help of Maurice Wilkins. The Nobel Prize that would have been hers was canceled out by her untimely death. Nobel Prizes are given only to living persons. Therefore, Wilkins, Watson, and Crick became the scientific icons who would dominate our times, our medicine, and our agriculture.

Radiation and chemicals of organic synthesis stand as realities that must be considered if we are to comprehend the health profiles of our times and the leap forward that the Olree Standard Genetic Chart represents.

At the start of the last century, Baron Ernest Rutherford of New Zealand expressed what he knew by intuition — that the atom was electrical in nature, that it was composed of protons and neutrons (as a nucleus) with one or more orbiting electrons. Atoms, he said were small, albeit divisible. It has been computed that if an atom were as big as the head of a pin, all atoms in a grain of sand would make a cube one mile high, one mile wide, and one mile long.

In 1905 Albert Einstein went straight to the heart of the matter, not by observing facts, but through pure reasoning. He said that energy is determined by the mass times the velocity of light squared, or $E=mc^2$.

Picture the earth as an atom. Start a gigantic bolt toward it from well beyond the Milky Way. Upon impact, splitting the earth in half would release a great deal of energy. In terms of relativity, a single atom has an equal amount of energy to release when split. Indeed, $E=mc^2$.

Standing on the shoulders of these giants, a German named Hahn reasoned that atomic energy could be released through nuclear fission, and in December of 1942 Fermi completed the first atomic pile. The world knows the rest — how the atomic bomb came into being, how fantastic energy release gave man explosive devices with cosmic violence. Not one of these developments flowed logically from eyeball facts. It took people of vision — with fantastic vision — to learn that much of the Creator's system.

Not many people really understand nuclear explosions, but they are convinced that atomic fallout causes mutations, cancers, and other unhappy conditions among human beings. The shock of Hiroshima gave this lesson to even the most illiterate. Almost immediately, people started pushing for a bomb ban. The use of products of organic synthesis on the cornfields has delivered similar mutations and cancers, but the drive to ban them is still short-winded. Trauma requires action. A lingering illness gets boring.

"We are rightly appalled by the genetic effects of radiation; how then can we be indifferent to the same effect in chemicals that we disseminate widely in our environment?" wrote Rachel Carson in 1962.

She meant the synthetic man-made poisons, and she also meant to compare these synthetics in mutagenic effect with atomic fallout. Later, Dr. Jerome Weisner, a science adviser to President Kennedy, repeated the Rachel Carson statement when facing a United States Senate Commission assembled to examine *Silent Spring,* her book. "Using agricultural pesticides," he said, "is more dangerous than atomic fallout."

This is not hyperbole. Several years ago, Dr. Americo Mosca of Torino, Italy, set out to illustrate how toxic genetic chemicals were, in fact, more dangerous than the atomic bomb. He made his computations because he had invented a fungicide. His battle with government illustrates how bureaucracy itself may be accounting for the greatest capital crime in the history of mankind.

For years it was assumed that when metallic compounds had fungicidal properties, this was due to the structure of matter. Scientists came to this conclusion in exactly the same way they have arrived at other conclusions — by observing the facts independent of the scientific principles that determined them. Observations based on empirical evidence are sometimes right, and sometimes they are wrong. Generally stated, when enough observations line up with enough suspected causes, man is said to have discovered a law. But it is also true that man's finite mind can easily line up certain facts with the wrong cause.

"For the first time in the history of the world," wrote Rachel Carson, "today every human creature comes in contact with poisonous chemical substances from the moment of conception till death." She went on to accuse the chemical industry of poisoning humanity with the consent of scientists whose knowledge and concept of toxicity dates back to the Stone Age, and she charged that we have become victims of "cancer, nerve paralysis, genetic mutations, and . . . are now in no better situation than Borgia's guests."

The atomic experience, its wild "success," and the frame of mind that saw chemicals of organic synthesis become considered inoffensive even while they accounted for deaths, poisonings, deformed and retarded children, all caused Dr. Americo Mosca to reach for the heart of the problem. Mosca took the proved knowledge of matter a step beyond the Stone Age. He reasoned that it wasn't the structure of matter alone that accounted for toxicity. He concluded that properties of all remedies are given "only" when they are ionized, that is, made electrically active.

Add a word to your lexicon: ionization. This is the process used to add or subtract one or more electrons from an atom. The hydrogen atom is electrically neutral. It has a single electron traveling around a core. A violent impact can knock the electron out of the atom. This ionizes the atom and creates an ion pair. When atoms in human tissue are ionized, they are damaged. This damage can be minor or so severe that it kills a cell. Sick cells have defective metabolic mechanisms that permit attack by bacterial and viral infections. Deranged cells "age more rapidly and may cause the appearance of these diseases of metabolism which are called cancer or thrombosis," noted André Voisin in *Soil, Grass, and Cancer.*

Protein molecules are formed of amino acids, and the amino acids are all long chains. What happens, according to Dr. Mosca, is that chemicals that are ionized to take electrons, as are synthetic poisons, reach up and grab electrons from the hydrogen atoms of amino acids. This might be visualized by taking a stout steel chain, stealing a link, and replacing it with a rubber band. Such a chain would not do its work very well. The amino acid chain that has been robbed of an electron won't build a healthy protein, and a sick protein won't build much of a cell. Sick and deranged cells are the authors of cancer, mental retardation, and mutations — and toxic genetic chemicals cause sick cells.

Chemicals used in agriculture have been ionized to subtract electrons from the hydrogen atoms of amino acids. They act in the same way as thermo, electric, and radiant energy from an atomic bomb, says Mosca. "Therefore, the damage caused by the ionization of atomic fallout and by chemical and physical agents is the same." The application of radioisotopes and fungicides based on Zineb in agriculture confirm this statement.

The Italian Committee on Nuclear Energy published the results of an experiment in which an apple tree was given a 30-Roentgen dose every day for about 18 months. The damage experienced became a matter of record in *Agricultural Progress and Nuclear Science,* First Italian Agricultural Show, 1961.

Knowing this much, Mosca computed the damage being done to human beings with the use of toxic genetic chemicals. Using power figures, he computed damage levels for farm chemicals in the U.S. and compared them to atomic bombs because he knew the degree of ionization of both nuclear fallout and farm chemicals.

Mosca's computations are too complex for instant comprehension by those not trained in chemistry, but this much can be understood by anyone: the power of the H-bomb exploded at Bikini was 14 megatons. A total of 500 kilograms of uranium was used. The number of ionizations obtained on the basis of data from the Atomic Energy Commission and the number obtained with theoretic calculus — considering the great number involved — was about the same.

The production of synthetic pesticides alone increased from 730 million pounds in 1962 to 1,158 million pounds in 1972, an increase of nearly 60% in ten years. In addition to pesticides, there are fungicides, herbicides, desiccants, rodenticides, and all manner of molecular combinations for which nature has never evolved a suitable disposal system. Mosca computed that 1,000 million pounds of these genetic chemicals presented the same danger to the American people as would an annual atomic fallout from 72,500 atomic bombs, type Hiroshima.

Besides fungicides, great quantities of toxic genetic chemicals are used as herbicides, insecticides, hormones, antibiotics, steroids — in agriculture and in foods for people and animals, in birth control devices, cosmetics, and in all sorts of pills used as medicine.

In the late 1940s, the animal feed industry came out with a 50-gram per ton antibiotic level. In the early 1950s, this doubled as drug-resistant strains of *E. coli* developed. By the 1960s, the level jumped to 250 grams, and it can be safely said that the antibiotic level in the so-called low-level feeding of the "wonder" drugs is now 500 to 1,000 grams per ton of feed. Instead of saving the swine producer, the miracle drugs have accounted for pig scours, and if *E. coli* is overpowered as a result of a massive dose, and scours are stopped, there is the situation of pneumonia and poor feed conversion. If a physician treated the average citizen with one shot of penicillin every day for a year, the likely result would be human distress and a suit for malpractice. And yet, this is exactly what feed companies have been doing to livestock and poultry.

To recite these details is not to suggest that official science agrees. As a matter of fact, official and government science say there is a safe level and a tolerance level for the synthetic chemicals, always on grounds that the concept of toxicity extant 200 years ago properly described man-made molecules.

Yet the fact is that toxic genetic chemicals do not qualify for homeostatic control, as do the natural compounds and sometimes lethal trace minerals. This is what Rachel Carson meant when she charged that all this is being done with the consent of scientists whose knowledge and concept of toxicity dates back to the Stone Age.

Even before Watson and Crick modeled the DNA, public policy elected to ignore the harsh realities of the toxic age. In 1949 the government set up Poison Control Centers so that toxic rescue chemical agriculture could proceed. The word was afloat that the chemicals were safe because the LD_{50} concept was correct, if not sacred. It meant such and such a dose per unit of poisons would kill 50% of the test animals. These were astounding statements in view of the fact that toxic genetic chemicals are radiomimetic. This means that they ape the character of radiation.

The arrival of a DNA model changed the level of knowledge, if not increased comprehension.

The DNA is a blueprint of sorts. It tells cells how to divide and produce copies of themselves. Picture a twisted rope ladder. All DNA structures are shaped this way — in a flower, a dog, a human being. The rungs of the ladder are made up of four components: adenine ($C_5H_5N_5$), cytosine ($C_4H_5N_3O$), guanine ($C_5H_5ON_5$), and thymine ($C_5H_6N_2O_2$). These are usually written as A, C, G, and T. A can only pair with T, and C with G. Base pairs reproduce themselves, and that is where genetic manipulation enters the scene. Millions of these base pairs form genes. Evolution has taken up the chore of directing the base pair reproduction, frequently and even usually improving the life structure. It was a small step to discover naturally occurring enzymes that act like molecular scissors, which genetic engineers have learned how to manipulate for the purpose of adding rungs to and deleting rungs from the DNA ladder.

Breaking the molecule has been applauded because of the potential for fighting hereditary disease conditions. Thus was born the idea of cutting and recombining at the molecular level. Thus was born the idea of finding a trait in one organism and transferring it to another organism. Thus was also born the idea of engineering the totality of life.

Two systems are before the world. One seeks to muck around with DNA, to interbreed species of plants and animals at the molecular level, to rescue mistakes with ever-more-powerful chemistry, to cure and salvage rather than to cause nature to reveal her secrets. Irradiation, not purity, is seen as the key to shelf life.

The second system is the one I have outlined. It does more than pay lip service to the conventional topics of humus, organic matter, mineral uptake, tilth, water conservation, line breeding, and humane animal husbandry. It seeks participation in the creation process so that future generations will inherit the land — a land improved, not degraded, productive, not degenerated.

The case can be made that public policy, economics, and technology are not different sides of the same coin. They are the same side.

No issue is ever drawn so sharply as a dead issue. The most violent arguments are between Tweedledee and Tweedledum. I submit that both the technology called "mainstream" and the economics of current public policy are sunset operations. No reasonable person can expect our soil systems to be managed another 50 years as they have been managed for the last 50 years — not when deserts expand, subsoil replaces topsoil, aquifers go dry, oceans become polluted, the air poisons our cells, and produce from the land becomes empty of nutrition. Nor can an agriculture assembled into a few strong hands pending bankruptcy do less than incubate fantastic adjustments in our political and institutional arrangements.

Even before the age of chemistry, cellular damage had become the issue for the farmer's crops and thus for the consumer. Cellular damage because of malnutrition has always been the primary cause of the classic diseases: rinderpest, brucellosis, foot-and-mouth disease, Johne's disease, etc. Much the same is true of toxicity. Both can cost a farmer part or all of his crop. The same damage in human beings can cost a nation its heritage and its future. Damage to the sperm or ova can cause malformation or mental retardation in future generations. It can also contribute to degenerative metabolic disease.

In the cell — plant, animal, or human — there are chromosomes that carry all the information needed to direct the cell's growth, division, and production of chemicals such as proteins. These chromosomes are composed in part of information-bearing genes. Radiomimetic chemicals, radiation itself, and almost all the chemicals used in agriculture can injure chromosomes, either by altering the chemistry of a single gene so that the gene conveys improper information, called "point mutation," or by actually breaking the chromosomes so that they become incomplete, called "deletion." The cell may be killed, or it may continue to live, sometimes reproducing the induced error. Cellular damage can cause genetic misinformation leading to uncontrolled cellular growth — cancer. Cellular damage, because of malnutrition or invasion of toxicity, can cost a farmer part or all of his crop and the consumer all of his health.

Jamie Whitten was chairman of the House Appropriations Sub-committee on Agriculture from 1944 until late in the century. His answer to Rachel Carson was a ghostwritten book entitled *That We May Live*. It was then that new battle lines were drawn. The goal of public policy was to drive people off the land because there were "surpluses" and "too many farmers," because the biological procedure called agriculture was perceived to have become an industrial proce-dure. The dissidents answered with old values, now named "organic."

The university professionals had their settled body of knowledge reaching back to the days of Justus von Liebig. They claimed that salt fertilizers trumped biotic life and even physical aspects of soil man-agement, and that very few trace minerals even mattered.

There were few who could answer. There were hardly any pro-fessional people who could discuss humus, organic matter, soil life — except to render lip service, so those who could pay for sound bites on television relegated such discussion to underground status.

Yet we are what we eat. We are what our farms and gardens pro-duce. The steady march of degenerative metabolic disease across the population of the nation and the world does not speak well for our prevailing form of agriculture.

The course of human events has ordered change, and yet change has been kept an arm's length away.

Now it seems that "living life" is again becoming the ultimate objective of select farm leaders. Now we can begin to construct an understanding of an ecology in the soil. We should now be able to benefit from its minuteness and wondrous patience. Nature has no time limit. She is ever forgiving. She is able to repair herself from the ignoble treatment of man, in spite of his capacity for destruction. But as we continue to replace nature, we assuredly prevent the develop-ment of the mental capacity to learn and fully complement nature, a requirement expected from us as permission for life.

Apparently the growing intellectual attitude confronting agrono-my and industry speaks a challenge. This virgin knowledge is finally emerging as a test and challenge to the introverted and integrated exploiters and absconders of our most precious resource. How farm practices relate to the immune system and the maintenance of health becomes at once apparent as the reader enters Part 2. For now it is enough to bring up the rear, so to speak.

It was this reality that the Friends of the Land sought to remedy. Meeting at Louis Bromfield's Malabar Farm in Ohio with most of the great professors of the midland land-grant colleges, Friends of the Land examined the premises of salt fertilizers and toxic-rescue chemistry. Bromfield had seen many of the world's worn-out acres. Before World War II, he came home. He bought down-and-out farms and started his restoration. One of the great mentors of Friends of the Land, William A. Albrecht, joined Rudolf Ozolins in serving as mentors.

Agriculture could no longer submit to amateurs, chemical or organic. The confusion touched off by J.I. Rodale's adoption of the word "organic" for "biologically correct" has never fully subsided.

"Organic" means carbon-based chemistry. The soil mineral becomes "organic" when it is taken up by the plant, having been acted upon by microorganisms, the size of almost all entry being the ion. As with most terms in the English language, "organic" has other meanings, it being the function of literacy to understand the meaning of a term in the context of its usage. Thus, "natural" — as opposed to synthetic — means organic growth. A town that expands naturally is said to grow organically. Semantic jousts cannot settle the issue.

This much stated, we still have to reflect that there is nothing occult about science — and I might add that there is nothing occult about the rationales constructed by the grant receivers to protect the commerce of their patrons. This being the case, the late William A. Albrecht joined me in outlining lessons and principles, each dazzling in the purity of its challenge. I state these now.

Simplistic nitrogen, phosphorus, and potassium (NPK) fertilization means malnutrition for plants, animals, and humans . . . this because of either a shortage or marked imbalance of plant nutrients, which prevents plant health, and therefore animal and human health. Plants in touch with exchangeable forms of soil nutrients that are needed to develop proper fertility loads can structure and stabilize hormone and enzyme potentials and provide their own protection against insect, bacterial, viral, and fungal attack. Insects and nature's predators are a disposal crew. They are summoned when they are needed, and they are repelled when they are not needed. Weeds are an index of the character of the soil. It is therefore a mistake to rely on herbicides to eradicate them.

Crop losses in dry weather or during mild cold snaps are not so much the result of drought and cold as they are of nutrient deficiency.

Toxic rescue chemistry hopes to salvage a crop that is not fit to live so that animals and humans might eat it, always with consequences for present and future generations of plants, animals, and human beings.

Man-made molecules of toxic rescue chemistry do not exist in nature's blueprints for living organisms. Since their counterparts in nature are few and tardy, they will not likely break down biologically in a time frame suitable to the head of the biotic pyramid, namely: humanity. Carcinogenic, mutagenic and teratogenic molecules of toxic-rescue chemistry have no safe level and no tolerance level.

Now, over 55 years after the foundation of the Poison Control Centers, and 55 years after the modeling of the DNA molecule, we have harvested the consequences of errant technology. Centers for Disease Control tell us statistically that one out of every three persons in the United States can expect cancer during his or her lifetime. The inventory of degenerative metabolic diseases is too long for recitation. Mental retardation, deformed births, and medical costs as a percentage of gross domestic product — much of it a consequence of poisons in, around, and on the food supply — have indicted our crops as a disgrace to a civilized society.

Blame for this state of affairs has been handed off to the gene and to God, who incorrectly designed it and permitted its evolution. A revision of the Gospel according to St. John is less hyperbole than one might imagine.

A platoon of daring designers of nature has come onto the world scene. They promise a world without hunger, cancer, AIDS, and medical anomalies that destroy human life.

Some honor the memory of the German philosopher Nietzsche; some envision designer genes. The idea of the Superman may have faded, but the ghost of Nietzsche hangs on with genetic engineering.

Even so, a measure of confusion hovers around gene splicing, its potential for disease control, cloning, and genetic modification of organisms. For this reason and for reasons left unstated, a short précis of the vast literature on the subject requires added attention.

All living organisms contain genes. They store more information than a modern Carnegie library. This information literally governs life. Genes benchmark heredity. Scientists have extrapolated this to mean that they can order up traits, even human evolution. Farmers are led to expect an increase in food production, and they even smile at the promise of beautiful progeny. But mature reflection suggests that mucking around in the dark is bad policy.

The transfer of specific traits from one organism to another is now current coin. The scope of this activity is less well known. It seems to promise modification of plants and food to comply with the unreal world man has manufactured for himself, or as William A. Albrecht pointed out, "An attempt is being made to modify one and all to withstand starvation." The metes and bounds of this development will be examined in the next chapter, which looks at the Genome Project. Here it is enough to note that scientists have identified almost all potential for gene and DNA transfer across the species barrier. This has meant use of the base pairs that make up the DNA.

Suffice it to note that geneticists now take specific gene traits from one organism and install them into the cellular makeup of another: plant, animal, or human being. The end product is to be superior to the one that God and evolution have accounted for.

The novel food crops thus produced ask more questions than have so far been answered.

The argument that consumers of such products make it to the door, as under the LD_{50} code, is not a comfortable one. For one thing, allergies are becoming pandemic. The entire population now made 50% sterile suggests interference with sexual development, this probably a consequence of radiation, chemical and soybean consumption with its estrogen overload.

Jeremy Rifkin, writing in *The Bio-Tech Century,* put it this way: "Imagine a wholesale transfer of genes between totally unrelated species and across all biological boundaries, plant, animal, and human — creating thousands of novel life-forms in a brief moment of evolutionary time, then with eternal propagation producing countless replicas of these new creations, releasing them into the bio-sphere to propagate, mutate, proliferate, migrate . . ."

It is strange to observe that children *en masse* have become lactose-intolerant, consuming grocery-store milk, and yet these same children seem to lose their lactose intolerance when given fresh, unpasteurized, unhomogenized cow's milk. Much of the U.S. milking herd, of course, is now treated with a bovine growth hormone, the product of GMO engineering, namely bovine somatropin. Even the public prints now report pig genes inserted into vegetables, chicken genes into potatoes, fish genes into tomatoes, strange genes into lettuce.

Indeed, the very idea stands in contrast to the quite simple Standard Genetic Chart developed by Richard Olree over 25 years. That development invites an in-depth look at the genome projects that have guided the progress of science in recent years.

Withal, cells create their own kind, which die after seven years. The control center of a cell is called a nucleus. Herein resides the cell's own genetic program. Chromosomes are thread-like substances composed of DNA and certain proteins.

The argument for fast-track use of genetic engineering in crop production stays with us — hang the dangers and the consequences!

But history reveals that the fast track in science is full of potholes and axle-breaking bumps. The debate is emerging from the shadows. In the case of BGH — bovine growth hormone — citizens generally vote with their dollars to reject the "shooting-from-the-hip" assurances of officialdom.

The brashest of the engineers look to designing animals and even infants. Ethical considerations are either ignored or swept aside.

As with DDT and atomic hazards, the voice of the people has to be heard in the fullness of time. Splicing genetic material into a hog has no ethical implications for some modern Neanderthalers, but it is something we all need to think about. There are too many people who rarely trouble themselves thinking about ethics or consequences.

It is now possible to buy human ova from stunningly beautiful women on the Internet. George Bernard Shaw was once approached by a very beautiful woman with the proposition that he father her child. She suggested that with her good looks and his brains, the progeny would answer Nietzsche's fondest dreams. Shaw answered, "But what if the child has your brains and my looks? Wouldn't that be tragic?"

The GMO Fallacy

In January 1998, a firm named after the mountain of the saints, Monsanto, became an institutional advertiser in the *Washington Post*. The firm basically decided that it had a new outlook on life. It was done with the business of fighting nature, fungus, bacteria, and weeds with harsh chemicals that offended the environment, and promised an end to the dreaded toxins DDT and the full range of toxic genetic pesticides. The ad did not point out that those same chemicals of organic synthesis, while a blunder, had built Monsanto. Now was the time to put those dark days behind everyone. A new paradigm was announced together with a new motto: food, health, hope. The author of pollution said it was taking on the mantle of life giver. The trail to this epiphany was well traveled before that January day. In 1980 new statistics came about as a result of experiments in biological sciences. They hired people such as medical geneticists and plant cell biologists.

All were people from academia and all were dedicated to pure, bona fide research. Monsanto sold off its interests in Conoco to DuPont. Next the firm started buying up seed companies, genetic firms, and not least, soybean companies. A few years later Monsanto procured the pharmaceutical firm G.E. Searle. Even before that famous ad in the *Washington Post*, Monsanto announced that the future of plant protection was seated in the new science of genetic engineering. In truth, Monsanto went on a buying spree spending 6.2 billion dollars to gain a stranglehold on soybean and corn production.

The prime target was the seed industry. "At 97 we have a new outlook on life," the arresting streamer announced. It could be a better life for the planet. How could anyone do other than applaud the altruistic firm that was to take us out of toxic technology? The new science that would erase the legacy of that toxic technology was genetic engineering.

The idea may or may not have been suggested by a battlefield incident during the Civil War. According to historians, a soldier was wounded in the gonads. The bullet continued a hundred yards or so and was stopped when it wounded a young lady who became impregnated. The missile had carried sperm to fertilize that ova. The concept of inserting a foreign substance into a cell to breed new life at the molecular level awaited the discovery of the DNA and RNA by Francis Crick and James Watson. A number of firms took on the challenge and then bowed out because of the difficulties and the expected revolt of the people. Since the early days, all sorts of entrepreneurs and capital providers have been involved in the hunt for genetic gold. Scientists with career interests are quite defensive when their type of genetic engineering is questioned.

Some understanding of genetic engineering is a necessary prelude to the Olree Standard Genetic Chart. I have recorded conversations with at least two geneticists in order to get at the full range of the story. The various agencies of government have assured us that biotech products are exactly the same as those served up by nature and her millions of evolutionary years. Those who hold up their wounded bodies as exhibits are dismissed as dilettantes and carping naysayers without credentials or standing. One doesn't get the impression that a government post and heavy political contributions to supporting politicians equals scientific veracity. Just the same, the challengers to this errant science have also presented their credentials and have made their findings available to the press. I have conducted lengthy interviews with some of these scientists and presented some of their answers to the questions the public has been asking. These answers are delving into the foundation of genetic science, including the Olree Standard Genetic Chart made a matter of record in the next section of this book.

John Fagan is a Ph.D. who has spent the best part of a working lifetime researching cancer. A product of the Cornell educational system, he assembled metes and bounds of what there was to know about molecular biology and biochemistry before moving on to seven years of research in molecular biology at NIH, National Institute of Health. In 1984, Fagan moved to a research laboratory at Maharishi University of Management, Fairfield, Iowa, where he is presently professor of molecular biology and biochemistry and Director of Physiology and Molecular and Cell Biology, as well as Dean of the Graduate School.

This schoolman has filed for and received grants from the National Cancer Institute and the National Institute of Health, the objective being the identification of cancer genes and how pollutants offend the immune system. On the hunt for gene expression he encountered what the trades call genetic engineering. Fagan has written more than 30 articles in peer-review literature on these topics. In November of 1994 he took an ethical stand against genetic engineering by asking scientists to follow safer and more productive research and to focus more on protection and less on high tech operators. He underscored his position by returning a $613,000 grant to the National Institute of Health. He also withdrew a grant application for another $1.2 million. To have accepted the money would have been tantamount to going along with the official stand of the government, supporting Monsanto, genetic engineering, Roundup Ready soybeans, and fancy footwork molecular engineering that appears to hold in escrow so much mischief for the human being.

He has now directed his attention to disease prevention systems and sustainable agriculture. His book is *Genetic Engineering: The Hazards — Vedic Engineering: The Solutions.* Currently, Fagan is conducting a global campaign to alert the public to the hazards of genetically engineered foods and reshape national and international policy and regulations regarding the safety testing, labeling, and importation of genetically engineered foods. This work has taken him to the capital cities of Austria, Belgium, Croatia, Denmark, Finland, France, Germany, Ireland, Italy, Netherlands, Northern Ireland, Norway, Sweden, Switzerland, and the United Kingdom, as well as Japan, Canada, and the United States, where he has conducted meetings with legislators, representatives of national governments, the food industry, the press, and the public.

Q. Before genetic engineering became a reality, how did nature transfer genetic information?

FAGAN. The transfer of genetic information occurred through natural reproductive mechanisms such as pollination or with animals, insemination. And this natural reproductive mechanism put very strict constraints on what a breeder could accomplish. You could cross closely related organisms, but as soon as you began to go too far afield, barriers were there that blocked the whole process. Even if you take the product of a donkey and a horse — a mule, that hybrid isn't fertile. You have run up against a reproductive barrier that has limited things. In traditional breeding what you are really doing is dealing with an existing pool of genetic characteristics and selecting from that pool certain characteristics you are interested in. But you are working with a limited, very defined pool of that species and possibly very closely related species. That is good because it means that you can't screw up nature too much.

Q. What limitations exist within genetic engineering?

FAGAN. With genetic engineering, we are really in a situation where there aren't any limitations. We know we can cross a tomato with a tomato using traditional breeding techniques or a fish with a fish. There is not a way you can get a tomato and a fish to mate. When was the last time you saw that kind of thing happening? And yet with genetic engineering, you can take genetic information from fish and put it into a tomato. It has already been done. You can take genetic information from a fish and put it into sugar beets. The Chinese have developed a fish-sugar beet. With this technology it is possible to take genes from virtually any organism on earth and put them into any other organism. This can be described as genetic surgery. Using these techniques which are not natural and are very invasive, they have taken genes not only from fish and other plants and bacteria, but also from viruses and pigs, even from human beings, as well as insects and other weird things and put those into the crop plants.

Q. How do they do this? How do the DNA and the messenger RNA really work?

FAGAN. The simplest way to describe it is as genetic surgery. There are little enzymes that the molecular biologist uses that function as little scalpels or knives and other enzymes that function as little sutures that link little DNA pieces together. What they do is isolate DNA from fish, then use one of these enzymes that are capable of cutting the DNA to slice out a specific gene from that fish DNA. Using some quite complex things they will isolate that single piece of DNA. It is quite a long involved process. The principle of it is that you cut out a specific gene, isolate it, and then take that gene and put it in the cells of another organism.

Q. What is the purpose of that?

FAGAN. In the case of the sugar beet, the purpose of the fish gene that they isolated was to acquire a gene for a protein. A gene, basically, is a blueprint. This fish gene was a blueprint for protein that was present in the blood of the Arctic flounder. That protein in the blood of the Arctic flounder functions like an antifreeze. In very cold temperatures the fish will not freeze. The rationale was to put a blueprint into the sugar beets so they would produce an antifreeze protein and be grown in a colder climate or in a place that has a shorter growing season. The problem is that when we put a single new gene into an organism, it isn't a perfectly controlled process. Sometimes, quite often, unexpected effects occur when you put in a new gene. These effects can cause the food that is produced to be allergenic or toxic or reduce its nutritional value. All of these things are possible. This is because when they put this new gene in, it isn't like surgery, *per se*. It is a very sloppy, random process when it is inserted in this way.

Q. Would it be akin to inserting a drug in your system?

FAGAN. Yes, to a certain extent. When you put a drug in your system, you know that it has a certain effect. You also can't predict what other side effects it may have. A drug just doesn't do one thing; it may interact with many different components in your body.

Q. Is that the reason the *Physicians' Desk Reference* has so many pages of side effects as compared to the purpose of the drug?

FAGAN. Absolutely. They can't control all of those effects because living organisms are so complex. The same is true with these genes. You put this new gene in, and it doesn't function in isolation. It interacts with all different components of the organism. We don't even know what all the components are. We can't predict the full range of effects.

Q. So we are approaching this genetic technology blindsided to a certain extent.

FAGAN. We do not know completely and fully where we are going with this. Therefore, to be safe in the way we carry forward with this, we need to test each of the products very thoroughly in terms of their safety effects, in terms of their environmental effects, and also in terms of the agronomic effects. There have been quite a few surprises that have come up with genetically engineered crops already. The Flavr Savr tomato was the first genetically engineered vegetable or fruit that got out there. They engineered it so that it was supposed to stay looking fresh on the shelf longer. But it turned out that those same genetic manipulations caused the skin to be weaker. So that when they were ready to harvest, they couldn't use the standard mechanical harvesting equipment. It made tomato puree out of the tomatoes. They had to develop a whole new way of harvesting. Because of that, this tomato has been a financial flop. You don't find it on your grocery shelves now.

Another example is genetically engineered cotton that was sold to farmers across the South and Southwest. This cotton was engineered to be resistant to the bollworm. They got it out in the field and in some areas of the country, the bollworms ate this stuff like it was cotton candy. There are now class-action lawsuits against Monsanto for deceptive advertising of this product.

Q. Cottonseed meal is used quite widely in agriculture. What effects could genetically engineered cotton seed have on an animal?

FAGAN. We don't know. I don't think it has even been tested. It has been put out as a transgenic plant for producing cotton. I haven't looked at the FDA data on this crop in detail. I am not certain that they have even tested this.

Q. But it has proved to be a disaster as far as cotton is concerned.

FAGAN. The fact is that even if they did some short-term animal testing on this new gene present in the cottonseed, it would not be enough to tell us the long-term effect on animals or on human beings (cottonseed oil is present in a lot of foods). My question is how and why are they being allowed to put this out there unlabeled and inadequately tested? That is what is happening these days. If we don't have adequate testing of these things, then this technology is not moving forward based on science, but it is simply being propelled forward on the basis of commercial and, in some cases, political pressures. It is not a good situation. At this point, genetically engineered foods are not required to be labeled by the FDA. Therefore, we are being used as guinea pigs in this huge nutritional experiment.

Q. Doesn't this have wider implication in the case of soybeans, where we now have glyphosate-tolerant soybeans and the danger of those soybeans being mixed or blended with other types of soybeans, some of which are grown to produce engine oil?

FAGAN. Absolutely. Yes, it is clearly a situation where this blending is resulting in genetically engineered products being pervasively present in our food supply, in the feed supply for animals, in engine oils, and also in dyes and printing inks. The real concern, of course, is human and animal nutrition.

Q. What happens when a human being eats genetically engineered product that has not been tested, but is out there on the market? What are some of the specific dangers?

FAGAN. The biggest danger is that the product might be allergenic or toxic to consumers. If the product hasn't been tested thoroughly, we don't know what the specific effects will be when we get out there.

When unlabeled, a product that's harmful may bounce around making people sick before we really nail down the problem. The fact is that when you put a new gene in, that gene programs the soybeans to produce a new protein. You are putting new protein into those foods. If these proteins haven't been part of the human diet before, we have no idea whether they are toxic or allergenic.

Q. But we do have some horrible examples of what has happened?

FAGAN. Yes, we have the example of tryptophan that was produced by Showa Denko, a Japanese chemical company. This chemical company had been producing tryptophan as a nutritional supplement for many years using fermentation and natural bacteria. Then they decided that by genetically engineering the bacteria they could produce tryptophan more effectively. The FDA allowed them to put this genetically engineered tryptophan on the market without further testing. They argued that the tryptophan was still tryptophan, just produced by another method. They felt it was the same thing. They put it on the market and within a few months 1,500 people had been disabled by it.

Q. Permanently disabled? In what way?

FAGAN. Seven were killed. The toxin that these genetically engineered bacteria were producing was present in the tryptophan. The genetic manipulation that caused the bacteria to produce more tryptophan also caused them to produce a powerful toxin which was present in the final tryptophan product. Then people ate it, and it made them sick. In some cases so sick, they died. The disease is called *Eosinophilia myalgia.* It is named after the initial symptoms, which are high levels of eosinophiles, a certain kind of blood cell, and myalgia, which is muscle pain.

There is range in the toxic effects of this product. The basic thing is that an immune disease comes out of it. It alters the functioning of the immune system, so that a lot of problematic things come up. Some people are suffering from cognitive deficits, emotional problems, paralysis, heart problems, problems with joints, rheumatism and arthritis. Muscles become very painful. The skin swells to the point that it cracks. There are excruciating headaches and sensitivity to light. A whole range of symptoms exist. It seems that this toxin really disrupts functioning at a cellular level and can interfere with health. I talked to a man who was going to speak at a conference we were holding. He had been poisoned by the genetically engineered tryptophan.

This man was absolutely ready to come and speak, and yet, on the day of the conference, he was so sick, he couldn't make the short trip required. He was an athlete, and he had taken the product to make him healthier. Because it wasn't labeled as genetically engineered, when he began to have some symptoms, he took more of it because it was a health product and was supposed to make him feel better. It took quite a while before he sorted out what was making him feel sick.

Q. What did the Centers for Disease Control do about it?

FAGAN. A couple of alert doctors in the Southwest put the first insight together and suggested that it might be tryptophan that was the problem. They alerted other physicians and The Centers for Disease Control (CDC), and, over a period of three or four months, physicians sorted out that it was this new preparation of tryptophan that was making people sick. CDC did some very careful epidemiological studies that nailed down very clearly that it was this tryptophan at fault. There are over 200 scientific studies that have been done on this. There have been hearings in Congress, albeit sort of small scale, that explored the whole problem.

Q. The product L-tryptophan, however, is perfectly safe, if made in a natural way.

FAGAN. It isn't the tryptophan itself, it is the contaminants that were present. Those contaminants were produced by genetically engineered bacteria, but not in natural bacteria.

Q. That's the reason L-tryptophan disappeared off the shelves of health food stores.

FAGAN. Interestingly, there is a story around that. Here we have a product of biotechnology that was embarrassing to the FDA and potentially embarrassing to the biotechnology industry. They got their heads together and put a spin on it that made the food supplement industry the scapegoat for the whole thing. To this day, there are many people out there who do not understand that it wasn't a food supplement problem but a genetic engineering problem, a biotech problem, and a regulatory problem. The FDA was being too sloppy in the way they were reviewing genetically engineered products that came on the market.

Q. In this case it was a toxin. Are there any other conduits?

FAGAN. There is the allergen problem as well. The big multinational feed company, Pioneer Hybrid, had the idea of genetically engineering soybeans to contain balanced amino acids — all the amino acids that you need for complete nutrition. What they did is take a gene from Brazil nuts and put that gene into soybeans. That did balance out the amino acid composition, which on the surface seemed like a great thing. But, unexpectedly, those same genetic manipulations caused the soybeans to produce a powerful allergen that caused strong allergic reactions in many people. If this product had gotten to the market, it would have killed people because there are people that have anaphylactic shock reactions to the Brazil nut allergen that was present in these soybeans. Fortunately, when Pioneer Hybrid discovered that these soybeans were allergenic they decided not to commercialize them, even though the FDA ruled that it was acceptable to put these things on the market with a few little restrictions. We have to give Pioneer credit on this one. They did the right thing and fortunately, no consumers were harmed. But it is, again, an example of how genetic manipulations give rise to unexpected events. They expected it to produce a soybean that contained balanced amino acids. They didn't at all expect a soybean that was allergenic. They lost millions of dollars on the project.

Q. When you consume a genetically engineered product, something mankind has not consumed before, are there other inherent dangers in addition to the toxicity and the allergens?

FAGAN. Basically what human beings have been eating through most of our existence as a species has been a pretty consistent diet. What that means is that we have, over time, evolved to handle the foods that we have available. There has been this evolution of the diet and of the capacity to deal with foods. Now overnight, we are changing our foods at a very fundamental level, at the level of the DNA blueprint of these foods. This is happening not just with one food, but with virtually every grain, legume, vegetable, fruit, nut and berry out there. They have already been engineered by the biotech industry. These things are not all on the grocery shelves yet, but they are in the developmental pipeline heading for our dinner plates. What is happening here is a radical re-engineering of our food supply over a very short period of time. There is no way we can adjust. These fundamental changes are very likely to give rise to characteristics in the food that will not be easy for us to deal with. As a result we will be finding nutritional problems coming up, either reduced nutritional value or allergenicity or toxicity. There could well be other kinds of less striking side effects that will come out of this. Think of the fact that every genetically engineered food that you eat will have some minor side effect associated with it. I can say that because over the history of scientific biological research virtually everything we do to a biological system will have some unexpected effects. Think over your life, how every drug that you take has some desired intended effect, but some side effect as well. In every case, there is some side effect.

Q. Isn't this exacerbated too because this is a synthesized product?

FAGAN. Synthesized means that it is artificial. It is a situation where we have altered nature in some way. Whenever we do this we have these unexpected side effects because of the complexity of nature. This is the case of altering nature at the genetic level and as well as chemical. Drugs are usually chemical alterations. Genetic engineering is a genetic alteration. Almost certainly these genetic alterations will give rise to side effects associated with each of these foods. What that means is that when our diet (ten years from now) contains many of these foods, it may be predominantly genetically engineered foods, and virtually every food we eat will have some small side effect associated with it. That adds up to a significant degradation of the quality of human food supply.

Mae-Wan Ho is one of the world's leading critics of the pseudo-science called genetic engineering. In 1967 she won a post-doctoral fellowship at the National Genetic Foundation, graduate credentials from the University of Hong Kong and doctoral work at the University of California and the University of San Diego. Later, as a research fellow at Queen Elizabeth College, U.K., she achieved an intellectual reputation for scientific excellence that covers the problems of genetic engineering today. Ho has been one of the most influential figures of the last decade in the debate within the scientific community regarding the use of genetically modified organisms. She is a highly consulted scientific figure with many theories relating to her powerful anti-GM stance. She is also a well-known critic of neo-Darwinism and reductionist thought in biology and physics.

Mae-Wan Ho joined the genetic engineering fray because of a deep-seated disgust with the quality of information going out to policy makers, and as a scientific advisor to the Third World network, who apparently came to her asking for help.

In an interview with this writer, Ho scoffed at the crudeness of the laboratory techniques used by the modern laboratory workers. The first subject at biochemistry genetic institutions was in finding a slot. Genetic material was inserted via a BB gun. The scientist simply fired away. Pulp decorated the walls, but some genetic material managed to enter a cell. It was a case of hip, hip, hooray! The new gene guns are more sophisticated. Nowadays, a .22 blank shell is used, and a buffer pad keeps the Petrie dish from being shattered. Vectors enable cell penetration with bacteria and viruses. These are joined to make new combinations with the imaginations of the scientists running rampant.

In the business of creation you have to push the envelope. "You use laboratory copies of this new engineered material, all of it unnatural," Ho said. "Then they use more lab techniques to insert these strange combinations of genes into organisms, into the cells of cows and sheep, anything," she said. "The idea is to make genetically modified cells." In the case of plants, cells are regenerated into whole plants. Out of this comes a transgenic line with cells that have broken up the genetic material.

In the case of animals, the frozen gene is injected into the egg. The hope is that the frozen construct will be taken up, given room and board, a transgenic animal resulting. Hope is the right word. The technique is literally uncontrollable and certainly not stable.

Once inserted in a cell, the new material is completely out of control. "It can become completely scrambled when it leaves the gene," Ho said.

"If you start with the same cells, the same construct, the same kind of genetic material, you can end up with completely different organisms. There is a reason for this. Code transferred is actually the cell that has taken up the genetic material."

Wes Jackson of the Land Institute, Salina, Kansas, tells us that if we had the complete working blueprint of a corn plant, it would fill the shelves of a major library. The interplay of cells, materials, enzymes, and a raft of DNA and RNA makes the outcome that complicated.

To this side note Mae-Wan Ho responded, "We don't know it all. The entire discipline has been terribly inconsistent. Where has this headed, and where does it stay?"

What has been found so far has been characterized as terribly complicated. Therefore, when a foreign material lands in a cell, it tends to scramble the site. The scrambling is so bad they can't even clarify the genetic sequence. "This is why a lot of the lines are unstable," Ho stated. The proprietary company will claim they have stabilized a transgenetic line.

The truth is something else. French and Belgian scientists have noted quite a deviation from the stated order, bits and pieces having disappeared. The chromosome order has been disturbed.

Here let me depart from our narrative to transcribe the exact words of the scientist, Dr. Ho.

Q. What actually happens when we eat foods that have been created this way?

HO. These modified genetic materials were designed to overcome the natural barriers between species. What happens when we eat ordinary vegetables and animal protein is that the DNA is broken down by our enzymes. Then, our cells also have enzymes for breaking them down further, and ultimately they will be nutrition for the cell. Unfortunately, if you design genetically modified DNA to jump into genomes and to overcome species barriers, then there is a chance that this DNA can avoid enzymatic breakdown and get into other unrelated species.

For example, one of the dangers of these organisms is that they are mainly made up of genetic material belonging to viruses and bacteria. So if these genetic materials meet other viruses and bacteria, they can join up to make new combinations — new viruses and bacteria that cause diseases and resist medical treatment.

Q. What we're attempting to do here is to intermarry unlike species at the molecular level. Is that a correct statement?

HO. Yes, absolutely! And there is no barrier whatsoever now because you can do all these things in the laboratory. The other thing that is immediately worrying is that they also use antibiotic-resistant genes. It's part of the tools of the trade that enable them to select for traits presumed to have greater economic value.

Q. Is that what they mean by the term "recombinant?"

HO. Yes, recombinant — that is, a recombination. Horizontal gene transfer and recombination form the major process for generating new viruses and bacteria that cause diseases.

Those cells have taken up the foreign genes. They put some antibiotic-resistant marker genes next to the foreign genes. Now, these genes can actually pass on — they very often stay in the GM crops that are released into the environment, and the antibiotic-resistant genes — if they get into bacteria that cause disease — would make those infections untreatable.

Q. Is it a possibility that this procedure has something to do with the prions implicated in Mad Cow disease and things like that?

HO. We don't know, because there have been so few targeted investigations. But this is the other thing: these DNA can also get into our cells, and the danger of rogue DNA getting into our cells, or the cells of other mammals, is that they often contain very aggressive promoters.

It's not easy to get a foreign gene to work in a cell. In order to do that, you really have to give it a very aggressive gene switch — which is called a "promoter" — that says to the cell, "Copy this gene and make a lot of the protein that's involved. Express this gene at a higher level." In order to do that they use the promoter from viruses. A virus, as the name implies, has the ability to hijack the cell to make many copies of itself, and that is essentially the basic technology that enables many foreign genes to become aggressive. They put it next to this kind of aggressive viral promoter. Now, if such an aggressive viral promoter gets into an alien cell, and if this promoter should work in that mammalian cell, and if this cell is involved in controlling cell division, then it could make this cell multiply out of control — and that's cancer by another name.

Q. It goes into wild proliferation?

HO. Exactly, and this is not merely a theoretic possibility — you've heard of gene therapy? Gene therapy is the genetic modification of human cells, and it uses techniques and constructs very similar to those used in genetic modification of plants and animals. In gene therapy there are two major side effects that people worry about. One of them is cancer, because if it gets into the wrong place, it turns on the wrong genes, and you get cancer. The other concern is the regeneration of live viruses, because in order to make this foreign DNA go into the genome, very often they use what is called a "gene carrier" or a "vector," which is itself a virus, a disarmed virus. Disarmed or not, a virus can still pick up genes from our genome or from the cell's genome and turn back into a fully armed virus by recombination. Those are the two major acknowledged dangers, or side effects, of gene therapy. Several years ago a group of scientists in France devised a method where they would genetically modify bone marrow cells outside the patient. They took the patient's own cells, genetically modified them, and then selected the "good" transformed cells — the cells that have taken up the foreign genes and then put them into a patient. It was hailed as a great success that avoids the complications I've just described. Unfortunately, about a year and a half later, two of the nine successes developed leukemia. So this is the other problem that we have to worry about.

Q. What about research on the effects of these foods?

HO. There have been so few experiments really addressing food safety. Proponents will say, "The Americans have been eating it for maybe a decade now, since 1994, and there is no evidence at all that anybody has died from eating GM food." But of course, nobody has really been looking, and as you have no labeling, you don't even know if you have eaten GM food directly. In any case, most of the GM goes into feeding your animals, so at least you're probably once removed from direct GM food. However, the Centers for Disease Control's own study, published in 1999, found that incidences of food-borne illness have risen from twofold to tenfold as compared to a 1994 study. That was when the first GM food (a transgenic tomato — "Flavr Savr") was grown to become available. Of course, that's not evidence that these illnesses were caused by GM food — critics could question whether the earlier study was done using different methodology — but at least this is something worth investigating. Plus, in Britain, we do have scientists such as Arpad Pusztai, a senior food scientist in Scotland, who was supported by the government to do food safety research.

Arpad Pusztai has been something of an enigmatic annoyance to members of the genetic engineering fraternity.

I have never been able to reach that great scientist, but his recorded message became a part of the BBC archives after much drama attending his research at Rowett Research Institute in Scotland. Dr. Pusztai demolished a concept that was espoused in the late 1900s, that genetic engineering was essentially the same as seed hybridization. The explanation of the Hudson Institute and all like-minded professors, so distorted findings of this type, it became an embarrassment to print them by our scientifically oriented editors. On August 10, 1998 Pusztai gave a television interview regarding his study on potatoes. On the air and in print, Arpad Pasztai revealed that genetically modified potatoes caused damage to test animals. Having done the research, Pusztai informed the interviewer "I couldn't believe it." Pusztai reported that the line of seeds used had been proven stable since 1992. When he fed the potatoes to test animal's stimulated growth resulted. Immune systems suffered damage. Hearts and livers decreased in size. Brains became smaller than controls. Speaking to the *Word in Action* program, Pusztai said genetically modified foods had not maintained stability before being allowed into the market. As with chemicals of organic synthesis, the new blunder was plied to expel the old, if the advertised intent of the modifiers is to be believed.

Subjects in the Pusztai experiments had been genetically engineered to produce a protein called albumin. Albumin genes had been taken from the bulbs of a snowdrop plant. Engineered into the potato, the snowdrops created a mix the stabilized potato couldn't manage.

At issue was the proactive idea that a pesticide could be built into a plant and still produce without significant change.

The same biological geneticists entreated the FDA to certify for use and sale BGH milk generated by the insertion of bovine somatropin into the animal itself.

Controlled experiments could easily name the damages and identify the victims, but proof seemed superfluous, when hearsay rules on the pivotal events. Withal, this side departure from the real purpose of the Olree Standard Genetic Chart merely confirms the complexity of the system in which we are all enjoined. It does not speak well for official and political science when unscientific sectors are lionized and foreign objectors are vilified. Officals seem satisfied to write new procedures as useless and irresponsible as the toxic era from which some few informed people are trying to escape.

The study presented here, nutrition — with special attention to the role of trace nutrients — is suggested as the key to immunity and health.

It rejects the practice of nutrition based on designer genes as being no more scientific than earlier attempts to turn base metals into gold.

It is now a matter of record that insects coming out of GMO fields are themselves genetically modified. This is not a consequence of sprayed fields, but rather because of the plants that are genetically modified. The literature nowadays tells us of monobacteria. These bacteria are said to go from the atmosphere into the human body, into the septic systems, and back into the environment. This suggests that genetically modified food is to become as prevalent as air. As we genetically modify our bodies, we genetically modify the monobacteria that live off us.

Genetically modified food means genetically modified bacteria that eat the genetically modified food. The wind wholesales and retails between farm fields, county to county. Genetically modified bacteria exchange genetic material not only within their own species, but more often with other species in an effort to stay alive. The host plant may absorb minerals from the soil, but now these genetically modified genes are causing plants never intended to be genetically modified to submit to the genetically modified bacteria, activity now moving from species to species to species. Weeds are not exempt from this modification. The last scare of all suggests a genetically modified world.

The Olree Standard Genetic Chart that follows in Part 2 has a subliminal suggestion. It is that the damage can be reversed if the appropriate minerals become the farmer's first line of attack and defense. Properly fed, the plants we use for food might then reverse the genetic manipulation. With the proper minerals, nature can then exhibit her patience and capacity for forgiveness.

From a genetic point of view, GMO simply means taking the weakest and giving it more strength. Bacteria are the weakest. Now they can multiply with reckless abandon.

Some plants are now exhibiting a capacity to spin away from the GMO blueprint in several generations, which may be one reason behind Monsanto contracts forbidding farmers to save seeds or replant saved seeds, and forcing them to buy the latest generation of seeds from the Monsanto corporation.

The scenario for plants is not the one that bacteria use for their choreographed existence. Once a bacterium gains the knowledge needed to resist pesticides or GMO intervention, there is no evidence that the new knowledge is ever lost. For instance, several hundred weeds are now immune to herbicides that once annihilated these same weeds with ease. Bacteria are several times more capable of incorporating survival capability into their genes.

After all the pros and cons have been considered, the advocates of GMOs always reach for their hole card. It has a name: yellow rice. This GMO product has been trotted out as an answer to malnutrition and poverty. Its major claim is that of a vitamin A product, no different than fortified orange juice, vitamin D manufactured milk, salt with iodine, or breakfast drinks with calcium. Most importantly, golden rice is the trump card in getting reluctant consumers to accept a concept advertised so heavily in metro dailies.

As a result of specious argument, some international leaders have been swayed, the instrument of their conversion being golden rice. This so-called miracle crop is said to require less pesticides, less nitrogen and phosphorus, all the while offering impoverished people better nutrition. Presidents Clinton and Bush II have added their bully pulpits to the PR effort. The conjured fact of 40,000 lives saved each day supported the presidential imprimatur.

Turning base metals into gold has never had the promise claimed for golden rice, but when we turn to science and database information, golden rice appears to be little more than a public relations ploy. After all, public support has to be revived if GMOs are not to die aborting. Greenpeace has challenged the claim that golden rice would prevent vitamin A deficiency among the poor. A report in the January, 2000 issue of *Science* asserts with damning finality that golden rice produces lower levels of beta-carotene than hoopla has suggested. It would take about nine kilograms of cooked rice to support the required dietary intake of vitamin A. Greenpeace extrapolated that three servings of golden rice would deliver only 10% of the required dietary level.

Withal, the tent pegs seem surely anchored, but in fact the ground is sandy and routine uprooting can be expected. I will reserve other suitable commentary for its outlined place in the last chapter.

The Trace Mineral

Around 1980 Richard Olree woke up from a dream state with a memory not unlike the half-dream Kekulé saw in his fireplace. For Kekulé, the smoke gamboling as the embers burned had carbon grabbing its own tail: the hexagon. The double helix came to the fore again when Watson and Crick modeled the DNA and RNA for *Nature* magazine in 1953.

In 1981 Richard Olree wrote down his first master chart revealing the relationship between minerals and subatomic particles of the human spine. That exercise kicked open the door to an understanding Dean Saunders had announced a half century earlier. Racing ahead of the state of the arts, Olree also made comparisons to color therapy, aroma therapy and acupuncture. Alongside his chart he made reference points of 1 to 64 — 1 being at the top, 64 at the bottom. Olree then added Eastern philosophy to the mix. In the process he came across the philosophy called *I Ching.*

"I started studying the psychological profile of the *I Ching* in relation to the minerals in the human spine. When I saw people having certain bones out of place, I found a relationship to certain natural dispositions," Olree explained, as these principles were developing. In 1995 Olree came across a book by Johnson F. Yan called *DNA and the I Ching.* The writer had a mathematical expression revealing how the *I Ching* tied in to DNA. Archimedes, discovering how to measure the king's crown for gold while in the bath tub, was not more excited than this modern geneticist at his own revelation: the mineral-amino acid connection for the messenger RNA.

The lesson was clear. When the DNA makes a copy of itself, whatever it wants the cell to do, it asks help from the RNA, the workhorse of our being. In effect, it goes out to the cell and says, "Make this!" The cell complies. If the messenger does not have the proper minerals, the copy of the cell is going to be faulty. DNA has its priorities. If one mineral falls on an acupuncture energy field called the heart, circulation will grab that mineral trumping other requirements.

Yttrium shortage, for instance, requires the brain to suffer. Calcium will step in as a poor substitute whenever yttrium is absent, a consequence being the construction of stone as a veritable contaminant in the organism.

Without upstaging the encyclopedic content of Part 2, it is now appropriate to point out that the degenerative metabolic diseases known as Lou Gehrig's disease, Alzheimer's, multiple sclerosis, and Parkinson's disease all relate to yttrium deficiency. Olree likes to think that some of these cases can be improved to some extent.

On the same frequency as yttrium is boron. It has the same oxidation state. It also affects the same acupuncture site. Yttrium and boron are the two brothers, albeit not identical twins. They hang out at the same place and do the same thing. The multiple sclerosis patient often responds to the yttrium-based *Bifidobacterium bifidum* and *Bifidobacterium longum*. Turmeric, a spice, also figures in successful therapy. Turmeric has been shown to cross the blood barrier carrying boron. Hopefully, it carries the bacteria-based protein for cellular brain regeneration. Yttrium has to arrive through the action of the bacteria in the intestinal tract. These bacteria have respiration. They have waste products. The human being absorbs the yttrium waste product. These get carried through the system after absorption.

The degenerative conditions cited above ask for yttrium, boron, and the spice turmeric, with a maximum dose of selenium.

When the time comes, we will go to the 63 position on the Olree Standard Genetic Chart. There we find lanthanum, an element that research suggests for kidney dialysis. Lanthanum carbonate picks up the calcium and phosphate in the most progressive dialysis procedure. Calcium is a major problem. It causes extreme arteriosclerosis, or hardening of the arteries, in patients on dialysis.

In writing these lines, I asked several doctors about lanthanum. They didn't seem to know about this mineral. One nurse recalled that the element had been seized and turned into a pharmaceutical under lanthanum carbonate, a pill.

When Olree took every chromosome and broke it down to minerals, and then tabled all the chromosomes, lanthanum turned out to be the most abundant mineral in the human genome, #63.

The genome calls for 64 minerals. To make this statement is to imply a simplicity that detailed study does not ratify.

The fact is, we do use a lot of trace minerals. Richard Olree annihilates the simplicity concept with a reflection on the discovery process. "I found chromosomes 1 through 22 sequenced from beginning to end using the four letters identified with the DNA ladder. Chromosome 1 is 1,400,000 pages long. It took 20 minutes for a fast computer to filter through all the numbers to produce a gross total of how many times a different mineral would be called for. Thus arrives the term "junk DNA" — DNA not used for anything in the state of the arts conceptualization now extant. But it is there for a reason.

The most abundant mineral is lanthanum. "I didn't understand why," recalls Olree, "at least not until I read about lanthanum carbonate, how it mops up the calcium and phosphorus. Even without peer-reviewed articles in the world's medical literature, the Standard Genetic Chart made the connection transparently obvious."

An aside is now in order. The hybrid automobile and mandated energy substitution for gasoline have brought lanthanum to the feast. Hydrogen fuel cells are now the popular science rage. The enthusiasm has been further energized by an extraction process based on lanthanum with a resultant drop in energy consumption by 90%, this to produce hydrogen.

If the human body permits such a drop in energy consumption in the presence of lanthanum by 90%, the role of number 63 on the Standard Genetic Chart becomes clear.

On the chart that details the values, number 63 comes first, not next to last.

Number 1 brings up the rear. There is a sound reason for this: it keeps the reader in the real world of minerals for most of the journey. From 22 to number 1, subatomic compounds figure. Subatomic minerals are the result of the ratios of calcium and magnesium, the positive value of subatomic particles. The ratio between nitrogen and phosphorus will deliver the negative 3 compounds.

Olree's understanding of the Standard Genetic Chart can be found in the valence expression. Position 64, lutetium, has a valence of positive 4.

Move up the scale to position 63, positive 3. 62 equals positive 2, 61 is positive 1, and 60 is 0. Position 59 is negative 1. The trip is from 0 to +1 to +2 to +3 to +4, then -3, -2, -1, and 0. That cycle repeats itself eight times, thus 8 x 8 = 64.

This is confusing only as long as the reader fails to comprehend the grammar of the subject. To assist in this regard it might be helpful to add gravity to our deliberations. The heaviest mineral is lutetium. Number 63, lanthanum, is lighter, and so on down the scale. Eventually we arrive at iodine, selenium, and all those traces holistic health practitioners talk about. Suffice it to say that those other lesser known minerals also figure. Some of the minerals have a bad connotation because they rely on homeostatic control, having the potential for being poisonous if present in certain excesses.

Reading the inventory of minerals in the ocean or even the minerals in the Table of Elements, a troubling discovery rises up to haunt our inquiry. There are trace minerals that are absent as prime entries on the Standard Genetic Chart. All are dragged into the process by cobalt, selenium or boron. Let this exploration rescue us from confusion.

If, all of a sudden, one takes in a mineral called iridium, the action is as follows. Iridium has a positive 3 electrical valence. It would displace yttrium or aluminum or boron. But because it has a different frequency from what is needed, there will be a three-dimensional shape to the enzyme being constructed. An amino acid is a simple protein. An enzyme is built by a group of amino acids held together by molecular forces.

Picture cars on an expressway. A chain linking all the cars together would preserve the reality of the individual cars. The chain is the workhorse RNA that tells the cars, the cells, to link together to make an amino acid. The RNA tells the cell that it wants a certain sequence of amino acids strung together to make an enzyme.

The source of the minerals usually, but not always, depends on food. Still, human beings, much like plants, harvest some minerals from the air. People who live near the ocean get iodine from the morning mist. This is also the case for some few particulates that we find magnified in that shaft of light entering a dark room. Speculation often enchants when questions have not been answered because they have not been asked. Associated with the 64 positions in the Standard Genetic Chart are the plants, food crops, weeds, forbs, and herbs that deliver some of the traces, source unknown. We like to assume that everything comes from the soil. This, however, is not always the case.

Richard Olree is more than a theoretical geneticist. He is a one-man advocate for remineralization of the earth, the use of minerals in dealing with metabolic disease conditions, and the installation of mineral therapy in the lexicon of all those who follow the lead of Hippocrates and his wisdom, "Let food be your medicine."

He writes to colleges telling them that, as a theoretical geneticist, he has a mineral counterpart, and they answer, "What in the world have minerals to do with genetics?"

It is not an easy thing to penetrate minds that believe they have all the answers, this when they've still to learn the question. Olree expects to revolutionize the professional's understanding of DNA in relation to minerals, and to exhibit a seven-league stride forward in reclaiming for humanity the health profile endowed by the Creator.

Richard Olree developed a periodic chart which included 22 subatomic particles that overlay the Standard Genetic Chart. DNA had adenine ($C_5H_5N_5$). RNA also has A, C, and G, with U (uracil $C_4H_4N_2O_2$) replacing T.

Any cluster of three stamps out a particular protein on the Standard Genetic Chart (SGC). As said, the Olree Chart overlays the SGC. Here, the development of the computer made possible scientific advancement far beyond the "simple" modeling of the DNA some 30 years earlier. Olree devised a computer program that digested an enzyme 2,000 proteins long, and it connected that protein sequence to a quantity of minerals broken down from the most to the least amount used.

All geneticists since the 1960s have used the Standard Genetic Chart. It is strictly a three-letter amino acid codon. Four letters make the chart look like an esoteric crossword puzzle. Decoded, the mass of letters turns out to be a message that is simple in the extreme. There are, as we have seen, four letters for DNA, with only three letters in each sequence. This translates into 64 possibilities, with none using the same letters twice.

The Genome Project merely denotes the breaking down of the chromosomes from one end to the other. This means taking all the genetic sequences in life — from a fly, a mouse, an elephant, a human, a willow tree, et al. If there was something magic about these 64 breakdown units, it lured the genetic masters who followed. But not all!

Richard Olree's mineral chart, which includes 22 subatomic particles, overlays the SGC. "Overlay" means that a connection has been installed. An explanation is now in order.

Instead of saying that UUU represents an amino acid, Olree now says that UUU represents phenylalanine and the mineral lanthanum. Each of the 64 valence sequences has a mineral key. The business of sequencing an enzyme consists of finding that this amino acid is hooked to that amino acid to this amino acid, on and on. Many pages and pages of these letters and the formula they represent are hooked together. Using a computer, Olree ran these sequences in a qualitative analysis of corresponding minerals. The concept is awesome and invites confirmation as in any scientific study. Convert genetic sequences into the qualitative analysis of minerals!

Olree laughs quietly, "When they say that this gene is broken, you'll get ovarian cancer, I have to say OK, when this gene is broken the most important mineral — based on the conversion of the protein sequence to minerals — is silicon."

Proteins have to develop into a three-dimensional object. If that three-dimensional object fails, then the tissue fails the plant, animal, or human being. The influence of the mineral allows the three-dimensional structure to perform. Minerals provide the electromagnetic influence supporting the structure's togetherness.

This much stated, we now arrive at the appropriate conclusion, and that conclusion is furbished and refurbished by every medical journal with peer-review status — blood, kidney, heart, brain, all receive the same message. When this gene doesn't work right, you'll get this problem! Problem, a prescription for drugs under the aegis of the medical establishment. A new drug to modify errant gene, output appears to be the Holy Grail.

Olree's findings seem to have faced the modern dilemma, and yet they have also complicated it. Since the same 64 minerals address every problem, it stands to reason that you can't affect one thing without affecting everything else. To create an enzyme, we rely on the Standard Genetic Chart with its 64 squares and 64 minerals in the squares. Outside the Standard Genetic Chart are minerals not accounted for. Take the mineral cobalt, usually missing in the soils of American farm acres. It is surrounded by five minerals above, titanium, vanadium, chromium, manganese, and iron and five minerals below, nickel, copper, zinc, germanium, gallium — trace minerals all. The body will rely on the SGC to create proteins to carry these trace minerals, to utilize them, but they are not part of the Standard Genetic Chart. Minerals on the SGC are used to make the protein sequences develop. Some of the protein sequences developed actually go out and bring in minerals from outside the Chart. They do this because they are made of carrier molecules for these metals.

Nature's plan makes the riddle of the Sphinx pale into insignificance by comparison. Thus, cobalt enters the Standard Genetic Chart, but the five minerals above it and the five below it rely on cobalt's presence to be utilized. Thus, iron, copper, nickel, zinc, manganese, germanium, and gallium all fall outside the SGC, yet they are always needed, for which reason enzymes are created to carry these minerals to their magnetic operating place.

Each enzyme has a beginning and an ending. The beginning of the initiation codon is methionine which is AUG. The number one ending is governed by hydrogen. The second ending is governed by sulfur. Sulfur is the 4th most abundant element in the body.

A third affirmation point comes into play via the mineral yttrium. Yttrium cannot be found in the body's tissue. Its action, it turns out, comes as a result of the bacteria in the intestinal tract. These bacteria utilize trace amounts of yttrium for their life cycle. We, in turn, absorb the bacterium protein sequences, all of which are created in the presence of yttrium. This pattern appears to be unique, a riddle inside an enigma.

One can speculate on, and one can rely on, settled science. Can it be that the Biblical patriarchs lived to such ripe old ages, often several times our lifespan, because they could make full use of all three minerals, permission for which was granted by their pristine environment? Research tells us that animals can have three times their normal lifespan when they make full use of all three minerals. They do not have to waste all of their trace minerals finding an alternative pathway for metabolic activity when radiation, starvation, or mineral toxicity closes down normal pathways.

The kidneys are basically governed by a mineral called sodium and by a subatomic particle. The main kidney energy field is situated in the subatomic field. It relies on a plethora of other minerals being in balance. The ratio of sodium to iodine is cause and effect.

Unfortunately, a long-term imbalance results in cells dying with no replacement — a broken-down piece of machinery! Attempts to initiate regeneration are a problem for which AMA medicine has no answer. Without working kidneys, the aging process becomes accelerated. The breakdown of cells is the consequence of toxic genetic chemicals in, on, or around the food supply, radiation, cellular starvation, or malignant nutrition.

Genetically modified fields are going to breed genetically modified insects. The resultant "creation" will be insects with a resistance commensurate with the so-called transgenic crop. How this errant crop will impact on the human being will be answered by time. Carbohydrates that feed the microorganisms will deliver genetic damage much as with insects. Genetically modified bacteria implies a change in the totality of life.

The creation of all sorts of modified bacteria is sure to shower mankind with allergies unnamed. An overview suggests that medicine is clueless, law is clueless, and society is clueless as to what will happen.

Two groups of people worked on DNA sequencing. One was a privately funded group which thought that it would copyright the genome findings. A second group was sponsored by the federal government. The first group threw in the towel after five years when it became evident that genome information did not open the path to profitable drug development. It was a case of refusal to allow conclusions to flow from the evidence. The conclusion came first, namely that only drug therapy belongs in health maintenance. The obvious connection between health and minerals was overlooked. Therefore, only test kits emerged from the study. Tests can identify genes that foretell predisposition to a disease because of a faulty gene, albeit the cash-cow benefits of the genome project never developed. Dreams of avarice portend ownership of patents with a corresponding drug evaporated the moment the sequencing was finished. This much realized, the entire body of knowledge passed into the public domain.

Panaceas die hard. In the case of the genome project, there remains afloat the idea that when this or that gene doesn't work, such and such a problem arises. Down track the information continues to be tantalizing with a breakthrough leading to a wonder drug — drug, drug, drug being the guiding light. The fairy tale for grown people has been and remains that everything can be solved with a drug and nothing but a drug.

First, the Standard Genetic Chart must be understood. This chart has a pecking order for the amino acids used to construct proteins. These are strung together by messenger RNA for the purpose of creating enzymes required for cellular function. The Standard Genetic

Chart now has a new meaning because each of the 64 three-letter codons has been assigned a discovered mineral equivalent.

The solution to all disease conditions appears to be seated in nutrition, not in pharmaceutical drugs panacea.

If you consult the eight squares composed of eight-letter entries (8 x 8 = 64), you will discern columns going down: one column U, one C, the next A, and the next G. Both RNA and DNA use three of the four letters. The fourth letter for DNA is T, thymine, and the fourth letter for RNA is U, uracil. In any case, they equal each other. They are interchangeable.

Only three of the four letters are used at one time in the codon. Thus, are the 64 squares achieved. The first square would be UUU, the second UUC, then UUA. All of these sequences progress, using the same three letters twice. All four letters are present, but only three comply with the Standard Genetic Chart. It is this chart and the development thereof that the Genome Project sought to explode into the greatest scientific development since Mendeleyev's Table of Elements.

On the Standard Genetic Chart with the mineral subatomic particle overlay, selenium has an extreme relevance when it comes to DNA-messenger RNA codon fixation. The four basic minerals are carbon, nitrogen, oxygen and hydrogen.

Consulting the Standard Genetic Chart, we find that carbon and nitrogen share the same amino acid with selenium. The amino acid is called arginine.

Oxygen has a -2 oxidation state, as with selenium. Bear in mind that selenium has other oxidation states. The periodic table lists selenium as having a -2 oxidation state, a +4 oxidation state, and a +6 oxidation state. Indeed, there are many minerals that have multiple oxidation states. The electron valence of any given mineral becomes as important as the mineral itself. If you consume the +4 or the +6 state of selenium, you can rapidly kill yourself because you are destabilizing the DNA.

All of the -2s in the mineral chart are governed by selenium. This means that selenium will govern oxygen. The relationship that carbon and nitrogen have is the same as arginine to selenium.

The most viable form of selenium is known as selenomethionine. Methionine is an amino acid used in all DNA to messenger-RNA starting points, also called the initiation codon.

All DNA sequences start with methionine, which doubles with rubidium, a +1 like cesium, sodium and potassium. The cesium-cancer connection causes rubidium to work better.

All DNA and messenger-RNA sequences start with methionine. Taking the supplement selenomethionine would be the best way to have selenium govern all starting points. The protection would be initiated by controlling sulfur, a termination point, and oxygen, a basic component of DNA. Selenium therefore becomes very important in preventing the formation of free radicals.

In 1981, when Richard Olree started developing his genetic chart, very little was known about selenium. Today, in the table of contents of almost every journal, selenium rates front-burner attention. "When I punch "selenium" into the search engine and find 400 or 500 or even 1,000 uses of the word," noted Olree, "I consider that a good database." It has come to our times to track a really good mineral. In a world of footnotes, this topic makes references outpace narrative, the research in selenium is that rich.

Item: The National Institute of Health suggests that dietary selenium decreases cellular changes that lead to prostate cancer.

Item: The tumor-suppressing protein, p53, found on chromosome 17, is a selenium-based gene that suppresses the formation of tumors.

Item: The human body makes 25 million cells every single day to replace the 20 or 25 million cells dying off. The white blood cells that line the small and large intestines to assimilate nutrients and challenge invaders, are replaced every seven years.

Every cell has a half-life and a total life-life. In its daily reproduction of 25 million cells, the body makes mistakes. If there is not enough p53 operative, then the defenses are down, and the body can allow mistaken reproductions to be put to work. Mistakes take on a life of their own. In other words, every form of cancer is a form of selenium depletion.

This shortage of selenium does not rely on complexity to understand. Simply stated, such a deficiency allows cells to be made and used that are creatively defective. The day comes in the seven-year cell cycle when also the defective cell has to die. Being defective in its role, it delivers its intention to live, in fact to copy itself and put wild proliferation into motion. That lethal deficiency could have happened at any time, up to years ago.

Selenium is second to yttrium as a lethal deficiency when it occurs. Its role is common knowledge among cattle producers, as Gearld Fry notes in *Reproduction and Animal Health*. Since the same genetic chart is used for cows, what applies to cows applies to humans.

Atomic Suicide

In 1955 Walter Russell wrote a book entitled *Atomic Suicide.* It contained his vision of the future for mankind as a consequence of using radioactive elements. As part of his study, he presented a periodic chart of the elements. The chart itself was written in 1926. It postulated the existence of 22 subatomic particles up to and including light, also known as photons. By 1955, in the wake of atomic tests around the world, he was inspired to explain to the literate reading public that radioactive minerals give off a radiation he called subatomic particles. Richard Olree has called Russell's chart a Biological Periodic Chart.

The chart itself was not fully understood at the time because no one examined, defined, or proved the existence of subatomic particles. A few investigators reasoned that Walter Russell was right. John Ott not only invoked the Biblical injunction, "Let there be light," he proved the health effects of full-spectrum light including the construction of vitamins by the agency of sunlight alone. Ott's several books on light and time-lapse photography are classic studies that engage the sun's energy as the prime mover, first through the agency of chlorophyll and photosynthesis, then through a subatomic presence so neatly defined by Russell.

A few years after Mendeleyev constructed his Periodic Chart of Elements, Walter Russell rewrote it. He agreed that there were primary minerals and isotope minerals. The primary minerals are the ones we use on the Standard Genetic Chart. The isotope minerals, or secondary minerals, are the ones that fall off the Standard Genetic Chart under the euphonious title, *trace minerals.*

The term *trace* must detain us for a moment. Take yttrium 89. It can be bombarded with radiation and made into 90. This isotope is quite different than what Russell called a full-toned mineral, as opposed to an isotope mineral. Walter Russell defined isotope minerals as the five elements that fit between scandium and cobalt, and the five minerals that fit between cobalt and arsenic. Those minerals fell under the operation of cobalt itself: the vitamin B-12 connection.

The 64-division is the Standard Genetic Chart. It is also the standard basis for the *I Ching*. Also, there is that same relationship between *I Ching* and DNA. Simply stated, Walter Russell postulated that there were 23 minerals lighter than hydrogen. These were all added onto the original periodic chart. In so doing, Russell found it necessary to construct a spiral-shaped chart. Turn the chart sideways and it looks like a sine wave, a half-circle going above the base line, then a full circle going below it, the cycles repeating themselves much like the oscillating wave of alternating current. "It was that chart," noted Richard Olree, "that prompted me to realize that the creation of the human spine in its earliest embryonic stages, called somites, brought the study back to chiropractic healing."

On a picture, somites line up. There are always spaces between somites. "What separates the spaces from the between-bone and non-bone eventually becomes disc material," Olree explained. "I realized," he summarized, "that the exact number of somites, if you include the disc space, comes to 64."

Somites can be found in any college biology text. Simply stated, the study of somites has to do with the earliest development of the human spine. There are 32 distinct somites. With a space between each, the count comes to 64. The human spine correlates to the 64 spaces on the Genetic Chart and also to the *I Ching*. Olree calculates that any time a segment in the human body is moved, this will change the outcome of the use of a particular mineral. "As it turns out," Olree noted, "we change the output of messenger RNA." Spinal manipulation for the most part enhances the expression of DNA through messenger RNA (mRNA).

In the presentation that follows, we hope not to create confusion between the Mendeleyev Periodic Chart of Elements and the revised Russell chart. Suffice it to say that Mendeleyev gave us a finding that we dare not abandon, that is the electron valence of the minerals. I mentioned this in the foreword when I noted the valence of 1 for fluorine, 2 for calcium, and 3 for phosphorus in the apatite crystal.

Most minerals have a single electron valence, but many minerals have multiple electron valences. The Olree Standard Genetic Chart lays out what mineral has to have what electron valence. He calls this the "mandatory valence." This cannot be underscored too much. If the use of the right mineral is correct, but the electron valence is wrong, then the output will be either wrong or fully compromised. In the final analysis, it is the Walter Russell chart that allows us to comprehend the electron valences needed.

At the University of Missouri pre-atomic era soil samples were sequestered, this because a professor or two realized that the world would never be the same again, and some reference to the past needed to be held in reserve.

Walter Russell was equally disturbed by those planes that flew over Hiroshima and Nagasaki. He "dreamed dreams" and "saw visions," as the Book of Joel has it. Like an Einstein who conceptualized $E=mc^2$, Russell saw what atomic energy would do to mankind in the fullness of time. In his book he wrote about the use of leaded gasoline, about contamination of the soil and the food chain. He scoffed at the idea of using atomic energy for a few years, then building containers to house radioactivity for thousands of years. It was as short-sighted as the medical society endorsing genetically modified food without even one database telling the population the long-range consequences. Russell would have agreed with the proposition that atomic energy belongs on the sun or miles beneath the earth, in the last case releasing radiation slowly in order to help create topsoil. In his books, Russell describes the role of subterranean radiation giving off particles to break down minerals.

This much stated, I believe that the Olree Standard Genetic Chart can be read in narrative form while at the same time its components are scrutinized, starting with 64 and moving down the chart in reverse.

The following 64 entries listing the minerals and subatomic particles in relation to the Standard Genetic Chart would lead one to understand why alternative medicine works without too much explanation. When research catches up to the level of understanding minerals and subatomic particles as related to DNA and messenger RNA, alternative therapy will likely come out on top without too much fanfare or "we told you so" reminders.

We may wonder aloud why chiropractic health management continues to gain in popularity. The answer is simple in the extreme. People

Walter Russell
He tapped the secrets of the universe!

Historically cited as a universal genius and an inspiration to others, that was Walter Russell — musician, illustrator, portrait painter, architectural designer, sculptor, business advisor, international businessman, natural scientist and philosopher. In 1925 he postulated the existence of the subatomic particles now validated as part of the Standard Genetic Code. Glenn Clark, one of the many writers who made Walter Russell their subject, once asked the great scientist about the secret of his life.

"I believe every man has consummate genius within him," came Russell's answer. "Some appear to have more than others only because they are aware of it . . . the awareness . . . is what makes each one of them into masters."

With more degrees than a brief biography dares to print, Walter Russell nevertheless believed in set study. For 50 years he and his wife Lao and associates operated a university without papers or exams, relying on solitude to inspire the self-taught student.

He wrote dozens of books. He faced the atomic age with the politically unpopular opinion that there were only two places where atomic energy belonged – on the sun and in the center of the Earth.

Often faced with a carping mediocrity, he said, "I believe mediocrity is self-inflicted and genius is self-bestowed."

Glenn Clark's world-famous biography, *The Man Who Tapped the Secrets of the Universe,* has been translated into several foreign languages. From commentary and from his wife's biography of him in *Atomic Suicide,* we learn of skyscrapers Walter Russell built, of cutting-edge research only now being embraced by physicists and geneticists, and of the University of Science and Philosophy that benchmarked an era. Real education "takes place up where the university leaves off" became the working philosophy of Walter Russell. Nowadays the Russell concepts are expanded via the Internet.

"We need to know and understand who we are," Walter Russell said, "and what is the purpose of our existence. We need to learn the science of ourselves, our creativity, spirituality, our process of thinking . . . our nature and destiny."

We can select paragraphs from the prolific writing of Walter Russell. Few will translate for us the reality of the situation as does the following.

"Ours is a dynamic, creative universe. Life is not static but ever-moving, ever-changing, ever-transforming, cyclic in seasons and cyclic in life patterns . . . we are co-creators of our destiny."

Because of our genetic makeup, we are partners in a creative process ordained for us by our blueprint for life and our penchant for genes to copy and replicate.

In 1921 Walter Russell had a creative experience. He drew inspired diagrams and wrote a far-seeing journal. He trained himself in science. He relayed the flow of his discoveries to some 500 scientists. They were not advanced enough to identify with what he was saying, for which reason a half century was to pass before fragments of his thought reached into credentialed chambers. His replacement for the Mendelyev table of elements is only now receiving the attention it has long deserved. It is the chart on which this study has relied and which now backbones the Standard Genetic Chart and Richard Olree's overlay of minerals.

We won't detain the reader with too many details. One, however, asks for reminding exposition. Russell experimented with transmutation at a Westinghouse laboratory in 1927. Meeting a measure of success, one can only wonder what would be his reception to Louis Kervran's *Biological Transmutations.*

Today, when peers of Russell's science gather, the work of this genius scientist is in their midst. His presence in this book is a reminder that we all stand on the shoulders of giants, earlier giants, and this new table of elements denotes a giant who passed from the scene on his birthday, May 19, 1963. He was born in 1871.

feel better. Illnesses vanish, often with little more than the movement of the spine, thereby changing how DNA perceives its environment and terrain, enabling the messenger RNA to invoke homeostasis. Unfortunately, research has still to validate, and the republics of learning remain tardy in supplying the required databases.

Add a phrase to your vocabulary: innate intelligence. Innate intelligence is the electromagnetic nature of the human being. This magnetism is directed toward and by the DNA through messenger RNA. It is an observed fact that the order of things has conspired to have chiropractors spend their time helping people rather than fill journals for peer review. Library shelves are swaybacked with journals proclaimed to be discipline journals, and yet there are no such journals reporting new research and vast databases for chiropractic healing as related to genetic research. The heart, the lungs, the kidneys, the specialized parts of the body, and the specialized diseases all have their journals, and all presumably consume ink by the barrels. As with one voice, these journals all speak of gene-related problems. It's always a case of "when this gene is broken, you get this kind of problem." No one can seem to answer the problem with a drug, for which reason answers have been found wanting. "I have cataloged between 1,500 and 1,800 genes reported broken, and I have analyzed the mineral chart in relation to the protein sequences confirmed by researchers," summarizes Richard Olree, "and I constantly see the same minerals as a high need in the genetic sequences. I see hundreds that never rise to the top as a requirement, always remaining in the middle of the pack, and I see minerals that stay at the bottom."

Some of the most important minerals like selenium, magnesium, and yttrium are called for heavily as a need for the gene, yet are absent, with the most devastating diseases as a consequence. As research in the future looks in on minerals and subatomic particles in relation to DNA, there will be a dramatic improvement in man's understanding of himself in relation to genes and genetics.

The future of medicine and healing cannot remain the property of pharmaceutical entrepreneurs. Health maintenance must fall under the purview of the farmer first of all. It must be the farmer's role to service the soil and those billions of unpaid workers, the microorganisms. The soils must feed the crops and animals, all of which require the proper minerals for proper genetic expression.

Modern medicine has a habit of making incredible assumptions. This is a harsh assessment, considering the primitive state of our knowledge. The pharmacy hopes to treat the symptoms and numb pain with drugs. Yet little attention is paid to disease. Research and pragmatic observation tell us that Alzheimer's disease is a consequence of aluminum in, around, and on our food supply, and in our water. Aspartame is indicted, and yet the Food and Drug Administration stays the course with its errant decision cemented into place during the first year of the Reagan administration.

Alzheimer's disease seems to claim age as its own. And yet even the natives of India know that turmeric added to the diet of the patient with Alzheimer's disease can help reverse the syndrome. The active ingredient in turmeric is curcumin and the mineral boron.

Chromosomes are the individual strands which often are broken by chemicals. One of the most produced chemicals in the United States is benzene. Recall how it was solution to the benzene ring that enabled scientists to construct the chlorinated hydrocarbons and organophosphates, and even enabled the analysis of the calabar bean with its tabun, soman and sarin. Benzene will rear its ugly head from five to 30 years later by breaking chromosomes 2 and 5. Portions of chromosome 2 then fuse to a portion of chromosome 5. The resultant abnormality is known as multiple myeloma and lymphoma.

A new example of the use of turmeric is found on the PubMed website *(www.pubmed.com)*, in the oncology section. All of the various cancers are listed. Also listed are the genes that are not working right. The inventory of information covers everything a physician might need. There is even a category called "alternative care." Under the heading of "multiple remedies" is the use of turmeric to dissolve cancer cells so that bone cells can return to a normal state.

Alternative therapy is gaining slowly among those who require highly scrutinized studies. As research shifts its gears out of its analytical mode, meaning "when this gene is broken, you get this," there will come an understanding of the play and interreaction of all the metals and minerals that the genetic code calls for and needs for proper functioning. There will come an understanding of the complexity and biodiversity of Earth itself. When the metals are adapted to the art of agronomy via the cattle, sheep, swine, poultry, and bread that we eat, then we will produce people capable of thought and reason.

I have hunted out new sources for these minerals; the ocean itself stands ready as a prime supplier. Coupling the Olree Standard Genetic Chart with mineral sources should be the beginning of a new science. Surely entrepreneurs will find a source for each mineral so it can be brought forth with the greatest quality and greatest efficacy. The ultimate goal is to answer a cry first uttered by Albert Carter Savage in his Depression-era booklet, *Mineralization: Will it Reach You in Time?*

More than 70 years has come and gone since Savage sounded his warning. Since then, the American health profile has become repositioned among the undeveloped countries of the world. Much of what Albert Carter Savage said has been validated by the strictest research.

Earlier in this volume Richard Olree and I noted that the human cell is quite capable of repairing itself, this as opposed to test-animal mice which have only a 17% chance of cell repair. But repair requires us to provide the living system with raw materials. The failure to understand minerals and their relationship to cell propagation and maximum life span has become a monument to wooden-headedness.

We are not required to seek the minimum for survival, but the maximum for human health. Some researchers state that it takes three to five human generations to cleanse the DNA of alcoholism. If it takes three generations for a mustard plant to produce the right flowers again, this when the DNA is clearly unaltered, we have our marching orders. If RNA is the template for all minerals, this is the message that DNA gets from RNA.

The cry goes forth. The necessary minerals are out there. Bring these magnetic influences back in, and let's straighten out our DNA.

Foods provide the necessary chemicals to fix broken chromosomes in the human body. There are basically two kinds of breaks. There is the single-helix break (DNA being a double-helix molecule) and there is the double-helix break. If you break one leg, you can move along on a crutch or with a walker. Getting both legs broken is a bit like a double-helix break. There is research, and there is more research. The single food most capable of repairing DNA is the red beet. This food has the necessary raw material to repair chromosomal abnormalities once they've been discovered. It's up to the body to make the discovery. The decision is made at the cellular level. "Can we fix it?" becomes the question. Cellular activity is shut down until the challenge is answered. If a cell is too badly damaged to be repaired, the message goes forth: die! The technical name for programmed cell death is cell apoptosis.

The first point of retreat is selenium. If there isn't enough selenium, then you can't tell the cell to repair itself or die. If a broken cell continues to live and manages to cope with the induced error, then cancer is made. Thus, we are required to put beets and the by-products of beets on a nutritional pedestal. Beets are the most powerful medicine in the pantry.

It is almost impossible to read all of the research that has been done on cardiovascular diseases, neurodegenerative diseases, connective-tissue diseases, indeed, the whole gamut of diseases. Diseases, organ by organ, are investigated by a gaggle of research people around the world, the objective being discovery of the causes for disease. Genes that do not express, genes that get broken, genes that are erroneously expressed as a consequence of broken chromosomes, all can be repaired because the central idea is to fix what is broken, express what is not being expressed, and shut off expressions that should not be expressed.

The Olree Standard Genetic Chart now fits in, as do the minerals that control other minerals. Not a part of this study are the Chinese acupuncture fields. Acupuncture meridian electric fields were discovered over 5,000 years ago. Superimposing these minerals on the laws of acupuncture reveals the husband-wife domination law, wherein six fields dominate six other fields. How these fields connect to minerals and subatomic particles, one mineral dominating another mineral, answers questions the healing disciplines seem reluctant to ask. These comments are more than mere hyperbole.

A classic example is the case of the urinary bladder connecting the three burner. There are 12 energy meridian fields. These are broken into four groups of three. Start with sacs: the gall bladder, stomach, and urinary bladder. All operate on the -1 frequency. The opposite of -1 is +1: the kidneys, spleen and liver. The small intestine initiates digestion, and the large intestine finalizes digestion. In acupuncture, the third energy field is called the three burner, an expression for the sum total of energy from food. Phosphorus governs the three burner. It is also the basis for all energy in the human body. A chemical process in the Krebs cycle goes from adenosine monophosphate to adenosine biphosphate to adenosine triphosphate. Adenosine triphosphate circulates throughout the body. In doing so, a molecule of energy is shed, releasing energy. It goes on and circulates as adenosine biphosphate. Another cell picks it up taking a phosphorus molecule, so now we're back to adenosine monophosphate. The intestines provide all this adenosine mono-, di- and triphosphate. They build the energy cycle.

These Chinese laws, to which we are obliged to submit, dominate certain fields. "I have discovered the energy fields for minerals and subatomic particles, enabling me to say that *these minerals dominate those minerals*," Olree explained.

If the working blueprint for a corn plant would fill a Carnegie library shelf, then expansion of this value into Chinese medicine would require a bank of libraries. The Chinese have broken down the regeneration cycle by hours, a rite of passage so to speak from one acupuncture meridian to the next.

Olree knows the coupling points, what mineral for what regeneration. Certain minerals dominate other minerals. This lesson runs like a clear blue stream through those 64 entries styled the Olree Standard Genetic Chart.

Some of these notes require memorization, much like learning the multiplication tables. Urinary bladder dominates three burner. Urinary bladder is iodine, and three burner is phosphorus. If you give yourself lots of iodine, it is always telling phosphorus what to do. But if you allow your iodine to run low, then that phosphorus is going to allow the three burner to short circuit the urinary bladder. A compromised bladder backs up into the kidneys soon enough, all with consequences that pharmaceutical pills a little less than answer.

In this summary, it is enough to point out that the food supply has become contaminated. Water leads the way. The Mississippi River has become the colon of the nation. Witness the dead zone in the Gulf of Mexico. Our water mains are full of chlorine, fluorine and aluminum. Agriculture since 1949 has been based on imbalanced salt fertilizers and toxic rescue chemistry. Almost immediately, in the wake of that errant science, the American eagle neared extinction. Quite late, the informed American public came to know that DNA walks with majesty through a dog, a horse, a human being, or a weed. One and all, we living things express our problems, all of us drawing our nourishment via a basic philosophy. Those genes have to be identifiable as Homo sapiens, otherwise the DNA might govern a puppy dog or a willow tree. Incredibly, the variation in genes is practically zero. There is a difference: the test horse will express its problem in tune with its lifespan. The *Homo sapiens* will take much longer.

As these trace minerals, halogens, noble gases, subatomic particles, and food notes are concluded, it seems necessary to ask the Food and Drug Administration, "What are you doing?"

Dr. Richard Olree has his opinion and solution. "They should disband the FDA, and start up a brand new agency of government named "The Genetic Stability Institute."

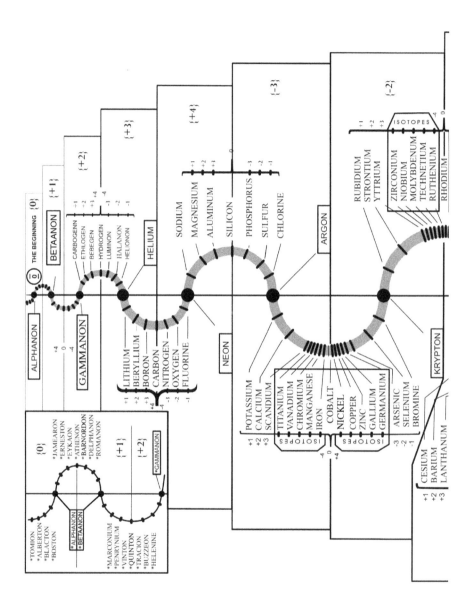

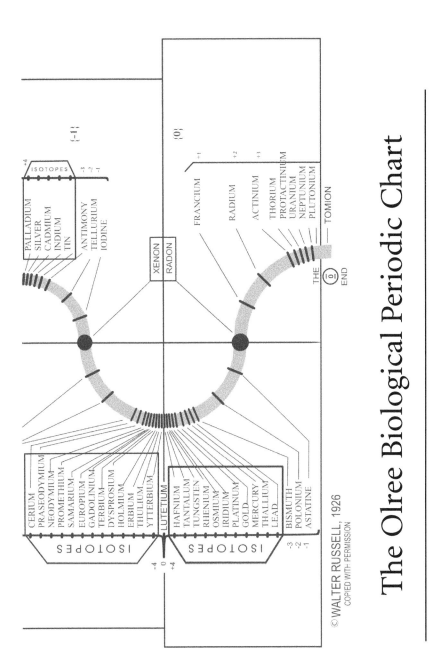

The Olree Biological Periodic Chart

© WALTER RUSSELL, 1926
COPIED WITH PERMISSION

Part 2
The Olree
Standard Chart

Understanding
the Olree Standard Chart

What, indeed, do we really know? Richard Olree asked, that is the Standard Genetic Chart. He has found that a periodic chart, including 22 subatomic particles, neatly superimposes itself over the Standard Genetic Chart, giving new meaning to that chart where each now has a mineral key.

Key

	I Ching Symbol	**#** Russell Number	
Three Codon Sequence			Location of Spinal Segments
Amino Acid Name	Number of Times in DNA		Acupuncture Meridian
Mineral	Electron Valence of Mineral		*I Ching* Number & Meaning

As a codicil to the above, it must be pointed out that a certain mastery of the grammar of the subject is required to read the genetic chart entries that follow in the next section. A step back in time to the 1950s, when Francis Crick and James Watson modeled DNA is indicated.

One entry in the genetic chart should serve to illustrate the language. There are 64 three-letter codons on the Standard Genetic Chart. Dr. Olree has superimposed a mineral chart over the Standard

Chart. Each codon is therefore affiliated with an amino acid and also with a mineral. However, there is an exception to amino acid sequencing when a termination point is reached. Sulfur, hydrogen and yttrium create the ending of a DNA to RNA sequence. Any segment of DNA created on any chromosome transferred to the cell to be made into a protein is called messenger RNA. The messenger almost always begins with methionine and ends with sulfur, hydrogen or yttrium. The second ending is hydrogen, and the third ending is yttrium. In the absence of sulfur, hydrogen and yttrium, the body can only make fragments of protein and these are degraded back to the original constituent makeup.

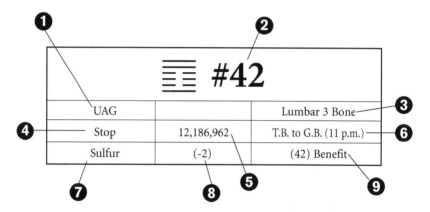

❶ Three Codon Sequence

This is the codon used in the Standard Chart. The letter U stands for uracil (from the RNA code), A and G stand for adenine and guanine respectively. The codon is now considered settled science.

❷ Russell Number

The number 42 designates the identifying position of the element and other parts of the code. The code itself runs from 1 through 64. Entries are listed in reverse so that subatomic particles postulated by Walter Russell take their appropriate place in terms of importance. This example fragment of the total 64 panels in the genetic chart appears on page 130 with complete commentary.

❸ Location of Spinal Segments

Lumbar Three Bone requires a background comment. Each three-letter codon is affiliated with an amino acid and a mineral. By superimposing the same sequence over the human spine as it is being developed from somites, it becomes the first development of the human spine in the embryonic state. There are 32 somites and there are 32 spaces between the somites, to be developed into vertebral disc space. In short, there are 64 points. When the Standard Genetic Chart is superimposed over the spine along with the acupuncture meridians, the master control panel is revealed. Three Bone designates one of those spinal links which is of maximum importance to chiropractic healing.

❹ indicates a terminal code in the DNA sequence.

❺ Number of Times in DNA

The number 12,186,962 denotes the number of times sulfur and this codon figure in DNA sequencing. This all is provisional and approximate.

❻ Acupuncture Meridian

The genetic chart and its individual explanations mention energy field meridians. These relate to acupuncture, a Chinese healing art. It has been in existence between 5,000 and 5,500 years, depending on the text one wishes to consult. Acupuncture energy field meridians denote lines of energy that travel through the body. There are 12, always grouped into threes. The first group has lungs, heart and the pericardial sac. All deal with pumping fluid, maintenance of vessels, and the heart sac. The second group includes the kidneys, the spleen and the liver. These deal with metabolic functions. The third group is composed of the small intestine, large intestine, and "three burners" (abbreviated T.B. on the chart). T.B. covers the sum total of energy garnered from the intestinal tract. T.B. denotes what one burns to keep warm, it was so named by the Chinese. The last grouping includes the stomach, gall bladder (abbreviated G.B.) and the urinary bladder.

Classical acupuncture holds that a two-hour reconstruction period governs each cycle. It takes 24 hours to regenerate the 12-energy-field meridian system.

Dr. Olree's chart superimposes the mineral involved on an hourly basis. This means there is one hour of complete regeneration and one hour of transition time. For instance, at 2:00 a.m., the liver meridian is in complete regeneration. At 3:00 a.m. energy passes from the liver meridian to the lung meridian in which calcium governs. At 4:00 a.m. the lung meridian is in full regeneration which is controlled by the mineral scandium. This goes on hour by hour, success being monitored by the minerals named in each entry on the genetic chart.

❼ Mineral
Sulfur is the mineral for the UAG codon entry.

❽ Electron Valence of Mineral
The designation –2 denotes the valence of the mineral. The range moves from positive to negative. All minerals on the face of the earth have electron valences. Indeed, some minerals have more than one electron valence. An example is selenium which often has a –2 oxidation state. Selenium also comes in the form of +4 and +6, both extremely toxic.

Iodine is also a classic example. Olree calls for iodine to be a –1. However, there are other oxidation states, +1, +3, +5 and +7 under certain circumstances. When this student of genetics laid out his chart, he noted the best oxidation state the mineral had to be in for metabolic use. The reader will note that there are only three termination or STOP codes, sulfur, hydrogen and yttrium. On all other entries the STOP position is occupied by the amino acid in question. In the case of codon AUU, position 39 on the genetic chart, mineral aluminum, the amino acid is isoleucine, as an example.

❾ Number 9
The *I Ching* and its corresponding meaning or impact are listed here. Each *I Ching* symbol comprises two halves, each containing a meaning; these combine to form a third, overall meaning.

These instructions stated, the reader can proceed to the chart itself with more complete understanding.

The Olree
Standard Chart

☰ #64		
CCC		Coccyx 4 Bone
Proline	12,362,927	Peri. to T.B. (9 p.m.)
Lutetium	(-4+)	(64) Before the End

We start with position 64 on that chart.

When DNA makes a copy of a portion for the cell to act on, the copy is called messenger RNA or mRNA. This is fundamental. CCC on the Standard Genetic Chart represents proline ($C_5H_9NO_2$), which is associated with the mineral lutetium. According to calculations by Richard Olree, this mineral will be found 12,362,927 times in the entire human DNA code, as constructed on May 14, 2004.

Lutetium is a mineral that apes cobalt. In fact, it is a carrier for other trace minerals. In turn, cobalt coupled to a cyanide molecule — carbon and nitrogen — creates vitamin B-12, the traditional link between metals and non-metals. Titanium, vanadium, chromium, manganese, iron, nickel, copper, zinc, gallium, and germanium do not appear on the Standard Genetic Chart, but they have a role in the genetic code through the use of carbon, nitrogen, and cobalt. Cobalt is a carrier, for which reason it is raised to a command position in the pantheon of minerals. The link between metals and non-metals is cobalt, simply stated and generally understood, hooked to an operative molecule called vitamin B-12.

Lutetium is a numbered mineral with the same classification as cobalt. If the human body has the use of the noted minerals, they must be affiliated with lutetium. The list reads as follows: cerium, neodymium, promethium, samarium, europium, gadolinium, terbium, praseodymium, thulium, and ytterbium. The role of this cited inventory has still to be established. Indeed, there may not be a role.

All of the listed minerals in the above paragraph have a +3 electric charge. They can easily affect the effects of boron, the master +3 mineral, or yttrium, a +3 mineral that controls one of the three termination codons.

Lutetium has a place in the genetic code, albeit a minor one since there is very little lutetium in our system. Finally, when the human genome was produced, and Olree had converted all the human genome into minerals, lutetium turned out to be either the most used, or 14th most used, mineral on the entire periodic chart. As we unfold the Olree Standard Genetic chart, the key at the beginning of this lutetium section must be kept in mind. The most abundant mineral and amino acid plant relationships that are applicable are listed in the "Sourcing the Elements" chapter.

☰☰ **#63**		

UUU		Coccyx 3 Disc
Phenylalanine	36,356,923	Pericardium (8 p.m.)
Lanthanum	(+3)	(63) After the End

UUU represents phenylalanine, which is affiliated with lanthanum. It has a +3 oxidation state, and it has an effect on the acupuncture meridian pericardium. Dr. Olree suspects that the use level will be downgraded by science because of the junk DNA concept. Of course there really is no junk DNA. DNA protects working genes with long protein sequences that have the ability to absorb electrical shocks and to disperse the electricity without damage to a working gene, a myelin insulation, so to speak. The mineral in trace amounts makes nerve function as an insulator for electric wiring, as well as to buffer events that can damage DNA.

Lanthanum simply has to be added to the common vocabulary. Few doctors are conversant with the mineral and fewer patients know of its metabolic role. Few worry about lanthanum supplementation.

Still, the DNA code calls for mass amounts of the stuff. The body uses the relationship between silica and lanthanum to act as the glue that holds "junk" DNA together.

We no longer need to speculate regarding the ability of animals in the wild to select nutrient sources endowed with health-providing minerals. Forbs in the field, leaves from flowers, nutritionally endowed grasses and herbs all point to nutritional excellence denied penned animals force-fed on highly refined carbohydrates. Botanists know how to grow and harvest plants that contain lanthanum, lutetium, and the trace minerals, but when the elements are not in the soil, plants deal with the shortfall by substituting trace minerals at a great expense of energy and trauma to their DNA.

Lanthanum is called for 36,356,923 times in the sequenced genome. Richard Olree warns that these numbers are not final. The definitive numbers await the final validation of decoding of DNA, a chore that challenges the capacity of DNA sequencing centers. Minerals also occur in the subatomic field. It is the protein that holds the calcium-magnesium ratio together. Subatomic minerals exist due to the presence and ratio of the same physical properties and the same and like electron valence.

☰☰ **#62**			
AGA		Coccyx 3 Bone	
Arginine	20,851,511	Kidney to Peri. (7 p.m.)	
Barium	(+2)	(62) Conscientiousness	

AGA designates the mineral barium. The amino acid is arginine. Barium has a +2 electron valence. It is attracted to -2. The AIDS virus thrives on barium. This appetite can be neutralized with selenium, which is a -2. The AIDS virus is spread via semen, and it loves barium. The AIDS virus is canceled by selenium-based molecules. Therefore, it feeds off the testicles. Since selenium is a resident of the brain, an AIDS infection will ultimately result in massive neurological deterioration. "If you shut off the light," counsels Richard Olree, "everything else fails. Your brain is the light. Everything that comes out of what we are is dependent on how we distribute light through our tissues via the subatomic particles and the human nervous system via all of the individual nerves."

This has long been a signal foundation for the chiropractic profession. Placement of the mineral nutrients in the spine governs how all minerals in the body work. The spine responds to excesses and deficiencies of the full pantheon of minerals. They are specific in their location and fixed in their oxidation state.

Barium is a +2 mineral, for which reason it has a major impact on the calcium-magnesium ratio. At this point, it is somewhat revealing to note that the skies are being filled with barium. "I don't think we'll ever see a barium molecule shoved out the back of an airplane in an aerosol operation that doesn't settle on land and sea," was the comment Olree handed off as these notes were set down.

Barium is inserted in the intestinal tract to enable photography. Barium also absorbs radiation. In X-ray photography, barium paints a picture in the dark. Barium falling from the sky answers the demand for some destruction of errant radiation. The offensive molecule is perceived to arrive from the sun. The cited reason for being of the barium-from-the-sky phenomenon is "holes in the ozone," and an attempt to do something about it.

Since it is called for by the genetic code, a trace amount of barium is probably necessary. In any case, every breath we take presents us with barium, give or take. Such a distribution system implies a damaging load. Barium will challenge only people who have no selenium to spare. For the person with a sufficient selenium load, and proper nutritional support, the arrival of barium merely means a -2 coupled with a +2 and a journey to the liver, gall bladder, intestinal tract and eventual disposal. People short on selenium will more likely have to endure barium toxicity. Those contrails in the sky are all calcium, magnesium, and barium, all +2s. The +3 minerals are titanium and aluminum because they both reflect sunlight at 90 degree angles, the goal being reflection of as much sunlight as possible back into outer space. The only antidote for aluminum toxicity is calcium, magnesium, and silicon.

Decades after the arrival of the AIDS virus, the signal question is: What makes these AIDS viruses tick? All the genetic sequences that Olree came up with are barium-based. Some barium is necessary or the genetic code wouldn't call for it. Yet an overload of barium appears to feed the virus. That much is simple enough. Could it be that poor nutritional support in effect incubates the AIDS virus when spray planes fend off sunlight over Africa? Are programs hatched by scientists educated beyond their intelligence delivering genocide?

Everyone conversant with the grammar of the subject that backbones this book knows that selenium is the nutrient that puts off the ultimate human experience — dying. All the AIDS cocktails, all the pharmaceuticals have less than marginal success in dealing with AIDS. People who go to medical doctors look for a magic bullet. Those who go to holistic doctors insist on adequate amounts of selenium. The word should go forth that selenium can either extinguish AIDS or quench its thirst. When the AIDS virus runs all the selenium out of the body, the immune system falls apart. Stated in another way, when selenium is spent, any virus that comes along can have a field day. The viruses we have in the body will prevail using our own machinery unless we have the buffering solace of selenium. With all its innate intelligence, the human body cannot comprehend the viral structure fast enough to do battle as fast as mutations occur, not unless selenium is present to lead the fight.

☰ **#61**		
GAG		Coccyx 2 Disc
Asparagine	15,860,260	Kidney (6 p.m.)
Cesium	(+1)	(61) Insight

GAG affiliates with the amino acid asparagine and is coupled with the mineral cesium. It is often linked to the concept, alkalize or die. It has an electron valence of +1. There appear to be three or four possible electron valences found in nature, but +1 alone assists the human being genetic sequencing. It also has a profound effect on the acupuncture meridian of the kidney, which regenerates at 6 p.m. Cesium's horn of plenty can be found in herbs and plants that are listed in the Sources section of this book. Cesium is a veritable sponge for the purpose of wiping out cancer, supporting the immune system, and short-stopping disease in the first place. Cesium can be purchased through the internet at various alternative cancer-related websites.

Cesium protects health. Accordingly, it is difficult to come by as a supplement because of the government's penchant for health destruction, not prevention. Much as nature loves fecundity, she also loves balance, and an imbalance of cesium is the reason for regulators saving us from ourselves. Cesium will suppress other +1 minerals such as potassium. It is always advisable to take cesium with potassium, thereby avoiding an acute potassium deficiency.

The observed facts of the situation tell us that cesium raises the temperature of cancer cells to a point where they simply die. Once dead, cellular respiration delivers them to the spleen, gall bladder and liver for removal.

Cesium has been shown to support the immune system to help individuals with severe health problems. It is an alkaline mineral that behaves similarly to sodium, potassium and rubidium. CAUTION: TAKE ONLY UNDER SUPERVISION BY A PHYSICIAN!

Cesium functions in the body: ion antagonism, cell osmosis, permeability regulation and maintenance of colloidal state of the living cell.

Signs of possible deficiency: compromised immune system, decreased cell osmosis.

☰☰ **#60**		
GAU		Coccyx 2 Bone
Asparagine	12,605,663	U.B. to Kidney (5 p.m.)
Xenon	(-0-)	(60) Limitations

GAU is another codon for the amino acid asparagine. Mere mention of this amino acid brings into focus xenon, a noble gas. The coccyx 2 bone is the spinal reflex for GAU and this connects the urinary bladder to the kidney meridian at 5 p.m.

How does a noble gas interact in the human body? Noble gases are supposed to be inert and have nothing to do with the human body and its functions. Richard Olree puts it this way, "I believe the genetic code calls for all the noble gases to have their play in our lives. We don't have many genetic sequences where xenon is called for as a really abundant element in any of the genes I've done. It hardly ever comes to the top, but when you sequence various herbs, you do find xenon at the top."

Every noble gas that occurs in the periodic chart actually enters all the minerals that have a charge. Square in the middle is the digit zero. To the left is +1 and to the right is -1. Then left is +2 and right -2; then +3 and -3. Since they have no polarity, they probably have more psychological expression in life than they do physical. If you have a 0 polarity mineral, you don't pull it this way or that. You can't push it into doing things. It can't be handled because it has no charge. To illustrate the point, radon gas can go through a concrete wall. Obviously, concrete and brick are not solid. Accordingly, officials tell us to vent the basement because radon can incubate radiation. Radon is in the ninth level of minerals, meaning that human beings want nothing to do with that level because that's the radioactive end of things.

The point here is that noble gases do have an effect. If we say that asparagine affiliates with xenon which has a polarity of zero, that is a correct statement. But asparagine shows up in other minerals with a charge, and this will influence how asparagine works. Xenon is the second most-called-for element in Egyptian onions. This merely hints at the vast complexity of nature's blueprints, and hints at the mystery of a noble gas so elusive in the human genome, yet so present in herbs. Xenon is number 1 in that sequence.

This short book cannot accommodate the encyclopedic inventory some of these passages might suggest. Suffice it to note that anything that has ever been sequenced anywhere in the world, whether plants, bacteria, or fungus, appears in a database styled www.kazusa.org/codon/. This is an alphabetized list, some parts of which are used to elucidate the point being made.

☰☰ #59		
CAG		Coccyx 1 Disc
Glutamine	19,084,067	Urinary Bladder (4 p.m.)
Iodine	(-1)	(59) Reuniting

CAG denotes the amino acid glutamine, and the mineral is iodine. The heaviest metal on the periodic chart, with a -1 valence, and the one with the most power is iodine. Iodine is stored and regulated in the thyroid and is a major component in the production of thyroxin, the number 1 free-floating hormone in the bloodstream. It is coupled to glutamine, the number 1 free amino acid in the bloodstream which controls the urinary bladder meridian with a coccyx 1 disc reflex. Iodine is the thermostat for the human body.

One of the most overlooked and important aspect of critical diagnoses, according to Richard Olree, has to do with the most common tumor found in women: the fibrocystic tumor, also called ovarian cyst. This is a caffeine toxicity with an iodine deficiency. It is a problem that causes potassium imbalance. Iodine is a -1. It is there to hold and pressure the +1 of potassium. Potassium falls out of solution into pockets called cysts. The most notorious are "fibrocystic breast disease" or uterine abnormities. The most common tumor found in women is a caffeine toxicity-iodine deficiency syndrome. When women are iodine deficient, they crave chocolate, the repository of more caffeine than coffee. The caffeine addiction is a near perfect insurance policy for the tumors mentioned above.

If you live in the United States, $1/10$ milligram of iodine will keep you alive, this according to the recommended dietary allowance. In Canada the government decrees that the dietary allowance is what it takes to maintain optimum health: 1 milligram. Therefore, it takes 10 American pills to equal one Canadian pill. One Canadian physician tells his patients, "Take about 16 of our Canadian pills a day for a couple of months, cut back to one a day for a couple of months, then go to one a week. You will get rid of all your fibrocystic tumors. They'll just dissolve and go away."

Anyone who lives near the ocean gets enough iodine out of the air. Anyone inland needs to give the iodine load serious consideration.

The brain can't develop without iodine. The classic name for such a shortfall is cretinism. A baby without iodine will turn out to be mentally retarded.

Astute monitors of the human creation routinely take note of metabolic mischief inherent in what passes for a culture. We are now looking at second, third, and fourth generations nurtured on phosphoric acid from soda pops. We are into the second generation on NutraSweet. Within ten years we will be in our second generation on Splenda. The intake of aspartame assures a pandemic of diabetes, and a fifth generation retarded by fluorine in the water supply. "We are in our third or fourth generation of DNA's being scrambled before reproduction, better genetic selection first being ruled from the field," is the Olree assessment.

Iodine does show at the top of many genetic sequences. People with low body temperatures are most commonly low in iodine.

One way or another, iodine and glutamine touch everything in the body. It constructs the most abundant amino acid found in the bloodstream. This much stated, we now put into clearer focus the devastating role that fluorine plays in trumping sister halogens chlorine, bromine and iodine. Fluorine inhibits iodine uptake by the thyroid gland, hence a deficit of thyroxin and an inability to metabolize sugar, among other things.

Hormones that are built with fluorine instead of iodine, or one made under the influence of fluorine instead of iodine, force the body to an awesome task: getting rid of the garbage hormone. The legacy is also awesome: a burned-out genetic code.

The urinary bladder finally presents the physician with an acceptable symptom. Even a cursory view of an acupuncture chart reveals that the bladder meridian starts at the little toe, runs up the back of the leg, covers two-thirds of the back, meanders up the neck, runs over the head, finally arriving at the corner of the eye next to the nose. "Sleepies" in the eye represent an iodine deficiency. "Sleepies" are matter in the corner of the eyes.

Eye doctors have other explanations, but kelp answers the problem. However, that is not what the eye doctors recommend as they reach for the prescription pad. The resultant pharmaceutical will cover up the symptom and leave the cause untouched.

As an essential trace element iodine is essential for the metabolism of fats and is important for physical and mental development. Iodine is concentrated in the thyroid gland and helps guard the brain and other parts of the body from harmful toxins that could have entered through the blood. This mineral helps with the assimilation of phosphorus and the utilization of calcium. Iodine must have the mineral selenium to make the thyroid work properly.

Iodine functions in the body: aids in the assimilation of minerals like calcium, silica and phosphorus; found in the blood, spleen, tears and perspiration, essential for thyroid, spleen, liver and brain function and neutralizes albumin.

Signs of possible deficiency: goiter, cretinism, numb fingers, nervousness, awkwardness, stitches, flabby skin, drooling and childlike behavior.

䷰ #58

GCU		Coccyx 1 Bone
Alanine	13,175,325	S.I. to U.B. (3 p.m.)
Tellurium	(-2)	(58) Encouraging

GCU affiliates with the amino acid alanine as shown by the Olree Standard Genetic Chart. The tellurium's reflex point is coccyx 1 bone and connects the small intestine to the urinary bladder meridian. Tellurium has an oxidation charge of -2. It's what gives garlic its smell and taste. It is extremely important in tumor-suppression protein sequences. It helps selenium in terms of helping the body ward off cancer, tumors, and virus infections. It is easily displaced by polonium 210, a -2 mineral that is released from cigarette smoke and is a radioactive mineral with 210 electrons which annihilates selenium and tellurium. With these two nutrients suppressed, tumor-suppression protein sequences quit working.

Protection by organic tellurium compounds against peroxynitrate — mediated oxidation and nitrate reactions. It was reported in June 2005 in *Acres U.S.A.* that nitrated lunchmeats increase your chances of getting cancer by 67%.

	☰ #57	

CUG		Sacral 5 Disc
Leucine	19,090,181	Small Intestine (2 p.m.)
Antimony	(-3)	(57) Penetrating Influence

CUG on the Olree Standard Genetic Chart affiliates with leucine, an amino acid that has to do with muscle function. It also is involved in the regeneration of the small intestine at 2 p.m., with a spinal reflex at the sacral 5 disc or the ligament connecting the sacrum to the coccyx.

Antimony is a -3 mineral, an alternative initiation code. Methionine is a primary initiation codon when DNA replicates itself to make messenger RNA. Not every genetic sequence starts with methionine. There is an alternative initiation codon with leucine, the governing mineral being antimony. The acupuncture meridian is the small intestine and the spinal connection is the sacral 5 disc or the ligament between the coccyx and the bottom of the sacrum.

Of its industrial uses there are plenty. Industry keeps antimony under lock and key because the heroin junkies are always on the hunt for its special effect as a cut or dilution for heroin.

There are two alternating initiation codons with sodium (UUG) being the other. Affiliation of antimony is with the acupuncture meridian small intestine. It has a role in maintaining nitrogen levels. Suffice it to say that antimony is a trace nutrient: a little goes a long way and too much can be lethal. Just the same, it is generally considered to be under homeostatic control.

Antimony rides along on the wings of xenon as portable passenger in the air. In the soil it attaches itself to iron, manganese or aluminum.

Classical chiropractic conditions of the coccyx areas known to receive nerve fibers from this spinal segment are rectum, anus. Some of the conditions that can follow a pressure on or interference with these nerves: hemorrhoids or piles, pruritus or itching, pain at end of spine on sitting.

☷ #56

AGC		Sacral 5 Bone
Serine	13,173,076	Heart to S.I. (1 p.m.)
Rhodium	(+4-)	(56) Traveling

AGC on the Olree Standard Genetic Chart affiliates with the amino acid is serine, which affiliates with others minerals like boron and bromine. As noted elsewhere, aluminum drives boron down, suppressing the boron-serine connection. This in turns drags all the bromine out of the equation leading to Parkinson's syndrome. Serine has its tryst with rhodium. Like cobalt and lutetium, rhodium is a carrier of other minerals into the genetic code.

The spinal connection is the sacral five bone and connects the heart meridian to the small intestine which regenerates at 1 p.m. just like carbon.

Rhodium is responsible for the absorption, utilization and excretion of zirconium, neodymium, molybdenum, technetium, ruthenium, palladium, silver, cadmium, indium, and tin.

Cancer and viruses may someday find themselves blinded by the light of therapies based on recent Purdue University chemistry research. A team of scientists has developed a group of rhodium-based compounds that, when exposed to light, can kill tumor cells and deactivate a virus closely related to the West Nile and Yellow Fever viruses. Unlike the ordinary substances used for chemotherapy, these chemicals are not harmful to the body in general — they only become lethal to DNA when activated by light of a specific frequency. While therapies based on the discovery are likely many years away, the compounds could have potential as anticancer agents and for blood sterilization. We have proven in principle that light and chemistry together can destroy tumor cells and the Sindbis virus, a member of a group of viruses that cause encephalitis, fever and arthritis. This type of rhodium research offers hope that someday we may be able to replace standard chemotherapy drugs with others that are far less generally harmful to a patient's body and guarantee safe, sterile blood for transfusions.

☷ #55

UGA		Sacral 4 Disc
STOP	18,468,491	Heart (12 noon)
Yttrium	(+3)	(55) Zenith

Yttrium helps the heart meridian regenerate along with boron at 12 noon. The spinal connection is the sacral 4 disc space.

Yttrium has been and remains the mystery element. You can look in vain for a library or even a volume on yttrium, and yet it emerges as an element of signal importance to human health. The diligent student will come up with Chaim T. Horovitz, the author of *Scandium and Yttrium in the Biological Process.*

Olree has merely codified existing peer-reviewed research done in the last 50 years. What he found fascinating with yttrium was obtained from test animals. These animals, repeatedly given daily doses of yttrium subcutaneously never had a bad reaction. The yttrium was hustled to the intestinal tract and mostly eliminated in 24 hours.

Olree found the yttrium connection a great puzzlement. Then, in 2002, a patient presented a multiple sclerosis journal. In that July 2002 article a geneticist was interviewed. MS, he said, came down to two broken genes. The analysis provided the answer, except that it didn't work. The components simply would not wrap around the nerve endings, the myelin sheath. This sheath sometimes calcifies. The body tries to prevent neurological developments by calcifying the area surrounding the offending development.

"I sought and found the FASTA sequences," Olree recalls, "and I converted those FASTA sequences to minerals. To my surprise, the most important stop-termination code to both sequences was yttrium. Not only was yttrium the most abundant stop-termination codon, it was the first and second most important mineral for the whole protein sequences."

It was a revelation no less startling than Newton's falling apple. Suddenly, clear cases of yttrium deficiency not allowing for protein synthesis were revealing themselves. Not so clear was where yttrium would fit into place. It took Olree from 2002 to 2004 to figure out how yttrium works in the human body.

It was back to Horovitz's testament and the intelligence that injection never resulted in illness. The only consequence of yttrium injection was extreme conservation of ultra minerals and a three-fold increase in the lifespan of test animals.

Olree concluded that a new lifespan was a natural consequence of the third termination codon on the Standard Genetic Chart requirements. The first termination codon is governed by hydrogen, the second by sulfur, the third by yttrium.

The second termination code should detain us long enough to point out that sulfur governing the second termination code leads us to the sulfur antidotes so much in use. Modern medicine adds antidotes to change the termination code of a microbe, which is the basis of sulfur-based antidotes. Yttrium has a +3 valence. The very word "yttrium" means "oxygen-seeking." Pure yttrium has to be packed with argon, an inert gas. If you spill pure yttrium, it'll burn a hole in the table, its affinity for oxygen is that great.

Since yttrium is always shuttled to the intestinal tract, the site of its greatest action, the idea of an yttrium-based probiotic suggested itself. Since there is no standard list of probiotics, Olree assembled his own. He next tapped into the genetic sequences in order to tie those sequences to probiotic and minerals and subatomic particles. He postulated that in doing this he would find something that dealt with yttrium.

It turned out that yttrium is barely used in the assembled list of probiotics. Indeed, most of the probiotics use aluminum as their most important mineral. Aluminum is the third most prevalent mineral in the earth' crust. All of Earth's bacteria have evolved using aluminum in their makeup and design, except for two probiotics: *Bifidobacterium bifidum* and *Bifidobacterium longum* do not utilize aluminum to any degree. Here's the scenario: When aluminum comes down to the middle of the sequence, yttrium goes up. This is an inverse relationship. Still, they share the same electron valence, +3. It is similar to sodium going up while potassium goes down. Calcium goes up, magnesium goes down. Any life form affiliated with the yttrium-based termination codon has a high requirement for the metal. In the presence of high aluminum, that life form would be suppressed. These few points indict the use of aluminum in foods and cosmetics. Aluminum suppresses yttrium.

Now we encounter selective starvation, always present in neurological diseases. Thus, the yttrium arriving through the foodchain is diminished or extinguished. "When you chew food," Olree explains, "and mix it with saliva, stomach acids, gastric juices, and gall bladder juices, this slurry that goes into the intestinal tract feeds the bacteria in your intestines. You actually have more bacteria in your intestines than there are red blood cells in your blood." These bacteria have a respiration cycle. They require food. If you do not have enough of the right bacteria, a new genetic sequence implodes. We absorb bacteria byproducts through our macrophages which line the intestinal tract. That is how selective starvation happens. No yttrium-based bacteria, no yttrium-based termination codon. If you have no termination codon the cells make a nonsense protein. The cells are able to recognize a nonsense string of amino acids and force the string to the centrosome for deconstruction back to the original amino acids.

The signal of the process going backward is fermentation. Gas means fermentation, not digestion. Fully 30 to 50% of the bowel movement is bacteria. Any cowman knows that a cow cannot be given access to a cherry tree when fall and frost arrives. Yttrium and its affinity for oxygen will assert themselves, almost always with lethal effect. Olree has a hunch that the cherry pit is a prime source of yttrium, a speculation that only investigation will affirm or deny.

India has an extremely low Alzheimer's profile. They use turmeric the way we use salt and pepper. Turmeric is an yttrium-boron-based life-form. Turmeric has three or four forms of boron in it. Turmeric can cross the blood-brain barrier, probably through the action of serine.

Current research has indicated that the UGA codon is governed by selenium. It is Olree's opinion that selenium is a secondary stop codon or may be used when yttrium is not present.

Research by Wei Sheng Yan in 2003 shows that yttrium enhances the absorption and distribution of selenium.

Yttrium also likes to attach to other elements and form compounds, including the following: yttrium oxide, yttrium bromide, yttrium chloride, yttrium phosphate, yttrium sulfate, yttrium vanadate and yttrium nitrate.

☰☷ **#54**		

GCA		Sacral 4 Bone
Alanine	13,560,712	Spleen to Heart (11 a.m.)
Strontium	(+2)	(54) Subordinate

The mineral is strontium. The amino acid is alanine. Much like tellurium, alanine and strontium are opposites. Alanine affiliates with tellurium -2 and magnesium at +2, with strontium +2. This arrangement enables strontium to have a significant impact on calcium-magnesium properties. At present strontium is being investigated for bone cells that regenerate or rebuild bones. These units are called osteoblasts. It is the function of the osteoblasts to make new bone cells. As age claims its prerogatives, bones break down faster than they are being made. The medical profession administers drugs to kill the osteoclast cells which are present to break bones down. By killing the osteoclast, the degree of function is slowed so bones break down at a medically acceptable rate. This takes about five years using approved drugs. Then the pharmaceuticals fail to function, at which point the body builds up an immunity to drug stimulation.

Strontium has come under the eye of the pharmaceutical industry. They see great profit potential in using strontium for bone regeneration. Accordingly, the FDA is attempting (and will probably succeed) in taking strontium away as an obtainable supplement.

Strontium has an effect on how spleen to heart meridians communicate. Regeneration takes place at 11:00 a.m. with the sacral 4 bone as the spinal reflex point.

	☰☰ #53	
AUG		Sacral 3 Disc
Methionine	17,323,574	Spleen (10 a.m.)
Rubidium	(+1)	(53) Developing

Rubidium affiliates with the amino acid methionine. Methionine only appears once on the Standard Genetic Chart. The mRNA sequenced in connection with rubidium starts up 99% of all DNA to mRNA sequences.

Methionine is sold in health food stores, not in combination with rubidium, but with selenium as seleno-methionine. This suggests that the initiation codon of methionine will be governed by selenium which has strong ties to carbon, nitrogen and oxygen. Carbon, nitrogen, and oxygen are main minerals in the B-complex vitamins.

Homocystein levels are the best indicator of methionine levels. High homocystein levels indicate a high degree of broken chromosomes. When about 38% of your chromosomes are broken you will perish. When homocystein is broken down by the vitamin B-6, methionine is released back to the system for further usage.

☰☷ #52			
AUC			Sacral 3 Bone
Isoleucine		12,589,650	St. to Sp. (9 a.m.)
Krypton		(-0-)	(52) Meditation

The noble gas is krypton and krypton affiliates with the amino acid isoleucine. Superman has done most to make krypton a household word. Unfortunately, the lessons seem to stop there. The Olree Standard Genetic Chart maps this one as shown above. The center of the largest bone in the spine is the sacral three bone. Sacral three bone is reflex to krypton.

Krypton has a profound effect on how the stomach moves magnetic energy to the spleen. It is near the top section of some genetic sequences. We breathe krypton with every breath as krypton is about 0.00011% of the atmosphere.

Classical chiropractic conditions of the sacral area known to receive nerve fibers from this spinal segment are hip bones and buttocks. Some of the conditions that can follow a pressure on, or interference with these nerves, are sacro-iliac conditions, and spinal curvatures.

☰ ☷ #51			
UCA			Sacral 2 Disc
Serine		18,475,973	Stomach (8 a.m.)
Bromine		(-1)	(51) Shocking

Bromine is found in trace amounts all through the body and is paired with the amino acid serine. It is a -1 polarity mineral. As the old Bromo-Seltzer ads used to have it, "Good for the stomach." It does have a profound effect on the stomach meridian. It is one of the minerals that control the stomach function. When you lose bromine, you get Parkinson's syndrome. Most of the drugs given to relieve Parkinson's disease are bromine-based drugs.

There is a portion of the brain called the *substantia nigra*, the part of the brain that gives your hands dexterity. A high aluminum level at a +3 depresses boron, which is also a +3. In fact, boron controls all the +3s. Boron affiliates with the mineral serine the way bromine does. Therefore, a suppressed boron level causes loss of control over serine. The loss of control over serine equals loss of bromine control. Parkinson's disease follows. It seems that if you allow the boron level to go low and the aluminum level to go up, bromine replacement is more than critical and almost impossible to restore.

		☰ #50	
CGC			Sacral 2 Bone
Arginine	2,228,188		L.I. to Stomach (7 a.m.)
Selenium	(-2)		(50) Cosmic Order

The Olree Standard Genetic Chart exhibits a -2 oxidation state for selenium and its amino acid counter part arginine. It is probably the most important of all agricultural minerals as well as the human DNA's longevity. Selenium has a profound effect on the stabilization of DNA strands of tumor-suppressing proteins, proteins that keep tumors from growing in the body. Selenium has a profound effect on oxygen, nitrogen, and carbon. All share the same amino acid, namely arginine. Selenium connects and allows for the stomach to pass on meridian energy to the large intestine energy field.

One of the most common forms of selenium for selenium consumption is called selenomethionine. Methionine is used to start almost every messenger RNA transcript that comes from DNA. Selenium is both a traffic cop and a wagon master, so to speak. It keeps the traffic moving. People and animals consuming selenium either diminish or eliminate cancer.

Selenium has a -2 oxidation, as we need it. In nature it is also available as +4 and +6 oxidation state, both very toxic.

A recent study performed by Larry Clark at the University of Arizona showed that the essential trace element selenium may reduce the incidence of and mortality from cancers in several sites in the body. In the *Nutritional Prevention of Cancer Trial*, Clark and colleagues found that the incidence of prostate cancer was decreased by 63% in a group of participants who took 200 micrograms of selenium each day as compared to a group of participants who did not take selenium. Decreased incidences of lung and colorectal cancers were also found in participants who took selenium.

Selenium is a nutritionally essential trace element that naturally occurs in the soil. It enters our bodies through our food (both plant and animal products) and, to a lesser extent, water sources. Plants absorb selenium from the soil into their leaves, stems, seeds and fruits. Animals eat plants containing selenium and this is stored in their tissues. Some foods that are good sources of selenium are grains grown in the Midwestern United States and animal meats, particularly organ meats. Certain foods like Brazil nuts are especially high in selenium.

The major functions of selenium in the body that have been discovered to date are as follows. Selenium is found in the active site of many enzymes, such as thioredoxin reductase, which catalyze oxidation-reduction reactions. These reactions help to protect against cancer by encouraging cancer cells to undergo apoptosis. Apoptosis is a form of programmed cell death that occurs when genetic damage is detected in the cell, thus preventing the transfer of mutations to a future generation of cells. An enzyme, glutathione peroxidase (or GSH-PX), requires selenium for its formation. This enzyme helps to prevent the oxidation process, which may cause injury in cells. Selenium appears to improve the functioning of the immune system and its response to infections. Selenium also appears to cause the formation of natural killer cells, which destroy foreign bacteria that enters the body. Essential P450 enzymes may be induced by selenium; these enzymes help detoxify some cancer-causing substances. Selenium inhibits prostaglandins which cause inflammatory reactions in the body. Male fertility may be enhanced by selenium due to increased sperm motility. At high doses, selenium may decrease the rates of tumor cell growth.

䷬ **#49**		
UGU		Sacral 1 Disc
Cysteine	19,051,284	Large Intestine (6 a.m.)
Arsenic	(-3)	(49) Changing

The Olree Standard Genetic Chart presents the following inventory for arsenic. Arsenic's spinal reflex point is the sacral 1 disc and influences the large intestine meridian with its -3 electron valence which regenerates at 6 a.m. Arsenic has an affiliation with the amino acid cysteine.

Arsenic has a bad reputation in the public prints because of detective novels and crime statistics. The mineral is a profound requirement for living systems just the same. In pregnancy, the arsenic level goes up tenfold if the child is to be a boy. Without such a level, spontaneous abortion becomes the inevitable result. Pine needles crushed and steeped as a tea in boiling water deliver enough arsenic to prevent miscarriage.

Homeostatic control and scientific use do not excuse the pandemic brought on by WHO (World Health Organization), which ordered up deep water wells that by now have turned at least one Indian state into a warehouse of cancer victims. This assertion is no hyperbole. One estimate has it that three million people are cancer victims because of this blunder.

A combination of two natural toxins — arsenic and bryostatin — may be a powerful new treatment for certain kinds of leukemia, claims a study published in the *Proceedings of the National Academy of Sciences.*

Researchers at Johns Hopkins Kimmel Cancer Center found that arsenic, long used to treat certain leukemias, activates the same cellular self-destruct mechanism as bryostatin — a toxin found in coral-like aquatic organisms called bryozoans which attach themselves to piers, boat hulls and rocky surfaces.

Arsenic is known to be effective against treatment-resistant acute promyelocytic leukemia (APL). It is a cancer of the blood and bone marrow characterized by unhealthy white blood cells. APL is a subtype of acute myeloid leukemia, the most common form of adult leukemia.

Until now, scientists didn't fully understand how arsenic actually kills cancer cells. The Johns Hopkins scientists used molecular studies to discover that arsenic activates NADPH oxidase, an oxygen-producing enzyme complex. "When normal white blood cells engulf invading bacteria, NADPH oxidase produces a big burst of bad oxygen species which they dump into bacteria to kill it and, in the process, kill themselves," Chi V. Dang, a vice dean for research and professor of medicine, cell biology, pathology, and oncology, says in a prepared statement. "We found that in APL, arsenic triggers activation of NADPH oxidase and uses this natural bacteria-killing mechanism against the leukemia cells — in essence, a self-destruct switch."

☰☷ **#48**		

CUU		Sacral 1 Bone
Leucine	18,861,320	Lung to L.I. (5 a.m.)
Cobalt	(+4-)	(48) The Source

Cobalt affiliates with the amino acid leucine on the Olree Standard Genetic Chart. Everything alive needs cobalt, yet it seems to be absent everywhere. Carbon and nitrogen combine to allow the link between metals and non-metals to enter the human body. Carbon and nitrogen combine together with a double bond called cyanide. This one is a rover, always wanting to seek something else. If you take carbon-nitrogen into your system, it wants to play tag-team with oxygen and does not let carbon dioxide release. If cobalt is attached to that cyanide molecule, it is a powerful arrangement for allowing metals into the body. That combination of carbon-nitrogen-cobalt is vitamin B-12, which we cannot live without. Minerals not on the Standard Genetic Chart link with DNA, and DNA creates molecules enabling messenger RNA to utilize trace minerals through the action of carbon, nitrogen and cobalt. These are titanium, vanadium, chromium, manganese, iron, nickel, copper, zinc, gallium and germanium.

This inventory of minerals opens the discussion in so many directions it would take a telephone directory-like tome to touch upon all of the bases.

Most people have heard about chromium and glucose tolerance. Also widely reported is manganese and its capacity to mimic magnesium. Manganese deficiency can trigger myasthenia gravis. Manganese deficiencies and copper toxicity are of maximum interest. Myasthenia is a thymus disorder. Under stress, simple manganese supplementation restores the organ. The thymus has a unique role. Whenever a white blood cell arrives, it gets its marching orders for whatever it is that it has to protect the body against. Surgical removal of the thymus makes its own suggestion.

Aspartame has been indicted in earlier passages. Now it is Splenda's turn. Splenda is a sugar molecule that has had a chlorine molecule synthetically attached. Olree states that some studies show consumption of Splenda is related to a 30 to 50% loss of thymus function, which means immunity is being canceled out quickly.

Cobalt is responsible for iron's entry into the body. Without cobalt, iron is not welcome, whatever the source. Moreover, iron can't be absorbed without the presence of copper. As a practitioner, Richard Olree directs patients to put blackstrap molasses into a cup of fresh cow's milk with vitamin B-complex and vitamin C. Also taken would be a Certs candy with the green dots in them. The green dots are copper gluconate, and copper must be present to absorb iron.

Titanium likes to pair up with germanium, and germanium likes oxygen. Vanadium and gallium also pair, as do chromium and zinc. Zinc is the glue that holds DNA together. It is stored and regulated by the prostate gland. Women usually live longer because men spend their lives giving their zinc and selenium to women. White spots on fingernails denote a zinc deficiency. Zinc is the number one trace element on the insulin molecule. It is the role of the chromium molecule to enable the placement of the zinc molecule on the insulin molecule. Zinc is the sixth most abundant element in the brain.

In the wild, Chronic Wasting Disease is usually a consequence of a low ratio of manganese to copper.

Following are the dietary symptoms of the minerals from titanium to germanium which are all under the direction of cobalt.

Vanadium was shown to be an essential trace mineral in 1971. Vanadium inhibits cholesterol synthesis followed by decreased plasma levels of cholesterol. The body needs vanadium for proper regulation of the circulatory system. Vanadium functions in the body and inhibits cholesterol synthesis, mimics insulin, and stimulates glucose oxidation.

Chromium (especially in the form of chromium picolinate) is referred to as the master regulator of insulin, a potent metabolic hormone involved in protein, carbohydrate and fat metabolism. Chromium levels decrease with age and it is important to replace it on a daily basis. Chromium functions in the body metabolism of glucose (sugar), neurotransmitters, brain function, insulin performance, thyroid function, and in hormonal balance. Signs of possible deficiency include diabetes/hypoglycemia, aortic cholesterol, peripheral neuropathy, hypo-/hyper-thyroidism, excess body weight, depression and arteriosclerosis.

Manganese is the element that is often found in combination with lecithin. Lecithin is a brain and nerve fat. Manganese gives us strong nerves, coordination of thoughts and produces elasticity with quick recuperative ability. This element is required for bone metabolism and in many enzyme reactions.

Manganese functions in the body in many ways. It controls nerves, is an element in the body linings and connective tissues, increases eyesight, enhances the body's own recuperative powers, improves memory and enhances resistance. Signs of possible deficiency, mental confusion, depression, convulsions, infertility, impatience, cracking joints, loss of libido, carpal tunnel syndrome, gout, anxiety, schizophrenia, asthma and nightmares.

Iron is responsible for attracting oxygen to the body and carrying oxygen to all systems, tissues, and organs. Iron combines with other nutrients to produce vital blood proteins and is involved in food metabolism. Without iron the body cannot survive long since the metabolism would decrease and atrophy. Iron in the body ensures oxygenation of blood, converts hematin to carry oxygen to cells, improves circulation, augments tissue oxidation, and attracts oxygen to the body. Signs of possible deficiency include anemia, brittle nails, fatigue, irritability, confusion, dizziness, fragile bone, anorexia and constipation.

Cobalt is an essential element that normalizes cells in the body, especially the performance of red corpuscles. Cobalt is at the very center of the vitamin B-12 molecule and is a cofactor and activator for enzymes and fixes nitrogen during amino acid production. Cobalt functions in the body include that it aids in the assimilation of iron, stimulates various enzymes, normalizes cells, and builds red blood cells. Signs of possible deficiency include pernicious anemia, nerve damage and stunted growth.

Copper is classified as an essential mineral due to the fact that copper deficiency can produce various symptoms. Copper is involved in many enzyme reactions and for the body to work properly it must maintain the proper balance of copper and zinc. Copper functions in the body as an enzyme co-factor, formation of hemoglobin and red blood cells, protein metabolism, synthesis of phospholipids, vitamin C oxidation, production of elastin, and formation of RNA. Signs of possible deficiency are white hair, liver cirrhosis, allergies, parasites, hernia, anemia, hyper-/hypo-thyroidism, arthritis, ruptured disc and iron storage disease.

Zinc is needed for metabolism of nucleic acids and the synthesis of proteins. It is an integral part of the human DNA for cell division and synthesis. Zinc is found in all the body fluids, including the moisture in the eyes, lungs, nose, urine and saliva. Zinc functions in the body as an element in mucous linings in the body, is necessary for hormone production, essential for the prostate gland, is found in the bodily fluids, and is a vital part of the immune system. Signs of possible deficiency include angina, paranoia, body odor, hair loss, obesity, acne, infertility, infections, diabetes, PMS, thyroid disorders, hypo-/hypertension, depression and Crohn's disease.

Germanium is necessary for the optimum nutrition of the human body. This element is amazing as it raises the level of activity of various organs by enabling them to attract more oxygen. It is responsible for providing more oxygen to the body as well as expelling harmful pollutants and pathogens or rendering them harmless. Germanium functions in the body include maintaining a strong immune system, production of killer cells and T-suppressor cells, electron transmission, expelling pollutants and pathogens, and providing more oxygen to the vital organs. Signs of possible deficiency: asthma, cirrhosis, neuralgia, cancer, leukemia, hypertension, softening of brain tissue, and cardiac insufficiency.

☰☰	**#47**	

CCU		Lumbar 5 Disc
Proline	16,740,216	Lung (4 a.m.)
Scandium	(+3)	(47) Adversity

Scandium is possibly the rarest mineral on planet Earth. It is available as a subatomic particle while obtaining sunlight. Its role in space projects and weaponry is well known. Not so with the metabolic process. The spinal location is the lumbar 5 disc and it has its magnetic effects on the lung meridian at 4 a.m. through the amino acid proline.

Olree points out that a person must have boron in the body in order to process scandium. Boron controls all the +3s on the chart. Scandium is a +3. We bask in the form of electromagnetic radiation. Scandium always reveals itself in vitamin D metabolism, or something that deals with calcium. If we walk in sunshine, we pick up all the scandium needed. Wherever the peer-reviewed literature has articles about calcium metabolism and related genes, scandium is always at the top in terms of need for genetic sequences. It has a lot to do with vitamin D metabolism and calcium metabolism. Scandium iodide added to mercury vapor lamps produces a highly efficient light source resembling sunlight, which is important for indoor or nighttime color television.

Scandium is one of the rare minerals on Planet Earth in terms of quantity, yet it surrounds you every time the sun comes out. Scandium is the 12th or the 20th most abundant mineral on the sun, depending on where your information is coming from. The relationship between scandium and its counterpart amino acid is the consequence of light. Scandium affiliates with the amino acid proline.

The sun produces electrical magnetic energy from light via the agency of scandium. In the vitamin D FASTA sequences scandium shows up as 1, 2 or 3 in vitamin D-related function. Vitamin D comes from food. It is absorbed in the intestinal tract in one form, is transported to the liver in a second form, and is finally shuttled to the skin where it morphs into D-3. The skin actually utilizes sunlight. The sunlight's electromagnetic radiation specifically oriented to scandium transforms vitamin D-2 into D-3. Scandium seems closely tied to calcium metabolism. On the Periodic Chart, scandium is positioned next to calcium, the pattern being argon to potassium to calcium, then to scandium.

No one takes scandium supplements. People are told to avoid the sun, and in trying they subject themselves to selective starvation.

☷☳ #46

CUA		Lumbar 5 Bone
Leucine	12,174,376	Liver to Lung (3 a.m.)
Calcium	(+2)	(46) Advancement

CUA is the three letter codon for leucine that associates with calcium and regenerates at 3 a.m. and allows the liver to pass magnetic energy to the lung meridian. Folks who awake at 3 a.m. out of a sound sleep have a bad calcium-magnesium ratio. Any person with a broken bone knows this due to the high amount of pain during regeneration.

More mythology attends the role of calcium than most of the other minerals put together. Television commercials love calcium, pitch it with the fervor of a Chautauqua minister leading sinners down the tabernacle aisle to the mourner's bench. Orange juice is touted for its calcium. People are told to take Tums for calcium. Women with osteoporosis are given a bone density test and told to take 1,200 milligrams of calcium. They never tell patients what other minerals are needed to get calcium into the body and into the bone structure, or how to get it out of the kidneys when they're through using it.

Yet the literature reveals that 1,200 mg of calcium without the necessary companion dietary supplements is a ticket to real sickness. The result is constipation and more bacteria, fungi and aberrations growing in the intestinal tract than nature's design can accommodate. An acute magnesium crisis can be expected, as can faulty periods, feet cramps, leg cramps, headaches, eyelids twitching, heart palpitations, loss of sleep, and back spasms.

In genetic sequences, calcium always shows up at the bottom of the utilization chart. The key is magnesium. It always mobilizes calcium, moves it around, moves it out, and drags it in.

Taking high-calcium supplements is much like making rock candy. The process calls for heated water, added sugar to a super-saturated point, and as that substance cools, the sugar precipitates as crystals. Drop in a string and the sugar crystallizes onto the string — presto! Rock candy. That's all a kidney stone is, super-saturated kidneys with calcium and not enough magnesium to keep it in solution. The resultant agony of kidney stones and their passage is the stuff of legends. Added to the above must be the long-term effect of arteriosclerosis, or calcification of the arteries. The single governing factor is and remains magnesium.

Calcium is used in forming bones, also known as bone mineralization, and in the proper formation and maintenance of teeth. It is important in nerve impulse transmission, blood coagulation, and muscle contraction. Calcium functions in the body, solidity of the body, essential to fetal growth during pregnancy, found in cartilage, fluids and tissues and body alkalinity. Signs of possible deficiency — weakness, fatigue, hemorrhaging, rickets, catarrh, bone softening, cramps, digestive disorders, abscesses and excessive sweating.

Classical chiropractic conditions of the lumbar 5 areas known to receive nerve fibers from this spinal segment are lower legs, ankles, feet, toes and arches. Some of the conditions that can follow a pressure on or interference with these nerves include poor circulation in the legs, swollen ankles, weak ankles and arches, cold feet, weakness in the legs, and leg cramps.

	☰☰ #45	
ACU		Lumbar 4 Disc
Threonine	15,182,192	Liver (2 a.m.)
Potassium	(+1)	(45) Assembling

Potassium never comes to the surface in terms of genetic sequence. It has a profound effect on the functioning of the liver. It is regulated by iodine. Potassium has a +1 charge and is coupled with the amino acid threonine and the liver meridian which regenerates at 2 a.m. The usual take on iodine is the American salt route: sodium chloride, silico-aluminate and potassium iodide. That will keep you from dying, but it is not a health measure. The real function of iodine is to move potassium. This is possible only when iodine comes from an organic base (such as kelp).

Potassium is critical for heart function. It is a major player, but in terms of genetic sequence it never arrives in the top 20. It is never needed in great quantities, yet is always present. A wake-up routine of 3 a.m. usually designates a calcium or magnesium deficieny. A routine 2 a.m. wake-up designates a potassium imbalance. The culprit is often a medicine that keeps the liver too toxic to regenerate on schedule, according to Olree.

Fibrocystic tumors are made of potassium. Potassium has to be in ratio to sodium, cesium, rubidium and lithium, as well as iodine.

Potassium is known as the great alkalizer, as it is a primary electrolyte, important in pH balance and water balance. This element plays a vital role in nerve function and cellular integrity by regulating the transfer of nutrients into the cell. Potassium attracts oxygen to tissues; lack of it reduces tissue oxygenation.

Potassium functions in the body include that it supports the muscular system, increases tissue and blood alkalinity, acts as a nerve tonic, reduces acidity, promotes good health and vigor, and helps eliminate toxins and supplies healthy nerves. Signs of possible deficiency include over-acidity, reduced oxygenation, aches and pains, mental illness, restlessness, low energy levels, skin disorders, elevated cholesterol and triglycerides, nervousness, anxiety and hypo-/hyper-tension.

≡ **#44**		
CGG		Lumbar 4 Bone
Arginine	2,585,536	G.B. to Liver (1 a.m.)
Argon	(-0-)	(44) Temptation

With its zero polarity, argon remains a mystery of sorts. It's always there, always presenting a noble gas with each breath. There seems to be no written information on the interaction of noble gases. This makes discovery a looked-for event, since for now we know of no real interplay in the human body. We breathe argon with every breath while it is about 0.93% of our air we breathe.

Classical chiropractic conditions of the lumbar 4 areas known to receive nerve fibers from this spinal segment are prostate gland muscles of the lower back and the sciatic nerve. Some of the conditions that can follow a pressure on, or interference with these nerves, are sciatic, lumbago, difficult, painful or too frequent urination, and backaches.

☰	#43		

GGU		Lumbar 3 Disc
Glycine	10,965,848	Gall Bladder (12 midnight)
Chlorine	(-1)	(43) Resolution

The three-letter codon GGU denotes its regeneration time of 12 midnight where the gall bladder is preparing to pass magnetic energy to the liver meridian. The spinal segment is the lumbar 4 bone. Chlorine affiliates with the amino acid glycine, which is unique. It is under the gallbladder meridian, and the spinal connection is the lumbar 3 disc. All amino acids have mirror images. The problem is that mirror images in regards to DNA replication do not work, or only work as with phenylalanine. There is one amino acid that does not have a mirror image and that is glycine. Glycine also affiliates with a -2 electron valence oxygen. That it pairs with oxygen, a part of the DNA molecule, means that wherever oxygen is used with chlorine, now affiliated with glycine, glycine has only one configuration, which is a dextrose or right-handed configuration. So all amino acids that affiliate with glycine have to be left-handed. Why doesn't the body use the mirror image of arginine? The riddle is answered by oxygen, one of the basic components of DNA. Chlorine is used in the stomach under the regulation of the gall bladder in order to break down protein bonds from the food consumed. Without hydrochloric acid acting on the protein, there is nothing to separate the individual amino acids presented to the stomach in various combinations.

The greatest imbalance takes place when heartburn occurs. Heartburn reveals the lack of an acid that medical doctors respond to by handing off the purple pill, a consequence of which is the situation of hydrochloric acid shutting down digestion. This again throws people into selective starvation.

The body has two cells that produce a hydrogen and a chlorine molecule. There isn't a cell in the stomach that can handle a pH of 1. One cell releases hydrogen, and one cell releases chlorine. They join forces to make hydrochloric acid, which breaks the protein bonds and delivers amino acids into the small intestine for further absorption. The usual medical practice seeks to get rid of the heartburn but achieves, instead, selective starvation. Heartburn is a chlorine deficiency, not an excess.

☷☱ #42		
UAG		Lumbar 3 Bone
STOP	12,186,962	T.B. to G.B. (11 p.m.)
Sulfur	(-2)	(42) Benefit

UAG on the Olree Standard Genetic Chart controls another termination codon for DNA mRNA connection, sulfur being one of three governors. This is where the medical profession discovered antibiotics. They found that certain compounds would interdict the makeup of certain aspects of, not allowing them to propagate. The concept of antibiotic resistance changed the world. The sulfur-based beneficial sulfur sold in health food stores — many which include glucosamine sulfate, chondroitin sulfate and methyl sulfate (MSM) — are all sulfur-delivering systems.

If the sulfur load in the body becomes depleted, joint cartilage wears out. The delivery system available in health food stores puts the sulfur back in the chondrocytes, the cell that makes new cartilage. The locus of the greatest effect is in the knees.

Chiropractors have determined that lumbar 3 protects and regulates the nerves that go to the legs and knees. Life without sulfur is not possible. Without sulfur cells cannot reproduce.

Get the lead out of gasoline, and sulfur is in. Sulfur trioxide is released from car exhaust instead of lead. Now we have a new problem. Sulfur gases combine in the air to form acid rain. Acid rain makes aluminum turn from a solid to a liquid. The aluminum liquid now affects all living creatures. Just like aluminum being sprayed in the armpits to shut off the sweat gland, aluminum will neutralize the gills of water life causing them to suffocate due to lack of oxygen transfer to the cellular tissue. Sulfur works its way up the food chain and causes trees to die from the sulfur-oxygen reaction of sulfuric acid.

Sulfur is known as a healing mineral. This element is necessary for developmental and neurological processes. It is necessary for collagen synthesis. Sulfur detoxifies the body and increases blood circulation, reduces muscle cramps and back pain, removes inflammation, permits muscles to heal, increases energy and helps the liver produce chorine.

Sulfur functions in the body as an element in the nerves and myelin sheath; it promotes the flow of bile, regulates the brain and heart, stimulates reproductive processes, promotes healthy skin, nails and hair and serves as a lubricant between the joints. Signs of possible deficiency include impulsiveness, excess stomach acid, circulatory problems, diabetes, hypoglycemia, allergies, arthritis, muscle cramps, and cracking joints. Additional signs of possible deficiency include slow growth, elevated cholesterol, hyperinsulinemia, cardiovascular disease, obesity, infertility, elevated triglycerides, and increased infant mortality.

This is a -2 mineral under the control of selenium. Proper supplementation of selenium always prevents sulfur from being expended too rapidly and can reduce toxicity from sulfur's excess amount if this occurs.

Classical chiropractic conditions of the lumbar 3 areas known to receive nerve fibers from this spinal segment are appendix, abdomen, upper leg and cecum. Some of the conditions that can follow a pressure on, or interference with these nerves are appendicitis, cramps, difficult breathing, acidosis and varicose veins.

☰ #41		
GAC		Lumbar 2 Disc
Asparagine	8,898,448	Three Burners (10 p.m.)
Phosphorus	(-3)	(41) Decline

The codon for this entry is GAC and the amino acid is asparagine. GAC is controlled by the three burners acupuncture meridian which regenerates at 10 p.m. and is controlled by the lumbar 2 disc. Phosphorus controls all of the -3 minerals of the body, namely nitrogen, arsenic, antimony and itself. It puts all of these into balance and keeps them there. Phosphorus also has +4 and +5 electron valences. The DNA structure expressed above can only deal with -3.

Phosphorus activates all of the nerves and is found in all foods. Patients on kidney dialysis have to stay away from phosphorus because it rapidly accumulates as a waste product if not expelled via urine and causes bones to honeycomb.

The greatest depletion of magnesium and other minerals that creates havoc with people is the consumption of phosphoric acid, which is found mainly in the most popular colas. Some teas also add phosphoric acid. Phosphoric acid causes rapid depletion of magnesium from the body. This rapid depletion causes the depletion of selenium. It also upsets the calcium metabolism and disturbs all the minerals on the periodic chart. The immune system takes a severe hit, and muscles become compromised, as does mental acuity.

The phosphorus molecule holds DNA together. In fact, you can't live with too much of it, and you can't live without it. Phosphorus is the prime mineral coating all of the nerves of the brain. The phosphorus molecule creates phosphorus-based fatty acids that perform this insulation chore and speed up electrical impulses through the nerves. Halley's *Condensed Chemical Dictionary*, under the word *hazard*, says "toxic by inhalation or digestion." "There are times," notes Olree, "when young patients drink enough phosphoric acid to make their elbows turn green. The stuff is addictive and should never be available to children."

Phosphorus is synonymous with intelligence. This element is found in the nucleus of each cell in the human body, is found in body fluids and in solid tissue. It is the nutrient that makes up the outer bone and combines with several other elements such as iron, potassium, sodium, magnesium and calcium.

Phosphorus functions in the body are many as it is necessary for the reproductive system, essential for bone and brain, vital for muscle tissue, necessary for growth, stimulates sexual function, is present in the white blood cells, and is an essential nerve nutrient. Signs of possible deficiency include neuralgia, brain softening, bone density loss, slow oxidation, paranoia, fatigue, numbness and sensitivity to noise.

☰☷ **#40**		
CCA		Lumbar 2 Bone
Proline	17,358,160	Peri. to T.B. (9 p.m.)
Silicon	(-4+)	(40) Liberation

CCA affiliates with the amino acid proline and couples with the mineral silicon, which in turn controls the flow of magnetic energy of the pericardial sac to the three burners acupuncture meridian at 9 p.m. Silicon is the *cement* that holds the brain together.

Well-researched data on ovarian cancer reveals that a simple broken gene is responsible 87% of the time. This is the most prevalent cancer in women. The one mineral needed to keep the ovarian cancer-correcting gene functioning is silicon. A telling symptom to observe is fingernail integrity. When fingernails have ridges from front to back, that is a good indicator of low silicon levels. Chicken skin is high in silicon. The horsetail herb contains high levels of silicon.

Silicon is used in connective tissues of the heart. About the only way to prevent aluminum buildup in the human body is through the action of silicon. Diets high in silicon, along with magnesium and calcium, normally do not have high aluminum and are therefore excused from the scourge of Alzheimer's disease. Silicon is a natural aluminum deterrent. This mineral is high in the genetic sequencing that Richard Olree does, always dealing with structure and form.

Silica is found in all of the tissues, especially the resistive tissue such as the skin, dura mater, fascia, hair, nails and tendons. It reinforces membranes throughout the body as well as the ligamentous tissue, arterial walls, throat walls, uterine lining, walls of the digestive tract, the spinal and cerebral dura mater, nails and skin.

Silica functions in the body by increasing vigor, energy and strength, is found in all tissues, reinforces walls, linings, ligaments, membranes, nails and hair, increases alkalinity of the body, helps in transfer of nerve impulses, and aids in retention of electricity and body heat. Signs of possible deficiency include nervous stomach, ligament weakness, nerve sensitivity, gout symptoms, inability to heal, falling hair, depression, tender spine, sexual dysfunction, swelling joints, low body temperature, abscesses and fatigue.

Classical chiropractic conditions of the lumbar 2 areas known to receive nerve fibers from this spinal segment indicate effects on the appendix, abdomen, upper leg and cecum. Some of the conditions that can follow a pressure on, or interference with these nerves include appendicitis, cramps, difficult breathing, acidosis, varicose veins.

☰☷	**#39**	
AUU		Lumbar 1 Disc
Isoleucine	23,556,091	Pericardium (8 p.m.)
Aluminum	(+3)	(39) Obstacles

The Olree Standard Genetic Chart tells of codon AUU and isoleucine, an amino acid paired with the mineral aluminum which helps the pericardial sac and circulation is general. The meridian regenerates at 8 p.m. and the spinal reference point is lumbar 1 disc.

Aluminum easily turns from a solid to a liquid and often inserts itself into the food supply via the agency of acid rain. When the human gut senses the presence of aluminum, it shuts down the absorption process. Still, the body has a way of utilizing the aluminum in the food chain, and some bacteria actually use it. The key here is "trace," a trace amount. Excess is always the problem.

Aluminum-based deodorant must now be indicted. People are poisoning themselves by using these anti-sweat products. Most people now understand that aluminum cookware is hazardous. Insects and rodents do not like aluminum-based baked products. Such baking powders are anathema to human beings.

Among senior citizens the syndrome is Alzheimer's, an aluminum toxicity problem. Aluminum inhibits boron, with one aluminum molecule knocking out three boron molecules. The chief culprit is processed foods. American cheese best melts on the hamburger because of added aluminum.

Food coloring also stands out in detail. If the insignia *Lake* appears in connection with a food coloring, it designates an aluminum-based food coloring. Indeed, it has become commercial sport to poison America via concoctions that look like food and even taste like food. Magnification of the ingredient list will reveal at least one or two or three aluminum-based food colorings. These product colorings are in candy for any Halloween trick or treat run. Children are likely to come home with 75% of their booty as aluminum contaminated. All of the candies on the racks are aluminum-based food products, the agency of ill health being food dyes.

The opposite valence of +3 is -3. In the human body the +3 aluminum seeks out a -3. It finds it in the brain in terms of phosphorus, which is -3. Aluminum from Detroit drinking water has been fed to lab rats and showed up in the brain tissue in four to seven minutes.

In the presence of aluminum, boron drops out. In an effort to reduce aluminum, silicon is spent. The structure of the brain is compromised. Yttrium is canceled out. The tragedy of America can be seen in nursing homes full of healthy bodies without brains to tell those bodies what to do.

Almost all municipalities add aluminum sulfate into the water supply in order to clear up turbidity. A small part of this aluminum remains, to be added to the other sources of aluminum found in processed foods, baking powder, cosmetics, and ambient air pollution. The impact of this "technology" was felt immediately in clinics for dialysis of renal patients. Aluminum and fluorine soon required distilled water for dialysis, the alternative being sudden death, also known as dialysis dementia.

Few medical doctors seem to understand that by prescribing coated aspirin for nursing homes or over-the-counter use they are giving the patient 49.5 mg of aluminum per pill as in the case of Ecotrin-coated aspirin.

A final note is now in order. We are rightly concerned about the mercury component of vaccines. How then can we be so indifferent to the near universal acceptance of flu shots that increase the chance of getting Alzheimer's disease by 10% because of the aluminum directly injected into the bloodstream? There seems to be no end to contamination.

☷ #38

GCC		Lumbar 1 Bone
Alanine	11,189,927	Kidney to Peri. (7 p.m.)
Magnesium	(+2)	(38) Contradiction

The Olree Standard Genetic Chart exhibits magnesium in tandem with the amino acid alanine which controls the flow of magnetic energy of the kidney to the pericardial sac meridian that regenerates at 7 p.m.

As sunlight hits the Earth and the agency of chlorophyll brings green to the fore, the center of that chlorophyll molecule is magnesium. It is the basis for the food chain — or the food *web*. Magnesium is also the basis for cell economics.

Magnesium is the single mineral most wiped out by the consumption of phosphoric acid. Any alert physician can detect the symptoms attending phosphoric acid consumption. Feet deficient in magnesium have bad odor, muscles don't work, bowels get blocked, kidneys can't work, poor sleep results, the back hurts, heart palpitations result, eyelids twitch, osteoporosis, high blood pressure, migraine headaches, the whole bag!

Magnesium is ubiquitous. The easiest way to overcome magnesium deficiency is to drink enough water. Dehydration causes magnesium to be wasted. Supplementation of 3 mg of boron a day prevents loss of magnesium through urination. Taking calcium supplements is the fastest way to deplete magnesium. Too much milk consumption can throw a young athlete into a magnesium crisis. Geriatric patients on calcium often so deplete their magnesium that they perish.

A slow and insidious way to lose magnesium is with the use of diuretics. Eighty percent of people who use diuretics, including caffeine, lose magnesium on a daily basis, and the more diuretics that are used, the greater is the loss of magnesium. This starts a deep spiral in regard to one's health.

Magnesium, in the human body, serves many crucial roles and is involved in a quartet of minerals that also serve the same function. The human body needs magnesium, calcium, sodium and potassium in the processes of helping to transmit electrical impulses across nerves and muscles, regulation of blood pressure, bone building and more.

Magnesium functions in the body as being necessary for solid teeth and bones, essential for brain and liver function, calms nerves, promotes cell growth, supports the excretory process, increases tissue elasticity. Signs of possible deficiency include sleepiness, growth failure, menstrual migraines, organ calcification, fainting, asthma, vertigo, cramps, depression, muscular weakness, stiff muscles and neuralgia.

Classical chiropractic conditions of the lumbar 1 areas known to receive nerve fibers from this spinal segment include the large intestines or colon, inguinal rings. Some of the conditions that can follow a pressure on, or interference with these nerves are constipation, colitis, dysentery, diarrhea, and ruptures or hernias.

☰☰ **#37**		

UUG		Thoracic 12 Disc
Leucine	17,919,096	Kidney (6 p.m.)
Sodium	(+1)	(37) Family

On the Olree Standard Genetic Chart, sodium keys as codon UUG, the amino acid connection being leucine and sodium with a spinal reflex point at the thoracic 12 disc segment. The meridian's regeneration is 6 p.m., which is the kidney's time of daily regeneration.

Leucine also affiliates with calcium, but sodium has the ability to mobilize calcium, the common denominator being leucine. Sodium shows up as a major kidney meridian energizer. It has a +1 valence and has to be in correct ratio with potassium, lithium, cesium, and rubidium. The primary codon is UUG. In the absence of rubidium, sodium can be used as secondary initiation codon when called upon.

People cannot live without sodium, but too much sodium causes arteries to harden. The shortfall usually is a lack of organic sodium. Inorganic sodium conspires with calcium to redeposit the calcium on the insides of the arteries. Calcium has a +2 charge. Lacking here is selenium. Selenium is a -2 charge. Still, it isn't the charge, it's the action of leucine and inorganic sodium at issue, mostly from common table salt.

The most organic source of sodium is goat whey. Dr. Bernard Jensen's "Vegetable Seasoning" mix is another source.

Sodium never shows up at the top of genetic sequencing. Because of its biodiversity, magnesium has a top role, sodium being well down the ladder. When sodium shows up, it usually has to do with a kidney-related function.

Under certain stressful family circumstances, often unwanted divorces, a person can spontaneously lose almost all of the their sodium and end up in the hospital.

䷗ #36		
UUA		Thoracic 12 Bone
Leucine	19,678,400	U.B. to Kidney (5 p.m.)
Neon	(-0-)	(36) Censorship

Codon UUA and the amino connection with leucine are noted on the Olree Standard Genetic Chart as the controller of the urinary bladder to the kidney acupuncture meridian connection which regenerates at 5 p.m. and is controlled by the thoracic 12 bone. We don't encounter this noble gas due to its presence in the air. Neon is 0.0018% of the air we breathe.

The skies are lit up with neon, but we have no knowledge of how or why it works, or even why it has a select spot on the chart. It will be up to future researchers to fill in the space we are obliged to leave open.

Classical chiropractic conditions of the thoracic 12 bone areas known to receive nerve fibers from this spinal segment are the small intestines, fallopian tubes, and lymph circulation. Some of the conditions that can follow a pressure on, or interference with these nerves, are rheumatism, gas pain, and certain types of sterility.

☷☳ **#35**		
ACC		Thoracic 11 Disc
Threonine	10,952,504	Urinary Bladder (4 p.m.)
Fluorine	(-1)	(35) Progress

The amino acid connection is threonine, and like iodine is responsible for the regeneration of the urinary bladder and regenerates at 4 p.m. with a spinal connection at the thoracic 11 disc space. This amino has shown up before attached to potassium. This time it is attached to fluorine.

Fluorine is needed in very trace amounts to make calcium fluoride, but it is not a major player. However, when artificially inserted into the diet, it takes a position that iodine would normally have taken. When this happens the chemicals are worthless. The roster of enzymes annihilated by fluorine injected into the nation's water mains number in excess of 72. Listing them with citations of research to validate this statement would take a half dozen papers.

Excessive fluorine from Teflon has been linked to birth defects and illness. Teflon was first used in 1945. Some claim that aluminum and fluorine together speed up the various brain inflammation and degeneration.

Fluorine was first used in drinking water at Newburgh, New York, in 1945. In 1957 more than 58% of all deaths were from heart disease. Fluorides are linked to children's aggressive behavior according to the founder of "Parents of Fluoride Poisoned Children" *(www.poison fluoride.com)*. This website indicates that as many as two-thirds of the American population are being constantly exposed to fluorine.

Another organization is Paul Connett Fluoride Action Network *(www.fluoridealert.org)*. Paul travels the world helping folks learn about and take action against the dangers of the fluoride drinking water connection.

☰ #34		
GGA		Thoracic 11 Bone
Glycine	14,548,193	S.I. to U.B. (3 p.m.)
Oxygen	(-2)	(34) Great Power

The Olree Standard Genetic Chart points to the amino acid affiliate glycine at the thoracic 11 bone which regenerates at 3 p.m. where it helps the small intestine energy to be passed to the urinary bladder meridian.

Oxygen does not function well in the absence of selenium. The fastest way to become deficient in oxygen is to stop breathing or to stop drinking water. The hydrogen-oxygen bonding angle can be anywhere from 98 to 103.2 degrees. The higher angle causes the carbon to further slow the aging process. Oxygen deprivation can take form in the absence of fresh air or the inability to breathe deeply. Oxygen is about 20.95% of the air we breathe, second only to nitrogen.

Selenium is one of the most important minerals that makes cells live or die. *Cell apoptosis* is the name of programmed cell death which has a central role in homeostasis and maintenance of a DNA-based life forms. It is required for the removal of autoreactive immune cells, virus-infected cells, and with unrepairable genetic damage posing the risk of a cell transformation. While converting apoptosis sequences, oxygen always appears in the top ten elements needed.

It is the oxygen-glycine combination that makes all of nature left-handed as far as amino acid utilization is concerned. When the oxygen glycine relationship is called for, only one form appears. It has no mirror image like all of the other amino acids.

Classical chiropractic conditions of the thoracic 11 bone areas known to receive nerve fibers from this spinal segment are affiliated with the kidneys and ureters. Some of the conditions that can follow a pressure on or interference with these nerves are skin conditions like acne, pimples and eczema or boils.

☰☷ **#33**		
AGG		Thoracic 10 Disc
Arginine	16,721,585	Small Intestine (2 p.m.)
Nitrogen	(-3)	(33) Retreat

The Olree Standard Genetic Chart exhibits nitrogen as related to arginine with a spinal intervention of the thoracic 10 disc where it is utilized with the small intestine meridian which regenerates at 2 p.m.

Nitrogen is a basic component of DNA. It loads the atmosphere we breathe and is also one of the most prominent minerals found in B-complex vitamins. The air we breathe is 78.08% nitrogen. We try to assimilate our nitrogen through our food chain in our water-soluble B vitamins — B-1, B-2, B-3, B-6, B-12, etc. These are the critical forms of water-soluble carbon-nitrogen-oxygen compounds. Water-soluble relates to excretion. They have to arrive in the food supply daily.

Nitrogen is used in extreme cardiac problems. As administered via pharmaceuticals, the preparation instantly opens up the arteries, relieving cardiac stress when a body is being shorted of oxygen.

When converting cancer-causing genes, nitrogen is at the top of the list. Lunchmeat that contains nitrated compounds increases your chances of getting cancer by a whopping 67%.

Nitrogen exhibits all oxidation states from -3 to +5 but usually is found in nature at a -3, +3 and a +5 oxidation state. The Olree Standard Genetic Chart calls for nitrogen to be in a -3 oxidation state. Nitrogen is found in 99% of all pharmaceutical drugs at an unknown oxidation state.

☰☰ **#32**		

CGA		Thoracic 10 Bone
Arginine	2,072,480	Heart to S.I. (1 p.m.)
Carbon	(-4+)	(32) Continuing

The Olree Standard Genetic Chart shows carbon affiliates with the heart to small intestine meridian with a regeneration time of 1 p.m. and a spinal location of the thoracic 10 bone. We are a carbon-based life form. The center of life is carbon. It is a major component of DNA. It controls all of the negative/positive 4 valences on the chart. Through the action of nitrogen and selenium, carbon gets direction. More specifically, selenium does not allow carbon to go where it is not supposed to. Selenium is the enforcer. As a rule, carbon is always at the bottom of genetic sequences. An analogy may serve us here. Take an old-style 78 record spinning to deliver its encoded message. If you create a numbering system from the center of the record to its edge, then 64 on the edge is spinning very rapidly compared to number 1 at the center. Carbon goes slow at the center; at 64 it races to its conclusion. Everything rotates around carbon. Selenium hovers close to carbon, usually at 58, 59, or 60. When carbon is at the top of a genetic sequence, it will be a really powerful sequence. Vitamin C is really nothing but carbon atoms strung together. If one gets low on selenium, one will lose all of the vitamin C in the system. If the vitamin C levels get low, so will selenium.

Classical chiropractic conditions of the thoracic 10 bone areas known to receive nerve fibers from this spinal segment are the kidneys. Some of the conditions that can follow a pressure on or interference with these nerves are kidney troubles, hardening of the arteries, chronic tiredness, nephritis and pyelitis.

☰☷	**#31**	
AGU		Thoracic 9 Disc
Serine	15,198,623	Heart (12 noon)
Boron	(+3)	(31) Attraction

The amino acid that connects with boron on the Olree Standard Genetic Chart is serine which is a major mineral in regeneration of the heart meridian. The spinal segmentation is the thoracic 9 disc space. Boron controls all the +3 charges in the human body. It is easily displaced by aluminum, losing three boron molecules to every one aluminum molecule. It is a mid-fence straddler, rarely at the bottom or top in sequence.

Boron has the ability to absorb radiation and release it without changing the neutron. The heart is the most active part of the body, for which reason boron defends the heart. The story has been told that Soviet truck drivers were offered bonuses to deliver boron to the Chernobyl site, this with the knowledge that their trip would be fatal, but families would be paid. None realized that, fortified with boron, they could have made their decision with impunity. Boron stopped the "China Syndrome" from occurring in Russia.

Boron is known as the calcium helper and for the metabolism of calcium, magnesium and phosphorus. Boron improves retention of both calcium and magnesium and elevates circulation of serum concentrations of testosterone.

Boron works in the body toward brain function, activates vitamin D, promotes electrical brain activity, enhances memory, and promotes alertness. Signs of possible deficiency include ADD/ADHD, osteoporosis, arthritis, fatigue, decreased motor function, decreased short-term memory, decreased brain function, and increased loss of calcium and magnesium in the urine.

☰ **#30**		
UGC		Thoracic 9 Bone
Cysteine	13,574,966	Spleen to Heart (11 a.m.)
Beryllium	(+2)	(30) Synergy

The mineral beryllium holds a position on the genetic chart, probably awaiting further discovery to be made. As long as the selenium level is adequate, the body rids itself of excess beryllium. Beryllium deals with the spleen and transferring energy to the heart. No one supplements beryllium because even a minimum amount would annihilate the calcium-magnesium relationship. The spinal segment is the thoracic 9 bone and assists the spleen to the heart acupuncture meridian with regeneration taking place at 11 a.m. Too much beryllium lodges in the lungs and causes berylliosis.

Classical chiropractic conditions of the thoracic 9 bone areas known to receive nerve fibers from this spinal segment are the adrenals or supra-renal. Some of the conditions that can follow a pressure on or interference with these nerves include allergies and hives.

☷☵ **#29**		
CAU		Thoracic 8 Disc
Histidine	17,328,533	Spleen (10 a.m.)
Lithium	(+1)	(29) Danger

Lithium pairs with the amino acid histidine, as depicted on the Olree Standard Genetic Chart, and is the major mineral that will allow the spleen acupuncture meridian to regenerate at 10 a.m. and has a spinal connection of the thoracic 8 disc space.

Lithium is critical for emotional stability. It helps the spleen work. It has a lot to do with, if not actually governing, mental outlook, and at the same time assists the immune system. In short, the lithium-spleen-histidine connection is greatly tied to health, emotional health first, which is tied, of course, to physical health. In sequence, lithium always stays in the middle, an arbiter of sorts, commanding respect and subservience where mental health is the issue.

Lithium has been shown to protect brain cells involved in learning and memory from radiation damage. In addition to killing cancer cells, normal cells will undergo cell apoptosis and die from gene damage during cancer radiation treatment. Lithium can reduce this.

Lithium is usually associated with medical treatments for psychiatric disorders. In humans, lithium is only required in trace amounts as that is all that is found in tissues.

In the body, it stabilizes the neurotransmitter serotonin, activates glucocorticosteroid receptors, and affects the production of CAMP.

Signs of possible deficiency include behavioral problems, depression, alcohol cravings, manic depression, impotency and increased suppressor cell activity.

☰ **#28**		

CGU		Thoracic 8 Bone
Arginine	2,362,043	St. to Sp. (9 a.m.)
Helium	(-0-)	(28) Critical Mass

On the Olree Standard Genetic Chart, helium has a codon of CGU, with the amino acid being arginine and the spinal segment is the thoracic 8 bone. Helium connects the stomach to the spleen acupuncture meridian with regeneration at 9 a.m. Helium is but 0.00053% of the air we breathe.

Here again an amino acid is placed with a noble gas. This same amino acid is also paired with barium, selenium, carbon and nitrogen. The point here is that quite a lot of the nutrients we use are delivered via the air. Helium has a zero polarity. Otherwise, helium awaits discovery beyond what the peer-reviewed literature has to offer at present.

Classical chiropractic conditions of the thoracic 8 bone areas known to receive nerve fibers from this spinal segment are the spleen and diaphragm. Some of the conditions that can follow a pressure on or interference with these nerves are hiccoughs and lower resistance.

☷ #27		

UAC		Thoracic 7 Disc
Tyrosine	19,644,340	Stomach (8 a.m.)
Helionon	(-1)	(27) Nourishing

Helionon holds the 27th position of the Olree Standard Genetic Chart and has a spinal segment of the thoracic 7 disc area. Helionon affiliates with the amino acid tyrosine and is a major player in the stomach meridian regeneration which occurs at 8 a.m. Tyrosine also has a profound effect on the thyroid which is governed by another -1 mineral, iodine. Helionon is a subatomic mineral. Modern-day nomenclature calls it tritium. It is a heavy water molecule. It identifies with -1 and is under the direction of iodine, bromine, chlorine and fluorine. There are a lot of tyrosine enzymes that deal with the thyroid.

☰☰ #26		

GUC		Thoracic 7 Bone
Valine	8,907,151	L.I. to Stomach (7 a.m.)
Halanon	(-2)	(26) Potential Energy

Halanon has a new name that departs from the Walter Russell nomenclature, deuterium. It is used in the production of nuclear bombs. Its place in the Olree Standard Genetic Chart is depicted here as it relates to the human spine with a location of the thoracic 7 bone and the amino acid valine. Halanon has something to do with how the large intestine passes magnetic energy to the stomach which communicates at 7 a.m. Another mineral which regenerates at 7 a.m. is selenium. Deuterium falls under the auspices of selenium. We have to leave it to the DNA to deal with subatomic particles. Research suggests that valine has profound effects on muscles. That ties it up with the other branch chain of amino acids. This may be one of the lower sequences in the human body. It is only called for 8 million times using the above cited codon and DNA.

Classical chiropractic conditions of the thoracic 7 bone areas known to receive nerve fibers from this spinal segment are the pancreas, Islets of Langerhans, and duodenum. Some of the conditions that can follow a pressure on or interference with these nerves are diabetes, ulcers and gastritis.

☰☷ **#25**		
UCG		Thoracic 6 Disc
Serine	2,076,719	Large Intestine (6 a.m.)
Luminon	(-3)	(25) Innocence

Walter Russell called this subatomic particle luminon; modern charts call it protium. Luminon has a profound effect on the large intestine acupuncture regeneration time of 6 a.m. and a thoracic 6 disc spinal connection. This one is used only 2 million times in DNA sequencing.

Here we dispense with the table of elements symbols and close out the Olree Standard Genetic Chart with minimum commentary.

The lightest subatomic particles are single quarks. The second level of energy or mineral is the two quark system and the third level of energy is a three quark system. Quarks are the smallest subatomic particles and are pure electromagnetic energy. There is nothing smaller or lighter than a single quark. Quarks are held into place by gluons and DNA is the intermediary between the real minerals and the subatomic particles. The heavier minerals (or minerals heavier than hydrogen) are what make quarks have configuration and provide configuration of subatomic particles incorporated in the DNA structure.

Walter Russell describes a ninth level of minerals. This level is the radioactive end of the spectrum of minerals. All minerals in the ninth level should be avoided because they yield high concentrations of quarks called radiation.

After number 24 the elements depicted here are subatomic minerals. The skeleton of this display was first revealed to the physics community by Walter Russell, the author of *Atomic Suicide*, circa 1957. It was Russell's thesis that using radioactivity on planet Earth was to cancel out mental acuity. Russell believed in atomic energy, but he also believed it should remain in its own environment, the sun.

Russell's nomenclature has been followed here. These subatomic particles reveal the working relationships that enable robust health. All these particles are lighter than hydrogen. Russell developed a periodic chart in 1926. Its foundation forms the basis of the Olree Standard Genetic charts of the relationship of DNA to minerals. The Olree Standard Genetic Chart makes it a premier scientific development.

☰☰ **#24**		
UAA		Thoracic 6 Bone
STOP	19,644,340	Lung to L.I. (5 a.m.)
Hydrogen	(-4+)	(24) Repeating

Hydrogen's spinal location is the thoracic 6 bone and is a STOP codon or a termination codon which regenerates at 5 a.m. This means that it will close out a genetic sequence when called upon. It is never found in the middle of the genetic sequences. It only acts to stop a genetic sequence. If one of the three STOP termination codons called for fails, the protein that is required will fail and will have to be disassembled.

Magnetic resonance imaging (MRI) used to diagnose is a hydrogen-based test. It has a single electron. That hydrogen molecule in the presence of a strong electric magnet causes the electron spin measuring activity giving the picture of what happens to hydrogen. The MRI measures only hydrogen as it attaches to water — H_2O. But it is one of the most sequenced of activities, rolling up 19 million times in the DNA code.

Hydrogen and oxygen together make water, H_2O. The body is mostly water and there are billions and billions of hydrogen molecules in the body. Hydrogen is 0.000005% of the air we breathe. There are hundreds of books that deal with hydrogen.

A classic misuse of hydrogen occurs when one uses margarine. A good oil like corn oil is supersaturated with hydrogen and then sold for human consumption. One cannot find supersaturated oils in nature.

Classical chiropractic conditions of the thoracic 6 bone areas known to receive nerve fibers from this spinal segment is the stomach. Some of the conditions that can follow a pressure on or interference with these nerves include stomach troubles, including nervous stomach, indigestion, heartburn, dyspepsia, etc.

	☷☳ #23	
AAC		Thoracic 5 Disc
Asparagine	13,734,733	Lung (4 a.m.)
Bebegen	(+3)	(23) Deterioration

The genetic code AAC correlates with the amino acid asparagine. Walter Russell called this subatomic particle bebegen. It is a triple-bottom quark. The triple-bottom quark can be manipulated by the aluminum-boron-yttrium levels. The spinal connection is the thoracic 5 disc space which facilitates the flow of magnetic energy of the lung meridian which regenerates at 4 a.m.

Quarks come in simple pairs, double pairs, and triple pairs. Subatomic particles are developed by the ratios of all minerals below hydrogen. Their appearance here may seem esoteric, but no more so than the other elements outlined, comprehension being deferred for those who master the grammar of the subject. In any case, manipulation of subatomic particles relies upon manipulation of minerals below hydrogen.

Bebegen is a triple-quark system. The triple-quark B is in place here. *B* stands for the bottom quark.

#22

UUC		Thoracic 5 Bone
Phenylalanine	18,617,212	Liver to Lung (3 a.m.)
Ethlogen	(+2)	(22) Grace

This is the second time that phenylalanine shows up. It is governed by a mineral called ethlogen. It controls all the ratios of positive 2s in the body. Beryllium, calcium, magnesium, strontium and barium all figure in maintenance and control. Chiefly, however, magnesium deficiency creates most of the problems. This one, not only the +2s, also takes into account the cobalt +2 minerals starting with manganese. It regulates the energy field of the liver to the lungs. The spinal segment is the thoracic 5 bone which is the connecting point of the liver to the lung acupuncture regeneration cycle. This is a triple-quark T system. T stands for top quark.

People who awake out of good sound sleep at 3 a.m. should take a look at their calcium and magnesium intake with emphasis on the latter. One of the most interesting gene sequences that involves magnesium is the gene that triggers puberty in humans. Magnesium is the most important and the mineral selenium is the second most important mineral in puberty initiation.

Classical chiropractic conditions of the thoracic 5 bone areas known to receive nerve fibers from this spinal segment are the liver, solar plexus and blood. Some of the conditions that can follow a pressure on or interference with these nerves are liver conditions, fevers, low blood pressure, anemia, poor circulation and arthritis.

☷☳ #21		
UCC		Thoracic 4 Disc
Serine	14,542,369	Liver (2 a.m.)
Carbogenn	(+1)	(21) Reform

Carbogenn has a +1 valence. It is created by the formation of cesium, sodium, potassium, lithium and rubidium. It has a profound effect on the liver, regenerates at 2 a.m., and is affiliated with the amino acid serine. This is a triple-quark S system. S stands for strange quark.

There are many books on the liver. To summarize them is to say keep your liver clean and you will not have too many problems.

☷☴ #20		
AAG		Thoracic 4 Bone
Lysine	18,824,882	G.B. to Liver (1 a.m.)
Gammanon	(-0-)	(20) Contemplating

This is a noble gas. It comes under the guidance of lysine. This subatomic particle has the name, according to Walter Russell, of gammanon, now called neutrino, and has no electrical charge. The spinal connection is the thoracic bone 4.

Gammanon is one of the most important subatomic particles in herbs among the DNA sequence. Gammanon is derived from the ratios of the other noble gases. Some investigators believe that the noble gases come into play only under the aegis of thought.

Classical chiropractic conditions of the thoracic 4 bone areas known to receive nerve fibers from this spinal segment are gall bladder and common duct. Some of the conditions that can follow a pressure on or interference with these nerves are gall bladder conditions, jaundice and shingles.

☰☷ #19		
GAA		Thoracic 3 Disc
Glutamate	18,594,971	Gall Bladder (12 midnight)
Helenine	(-1)	(19) Promotion

Glutamate, also known as glutamic acid, triggers the brain into activity, and too much burns it out. We have now depicted the minerals contained in ocean water. These subatomic particles of which we speak are quarks of light, measurable only by the most sophisticated equipment. Here we have one of two amino acids that do not have a quantitative mineral counterpart. This helenine is a fragment of a triple quark with a -1 oxidation state, which means it is controlled by iodine. The gall bladder is the related organ, glutamate regenerates at 12 midnight, and has spinal reflex at the thoracic 3 disc. This subatomic particle is a triple-quark system. Who really knows what monosodium glutamate is doing to humans?

䷐	**#18**	
CUC		Thoracic 3 Bone
Leucine	15,863,027	T.B. to G.B. (11 p.m.)
Buzzeon	(-2)	(18) Repair

Walter Russell named the counterpart of leucine with the tongue-twister buzzeon. It is responsible for taking control of -2s in subatomic particles under the auspices of selenium, sulfur, oxygen and tellurium. The spinal segment is the thoracic 3 bone which regenerates the three burners to the gall bladder acupuncture energy field. The amino acid which bows to influence of this subatomic particle is leucine. The subatomic particle associated is a three-quark C system. C stands for charm quark.

Classical chiropractic conditions of the thoracic 3 bone areas known to receive nerve fibers from this spinal segment are lungs, bronchial tubes, pleura, chest, breast nipples. Some of the conditions that can follow a pressure on or interference with these nerves are bronchitis, pleurisy, pneumonia, congestion and influenza.

☰☰ #17		
UCU		Thoracic 2 Disc
Serine	20,882,456	Three Burners (10 p.m.)
Tracion	(-3)	(17) Adapting

The amino acid is serine, the same serine that has showed up earlier in this chart. It is a -3 in the subatomic field named tracion, a triple-U quark. U stands for the up quark.

The relationship best defined here has to do with acupuncture. "When I broke down the Chinese acupuncture chart," notes Richard Olree, "I found that the small intestine and large intestine and three burners go hand in hand. The end result is small intestine digestion sent to the large intestine for further digestion, the sum total of energy derived from food. That energy is called adenosine triphosphate."

Adenosine triphosphate gets broken down by losing one phosphate to become adenosine biphosphate, which is further broken down into adenosine monophosphate. Having given up all its energy, it must go through the Krebs cycle and get rebuilt into adenosine triphosphate again, all this through the action of the three-burner energy field. "When people come into my clinic with the thoracic 2 disc out between their shoulder blades, I can predict these people are so tired they can barely function and have no energy at all," states Dr. Olree.

☰ **#16**		
ACA		Thoracic 2 Bone
Threonine	18,992,012	Peri. to T.B. (9 p.m.)
Quinton	(-4+)	(16) Harmonize

Quinton is the subatomic particle that has a thoracic 2 spinal location and regenerates at 9 p.m. where the pericardial sac is transferring magnetic energy to the three burners acupuncture meridian. This is considered a neutral current. It is a current without charge. This mineral is created by the minerals of carbon, silicon, cobalt, rhodium and lutetium.

Classical chiropractic conditions of the thoracic 2 bone areas known to receive nerve fibers from this spinal segment are the heart including its valves and covering, and also coronary arteries. Some of the conditions that can follow a pressure on or interference with these nerves are functional heart conditions and certain chest pains.

☰ **#15**		
AUA		Thoracic 1 Disc
Isoleucine	19,461,167	Pericardium (8 p.m.)
Vinton	(+3)	(15) Moderation

A positive subatomic particle called vinton brings us to the double-quark system. This one is a quark B. B stands for bottom quark. Its effect is in the pericardial sac, is under the control of boron, greatly influenced by yttrium, and most likely heavily damaged by aluminum. The electromagnetic field of the accupuncture meridian is the pericardium sac which regenerates at 8 p.m. and has a spinal affiliation at the thoracic 1 disc area.

GGC		Thoracic 1 Bone
Glycine	11,190,258	Kidney to Peri. (7 p.m.)
Penrynium	(+2)	(14) Sovereignty

☰ #14

GGC, glycine, thoracic 1 bone, hooks to a glycine molecule, which always has a left spin. The subatomic particle name is penrynium and is a two-quark T system. T stands for top quark. It has a +2 charge and has the same flow as magnesium. It helps the flow of energy go from the kidneys to the pericardial sac at 7 p.m. Circulation is the living factor. When this one drops, there is a consequence of lost circulation.

Penrynium is a +2 mineral. This is the only positive magnetic field that affiliates with glycine. This connection has a profound nerve supply to the heart and will cause the heart to falter without the glycine-oxygen connection.

Classical chiropractic conditions of the thoracic 1 bone areas known to receive nerve fibers from this spinal segment are arms from the elbows down, including the hands, wrists and fingers, also the esophagus and trachea. Some of the conditions that can follow a pressure on or interference with these nerves are asthma, cough, difficult breathing, shortness of breath and pain in lower arms and hands.

☰ **#13**		
UGG		Cervical 7 Disc
Tryptophan	17,388,815	Kidney (6 p.m.)
Marconium	(+1)	(13) Community

The only time L-tryptophan shows up on the chart is with the subatomic particle named marconium. It controls a double-quark S system. S stands for the strange quark. Its subatomic particle existence is the sum total of all the +1 minerals that we have in our system from cesium, rubidium, sodium, and potassium to lithium. The opposite of +1 is -1. Its location on the human spine is cervical 7 disc, which happens to be the nerve connected to the thyroid, which is there to collect the negative polarity of iodine.

This makes iodine the most important element for kidney function. "From my chair," explains Olree, "the thyroid really falls beneath the kidney energy field in acupuncture meridians."

This one is used a whopping 17,338,815 times in the genetic code. The question asks itself: how does one accumulate subatomic particles and couple them to a protein? DNA can do this, but the research is still out there trying to explain how!

The heaviest, most important mineral in quantity is iodine. Imagine the strength of the subatomic particles to attract and hold iodine in the thyroid gland.

The question is really how to get L-tryptophan working in the kidneys to create a subatomic field called marconium. It's commonly held that, L-tryptophan was removed from the market in order to make way for Prozac. A Japanese product made with the aid of genetically modified microorganisms allegedly killed seven people. There is no record of ill-fated use of the natural tryptophan product. Replacement under the auspices of Prozac has become a disgrace to the medical profession. There are a number of fluoride-based drugs similar to Prozac. One must consult the *Physicians' Desk Reference* to check the chemical structure of any drug.

☰ #12		
ACG		Cervical 7 Bone
Threonine	2,356,907	U.B. to Kidney (5 p.m.)
Betaanon	(-0-)	(12) Stagnation

This is the second lightest of the noble gases with no polarity or charges. This regenerates at 5 p.m. as the urinary bladder passes the magnetic energy to the kidney acupuncture meridian fields. This is the least call for an amino on the Olree Standard Genetic Chart. The spinal connection is the cervical 7 bone.

Classical chiropractic conditions of the cervical 7 bone areas known to receive nerve fibers from this spinal segment are the thyroid gland, bursae in the shoulders and the elbows. Some of the conditions that can follow a pressure on, or interference with these nerves are bursitis, colds, thyroid conditions and goiter.

☷ #11		
GUA		Cervical 6 Disc
Valine	10,721,426	Urinary Bladder (4 p.m.)
Romanon	(-1)	(11) Prospering

Here is another branch-chain amino acid: valine, a double-quark C system named romanon. C stands for the charm quark. It is governed by -1 electrons so that the iodine, bromine, chlorine and fluorine ratio will have a profound effect on the primary regeneration of the urinary bladder. This regenerates at 4 p.m.

☰ **#10**		
GCG		Cervical 6 Bone
Alanine	2,231,822	S.I. to U.B. (3 p.m.)
Delphanon	(-2)	(10) Conduct

Delphanon is the second lightest subatomic -2 particle. Delphanon is a double-quark D system. D stands for the down quark. The amino acid is alanine and it pairs up with the communication at the subatomic level between the small intestine to the urinary bladder at 3 p.m. It is only called for 2 million plus times in the DNA sequence. It affects the sixth bone in the cervical spine.

Classical chiropractic conditions of the cervical 6 bone areas known to receive nerve fibers from this spinal segment are neck muscles, shoulder and tonsils. Some of the conditions that can follow a pressure on or interference with these nerves are stiff neck, pain in the upper arm, tonsillitis, whooping cough and croup.

☰ **#9**		

GUG		Cervical 5 Disc
Valine	14,164,470	Small Instestine (2 p.m.)
Barnordon	(-3)	(9) Restrained

Here we're back into a branch-chain amino acid called valine. It is a barnordon. It has a -3 valence. It affects the small intestine and regenerates at 2 p.m. through the cervical 5 disc. Richard Olree explains, "I like the third law of physics. For every action has an equal and opposite reaction. So I take the human spine and the 64 amino acids and concluded that number 1 equals 64, number 2 equals 63, and I laid it out on paper. The opposite of number 9 is number 54, the yttrium area of the spine. So treatment at the cervical 5 disc can directly have an effect on yttrium."

There are many in the chiropractic field who adjust the cervical 5 area as a matter of routine procedure. This segment will have a direct effect on the yttrium-based STOP termination codon based on the third law of physics which states "For every reaction there is an equal and opposite reaction".

☰ ☷	**#8**	

AAU		Cervical 5 Bone
Asparagine	23,529,409	Heart to S.I. (1 p.m.)
Athenon	(+4-)	(8) Unity

At this point asparagine is hooked up with the +4/-4 subatomic particle called athenon. This has to do with the neutral current in subatomic particle physics. Called z-boson, this electrically neutral particle is held together as +4/-4 by the other +/-4 elements, which are carbon, cobalt, silicon, rhodium and lutetium. The amino acid is asparagine and connects the heart to small intestine acupuncture energy meridian through the cervical 5 bone.

Classical chiropractic conditions of the cervical 5 bone areas known to receive nerve fibers from this spinal segment are the vocal cords, neck glands, and pharynx. Some of the conditions that can follow a pressure on, or interference with these nerves are laryngitis, hoarseness, and throat conditions like a sore throat or quinsy.

	☰ ☷ **#7**	
CAA		Cervical 4 Disc
Glutamine	17,851,044	Heart (12 noon)
Eykaon	(+3)	(7) Collective Force

The amino acid is glutamine. The subatomic particle is called eykaon, which is a single-quark system using the B quark. The B quark is the bottom quark. The electron valence is +3. On the acupuncture meridian it represents the heart regenerating at 12 noon in the cervical 4 disc space. It comes into being from the ratios of boron, aluminum, yttrium, scandium, and all of the +3 minerals.

This is the heaviest of all single quark configurations. Each one of the nine levels of minerals is controlled by an electron valence. The number one level of the mineral chart is governed by the -0- polarity. There are no overriding energy fields. This makes all of the single-quark systems pure electrical magnetic energy.

☰☷	**#6**	

CCG		Cervical 4 Bone
Proline	2,583,729	Spleen to Heart (11 a.m.)
Erneston	(+2)	(6) Conflict

The amino acid on the Standard Genetic Chart is proline, also on the Olree Chart. It has a +2 electron valence. It is called on 2,500,000 times in DNA sequencing. It allows the energy of the cervical 4 bone to be used. In the acupuncture energy field it links the spleen to the heart meridian, and regenerates at 11 am. Beryllium, calcium, magnesium, barium, and strontium ratios give permission for the formation of this subatomic quark to exist.

Classical chiropractic conditions of the cervical 4 bone areas known to receive nerve fibers from this spinal segment are the nose, lips, mouth and eustachian tube. Some of the conditions that can follow a pressure on or interference with these nerves are hay fever, catarrh, hard of hearing, and affects on the adenoids.

☷☰	**#5**	

GUU		Cervical 3 Disc
Valine	13,793,561	Spleen (10 a.m.)
Jamearnon	(+1)	(5) Calculated Waiting

The amino acid is valine. The subatomic particle would be jame-arnon with a +1 electron valence. It patrols the spleen, regenerates at 10 a.m., and relates to the cervical 3 disc in the neck. The life of jame-arnon depends on the lithium, sodium, potassium, cesium and rubidium ratios. This is a single-quark system using the S quark. S stands for the strange quark.

☰☷	**#4**	
CAC		Cervical 3 Bone
Histidine	14,137,650	St. to Sp. (9 a.m.)
Alphanon	(-0-)	(4) Inexperience

The amino acid is Histidine. Alphanon is the noblest of noble gases. It has a -0- polarity in the highest level of octaves that are governed by zeros. This would have to be the god gene and has the greatest impact on mental health. The right brain has a spin, and the left brain has a spin. Where the spins meet is a vortex of neutral energy called consciousness. Histidine becomes a very potent amino acid. It controls the stomach to the spleen and regenerates at 9 a.m. "If there is a god-based amino," notes Olree, "histidine would be tied to it." The spinal connection is the cervical 3 bone.

Lithium is the only other mineral associated with histidine, and lithium is a volatile mineral in terms of brain stability. When the lithium level drops, the individual develops bipolar disease, formerly known as manic-depressive illness. The brain itself has electromagnetic fields at the conjunction where the two brain spins meet. This one is called upon 14 million plus times in DNA sequencing.

Classical chiropractic conditions of the cervical 3 bone areas known to receive nerve fibers from this spinal segment are the cheeks, outer ear, face bones, teeth and the trifacial nerve. Some of the conditions that can follow a pressure on or interference with these nerves are neuralgia, neuritis, acne or pimples, and eczema.

☷ ☷ **#3**		
UAU		Cervical 2 Disc
Tyrosine	19,483,112	Stomach (8 a.m.)
Boston	(-1)	(3) Difficult Beginings

The amino acid is tyrosine, and the subatomic name is boston, a -1 charge. It relates to the second disc in the cervical spine, and helps the stomach regenerate at 8 a.m. In terms of how emotions affect one's health, this is a big segment of the spine. Any abnormal pressure on the base of the brain can make one very sick to the stomach.

☷ ☷ **#2**		
AAA		Cervical 2 Bone
Lysine	36,326,850	L.I. to St. (7 a.m.)
Blackton	(-2)	(2) Natural Response

The amino acid is lysine, and the subatomic particle is named blackton. It has a -2 oxidation state. Valence -2 are governed primarily by selenium, oxygen, sulfur and tellurium; -2 and selenium go hand in hand because there are 27 proteins that evolve around selenium found in the brain. It works its way to the subatomic level as the second lightest subatomic particle there is. This is the most or second most called for amino in all of the 22 chromosomes, including the X and Y chromosomes. Between this segment and the next segment is the starting point for all of chiropractic. D.D. Palmer started the first school of chiropractic on the premise that this is the original subluxation of the spinal column.

Classical chiropractic conditions of the cervical 2 bone areas known to receive nerve fibers from this spinal segment are eyes, optic nerve, auditory nerve, sinuses, mastoid bones, tongue and forehead. Some of the conditions that can follow a pressure on or interference with these nerves are sinus trouble, allergies, crossed eyes, deafness, erysipelas, eye troubles, earaches, fainting spells and certain cases of blindness.

☰	**#1**	

GGG		Cervical 1 Bone
Glycine	12,371,863	Large Intestine (6 a.m.)
Alberton	(-3)	(1) Creative Power

There is no lighter subatomic particle than the one associated with GGG. The amino acid is glycine. It has no mirror image. It affiliates with oxygen, a component of DNA. All of the other minerals and all of the other amino acids have to fit in around glycine because of glycine's left-handed nature. Walter Russell called this subatomic particle alberton and it is the lightest of the subatomic particles, the U quark. U stands for the up quark. It has a -3 electric charge. It has a profound effect on the large intestine and is governed by the cervical 1 bone.

Classical chiropractic conditions of the cervical 1 bone areas known to receive nerve fibers from this spinal segment are the blood supply to the head, the pituitary gland, the scalp, bones of the face, the brain itself, inner and middle ear, and the sympathetic nervous symptom. Some of the conditions that can follow a pressure on or interference with these nerves are headaches, nervousness, insomnia, head colds, high blood pressure, migraine headaches, mental conditions, nervous breakdowns, amnesia, sleeping sickness, chronic tiredness, dizziness or vertigo and St. Vitus dance.

So ends the periodic chart superimposed over the Standard Genetic Chart. For botanical sources of the elements described above, see Sourcing the Elements.

I Ching

The discerning reader will have noted the appearance of hexa-grams opposite each of the 64 genetic chart codons. It seems less than happenstance that the *I Ching* should tally 64 hexagrams. We have now seen the 64 number identified in the human spine in the Standard Genetic Chart.

In a manner of speaking, it has been the *I Ching*-DNA connection that has made the mineral-amino acid connection come clear. This number alphabet of the *I Ching* is a part of the South Korean flag. A series of lines makes a statement. There are solid lines and broken lines.

The 64 sequences that backbone this book can all be depicted with two sequences of three lines each. The series start with long-long-long, and then long-long-long. The next one is long-long-long, and then long-short-long. This graphical depiction of binary numbers, developed in the 11th century is a sort of Morse code of Eastern philosophy with each combination having related emotion or action. This code is presented on each of the 64 Olree Standard Genetic Chart entries. Eastern philosophers can be justified if they say, "You've decoded our bible."

A readout of the system thus presents itself. On 64, you read CCC, proline, and the mineral lutetium. Too many times the DNA sequence calls for the mineral, the electron valence, the vertebra in the back, and the acupuncture meridian, and finally the designation of the *I Ching* columns.

More than half the world is conversant with this subtle communication form — China, Japan, Korea, Taiwan, and everyone in the Asian East.

A Pantheon of Minerals

Every mineral can be accumulated, stored and released. Storage times are different for every mineral. Taking in too many minerals of almost any stripe can be detrimental. The biggest mass poisoning in history is taking place in Bangladesh where WHO has a program for supplying wellwater. For 30 years people have been drinking arsenic-contaminated water. The resultant lung and skin cancer promises to set a new world record. Thirty million people are affected.

People who become low on iodine have "senior moments." Their memories crash. In the end stages, they have acute Alzheimer's attacks. Patients who search for help in the usual M.D. channels will often be told that the blood test reveals nothing and to wait until a more definitive diagnosis arrives. Until the numbers say that you're sick, you're not sick, that seems to be the medically correct verdict. "But, Doc, my neck is swollen! My memory is gone. The miseries are flowing through me. My hands and feet are constantly cold. My thermostat is up. Are you sure, Doc?"

"We could reduce our national dependence on oil by 5% if everyone had enough iodine," is Richard Olree's verdict.

There are lifeforms in the Galapagos that do not use iron. They use vanadium instead of iron to carry oxygen, so their blood is green, just like Mr. Spock's.

Vanadium pairs with the mineral called gallium. Gallium seems to have no entries in the medical literature. It has been and remains one of those mysteries that still has to be unraveled. Next we skip five minerals from cobalt to arsenic because cobalt is the master dragger.

They base their identity as subordinate minerals since they all have to be paired with cobalt.

DNA has a way to use the protein frequency of certain minerals to drag still other trace minerals in and out of the body. In the absence of certain trace minerals the DNA makes use of substitutes. In terms of an allegory, this means 50 or 200 or 500 chemical conversions to achieve the same result. Recall, if you will, the experiments with yttrium. Yttrium lengthened the lifespan of test animals by 30% or more because all the energy wasn't being wasted performing the demanded function the hard way. Yttrium canceled out so many unnecessary pathways that debilitated and exhausted, it enabled the lengthening of life itself.

Ronald Reagan's transition team fired the FDA director and installed a bureaucrat who ratified the use of NutraSweet, or aspartame. Previously, aspartame had been turned down 16 times. In 1980 aspartame became legal.

In Iraq diet versions of Coke and Pepsi were kept in very hot conditions. The aspartame broke down into formaldehyde and wood alcohol. The heat changes aspartame with the breakdown product a neurotoxin.

Do we need strontium? Yes. Do we need aluminum? Yes. Do we need arsenic? Absolutely. There wouldn't be a man on this earth if arsenic wasn't a player in the DNA code. Every woman carrying a male child needs arsenic to carry that child. A woman who aborts at the end of the first trimester lacks in arsenic. Practiced holistic health can shut down the spontaneous abortion. Long, thin pine needles, crushed and steeped in one cup of hot water for 20 minutes, will bring the arsenic levels up to nature's requirement.

Pine needle arsenic always figured as a heart medicine before the advent of the nitro pill. The element has a bad name because of James Bond movies and mystery writers.

The mineral bromine affiliates with the acupuncture meridian of the stomach. The amino acid is serine. Boron also affiliates with the amino acid serine. "I speculated," recounts Olree, "that if you have high aluminum consumption and it suppresses your boron or runs it out of the system, this will alter serine metabolism. If you alter serine metabolism, you alter bromine metabolism."

That part of the brain that goes faulty, that delivers Parkinson's, has no bromine. So, Parkinson's is an aluminum toxicity, plus a boron deficiency which depletes or alters serine metabolism. When serine is depleted in that portion of the brain or shuttled somewhere else, the bromine leaves the tissue and the result is Parkinson's disease.

Alzheimer's is an aluminum toxicity-yttrium deficiency disease. Yttrium falls on the heart meridian. When there is a deficit of yttrium-based protein, the heart, not the brain, is the victim. American rest homes are full of people with an yttrium deficiency. The small supply services the heart to sustain life, but the deprived brain loses its function — Alzheimer's! Lou Gehrig's disease falls into the same category as Alzheimer's: high aluminum, low boron, and yttrium-based minerals suppressed — select starvation!

The Walter Russell chart is set up with nine levels: octaves, like music for a piano. There are nine levels of energy sequenced 0 to 4, and 0 which repeats itself. Taking that numbered sequence, you start off at the ninth level, the radioactive end. You avoid that end because it is radioactive. It gives off subatomic particles in heavier doses than we can use. They cause the DNA to break down in the presence of these minerals giving off subatomic particles. Radiation, in fact, is a concentration of subatomic particles. The life factor asks for the creation of a magnetic field with trace amounts of subatomic particles brought about by the ratios of minerals consumed. Radiation has a +2 form, but that disrupts calcium-magnesium. Such a disruption equals a short circuit with the DNA falling apart. Using the number system, you can start at the bottom of the chart, 0. The next level up is -1, then -2, then -3. The fourth level up is governed by +4/-4, silicon, and carbon. The next level up is governed by boron. The next level up is governed by calcium-magnesium. The second level from the top is the sodium-potassium ratio. The third level is a noble gas with a 0 polarity, the lightest of atomic particles.

The -1 of iodine controls all of the other -1s: bromine, chlorine, and fluorine. The next level up is -2. In that spectrum of 0 to 4 to 0, the -2 of the seventh octave is selenium. Selenium is there to govern all of the other -2s: tellurium, oxygen and sulfur.

It's all tied to the music scale and the light scale.

On the Olree Standard Genetic Chart one finds an amino acid-mineral relationship. If a person expects to take in, for example, magnesium, then it is mandatory to have magnesium paired with alanine, an amino acid. It is the function of alanine to harvest magnesium from the intestinal tract and move it around. The mineral counterpart of the amino acid must function as a carrier. Minerals do not act on their own, nor do amino acids act on their own. Minerals and amino acids get with each other at the discretion of the DNA to create a three-dimensional life forms.

Selenium mops up beryllium and arsenic toxicity. Richard Olree explains the sequence this way: "A person who goes into acute arsenic toxicity can be rendered healthy again in a short period of time via the administration of selenium. There are mushrooms that people consume that make them deathly ill by upsetting the intestinal tract. The chemical gets caught in a loop between the large intestine and the liver. The liver shuttles it to the gall bladder. The gall bladder puts it into the intestine. The intestine reabsorbs it and puts it in the blood-stream, and it goes back to the liver. Each time that it makes the loop it tears up the system chemically. Selenium stops that loop and expels the toxin instantly, often within hours."

Tellurium is a mineral in the -2 oxidation state. It's heavier than selenium. It's the garlic factor, the author of garlic breath. It's a phenomenal oxygen-consuming mineral. It has the same classification as sulfur and selenium. Polonium 210 cancels out tellurium and selenium. Indeed, it goes down one pipe, and then splits into two pipes: the right lung and the left lung. At every split into another set of pipes, a veritable bifurcation process, one tube becomes two tubes. Wherever the velocity of the air is the fastest, it will land polonium 210 into the tissue. Now this radioactive metal gives off its alpha particles, influencing the replication of the DNA, shoving out selenium and causing oxygen mutations. The result is an entirely new DNA-based cell that falls under the control of p53, the biggest and most important tumor-suppressing gene there is. p53 is selenium-based and has to work in order to identify normal cells that are not an exact copy of what they replace.

Polonium 210 inhibits the function of selenium-based proteins. The number one reason for lung cancer is polonium 210 toxicity caused by selenium deficiency. The number two reason for lung cancer is the noble gas radon.

A bit of doggerel supplies an explanation more easily understood than the above. Olree explains: *The cigarette is a blight on the human race. A man is a monkey with one in his face. Here's my take on smoking, dear brother: A fire on one end, a fool on the other.*

Small-cell cancer is a 100% tobacco-related cancer. It is an iodine deficiency, a selenium deficiency, and a polonium 210 toxicity. When the standard oncologist wants to radiate and apply chemotherapy, he'll do exactly what the tobacco does.

Nicotine, from the tobacco plant, causes addiction to a substance treated with arsenic-based herbicides that install cadmium and arsenic into the system via the agency of smoke. Modern technology shortens the tobacco farm drying process by saturating the product with propane, a methane-type gas which triggers an assembly of methyl changes to the structure of the tobacco. Thus, the smoker inhales raw toxicity. No one can continue to smoke, then use alternative remedies for a cancer, and expect to win. First, the chemical source must be eliminated. As with the consequences of aspartame-laced soda pop, you simply have to stop. Then, an immune system wakeup call must be invoked. These abnormal cells put up a chemical defense of their own. They attempt to hide tumor-suppressing proteins. It is up to the immune system to kill mutated cells.

A new problem surfaces soon enough. Suppose radiation and its cyanide molecule annihilate the cancer cell. Can the liver and kidneys and lymph system be capable of removing so many toxic cells as fast as they are destroyed?

University of Wisconsin researchers now find that magnesium has a central role in biochemistry and physiology because a substantial fraction of it is mono- to triphosphate. Magnesium is absolutely permission for life. There isn't a farmer on planet Earth who can live without sunlight striking the earth, causing the green coloring called chlorophyll to engineer into existence plant growth. The center of the chlorophyll molecule is magnesium. If you remove the magnesium molecule from the center of chlorophyll, and insert an iron molecule in its place, you now have hemoglobin. That's how closely tied is the chlorophyll-hemoglobin connection. The whole basis of the food chain is the sunlight-chlorophyll-magnesium factor. The cow eats grass. She avails herself of that instant conversion, giving man — the head of the biotic pyramid — meat and milk. It is a very efficient system — sunlight to meat! The mineral inventory found in beef is awesome. These great natural benefits are canceled out when the cow is restricted to a feedlot, fed carbohydrates, bypass protein, cattle cake, and bicarbonate of soda. "If they did that to humans," noted Richard Olree, "they'd be prosecuted and jailed for life. You can't treat life that way and expect to have life-giving properties."

As calcium goes up, magnesium goes down. Too often, calcium supplementation results in calcium precipitating into kidneys to build kidney stones or into the blood vessels to create arteriosclerosis or into the gall bladder to build gall bladder stones.

The University of Southern California and the Orthopedic Hospital of Los Angeles put it this way: "Dietary magnesium intake has been linked to osteoporosis. Previous studies have demonstrated that severe magnesium deficiency results in osteoporosis." They have assessed that more moderate dietary magnesium affects all bone and mineral metabolism and the effects of the parathyroid hormone.

A summary of the above is that magnesium is necessary to affect calcium absorption, calcium utilization, and calcium excretion. Organic magnesium is the magnesium of choice. It will most certainly stop the formation of any new kidney stones. A modest increase of magnesium is both indicated and absolutely necessary to stop osteoporosis in its tracks. Diuretics should be indicted as the wrong therapy in the wrong place at the wrong time. It causes the elimination of magnesium, and magnesium loss goes hand in hand with rising blood pressure. This is usually a consequence of the drug prescription. The 10-mg dose no longer works. The usual procedure is to increase it. Fully 80% of patients using diuretics lose magnesium. Once the magnesium wastes away, the slide to the floor and below picks up speed.

Magnesium controls the potassium level. When magnesium goes bonkers, the body tries to compensate by hoarding potassium. Reading the peer-reviewed literature, we find that the loss of magnesium drains the magnesium nutrient out of the heart, a serious miscalculation. Magnesium is the mineral needed for the electricity to conduct the heartbeat. All of the electrical modes in the heart run on magnesium.

Modern medicine tries to deal with this dichotomy via the blood test. Yet magnesium is supposed to be in the cell. The problem is that cell magnesium will leach out and service the blood. Once the blood shows low magnesium, the reserve is almost exhausted. If the blood test is marginal, how can a physician tell? Old-timers used signs and symptoms, an art that most physicians ignore nowadays. The fastest way to deplete magnesium is to drink soft drinks rich in phosphoric acid. A slower way to deplete magnesium is to take calcium supplementation or simply not drink enough water.

The signal question arrives: how can one preserve some of the magnesium? All of the levels of the spine are controlled by different master minerals: -1 is iodine; -2 is selenium; -3 is phosphorus. Phosphorus in turn controls nitrogen, arsenic and antimony. Antimony in very small amounts provides the body cycles their requirement.

On the positive end, there is silicon as +4; the opposite valence, -4, is carbon. The base of carbon is vitamin C.

The master +3 mineral is boron, the conservator of magnesium. Just 3 mg a day of boron stop urinary output of magnesium. The apple core is a good source of boron. Boron is fuel in the highest portions of the brain. It enables thoughts that go with pure and high ideals. It also figures in controlling the heart meridian.

Now consider the various forms of radiation that assault the human body. If you have adequate boron and iodine levels, the body is not affected. DNA is not altered when adequate boron levels are present. That's why the Chernobyl disaster called for boron to treat the place. Boron absorbs radiation and releases it without disturbing the protons and neutrons in the nucleus. Every other mineral on the genetic chart that is bombarded with radiation loses a proton or a neutron making it a radioactive mineral. Alone, boron does not become radioactive.

Boron stops urinary loss of magnesium. It is critical for the relaxation of heart muscles, for the relaxation of arteries, and for the electrical conductivity of the heart.

Magnesium, found in the kidneys, is essential for kidney function. Magnesium falls on the communication point between the kidney and the pericardial sac meridians. The acupuncture discipline tells us that the meridians are either in favored junction or they are giving off energy to the next energy field. At 7 p.m. magnesium is regenerating and couples to the kidney and to the pericardial sac. This pericardial sac is simply the arterial system. When people experience magnesium deficiency related to heart palpitations, it is not the heart at issue, it is the sac around the heart not beating in rhythm with the heart. It is usually beating twice as fast as the heart. The rapid heartbeat is simply saying, "Get some magnesium in here, dummy!"

Part 3
Sourcing the Elements

Sourcing the Elements

Meaningful dietary levels of the elements profiled in this book —tinctures, teas, plants, proteins from browsing and grazing meat animals, and nuts — all depend on sources close to nature. Meaningful suppliers of supplements are under assault worldwide by Codex amateurs. On July 4, 2005, a meeting in Rome, Italy, finalized the iron collar around the neck of the public, guided by the World Trade Organization and NATO.

A new world order is to take charge of health maintenance items such as minerals, vitamins, enzymes, probiotics, and the type of fare available in health food stores. Those with enough vision to see some part of the future take comfort as in Voltaire's *Candide* — that all will turn out well. Yet one has to wonder whether people will survive with enough mental acuity to take saving action. At issue is the Codex Alimentarius, the WTO document that takes off our hands the problem of self-government. On July 4, Codex Alimentarius installed its version of what the food supplement industry should be. That version complies with the designs of the pharmaceutical industry and the American Medical Association machine. Codex allows food supplements, but the dosages are to be so low as to be meaningless. Our betters expect to put our health in the hands of physicians, a discipline that knows little more about nutrition than a jackrabbit knows about Sunday.

The way WTO works is as follows: once a nation buys into this corporate world domination, congresses or parliaments are required to pass laws to bring the subject nation into compliance. This done, an unseen committee serves as a court. Should the United States elect to install environmental rules that affect a trader nation, for example, the new jurisdiction levies fines. There is no real appeal, nor will there be unless the United States or Mexico or Chile or any other nation tells WTO to stuff it.

The chance of the U.S. Congress standing up to the WTO is about the same as that of the Brooklyn Bridge suddenly levitating. The scheme calls for GMOs to be ratified by the Organic Standards Act.

Codex Alimentarius hopes to tightly control vitamins, minerals, enzymes and almost all essential nutrients embodied in food supplements. They will be treated as pharmaceutical drugs, ergo available only by prescription. More important, they are to be manufactured by pharmaceutical companies from synthetic materials and genetically engineered substances.

Since failure to adopt these guidelines can and will result in sanctions, you can make book that the talking heads in Washington will comply. Australia, Norway, Denmark and Germany were the early ones to adopt the food and drug guidelines. Canada moved supplements under the drug category on January 1, 2004.

The show may not be over. Article 152 of the EU Constitution forbids harmonization of medicinal and food supplements. This may be a solid legal argument. Legal arguments notwithstanding, the Codex proposes, and the legal puppets dispose.

Consumers will be shoved back into line, forced to rely on drugs —especially drugs that earn fantastic profits protected by patents. If the German experience means anything, we can expect food supplements to carry pharmacy prices! We're informed that $200 for vitamin E capsules is typical. Simple calcium carbonate, or blackboard chalk, may all be weighed out on the jeweler's scale. If this comes to fruition, you can still source the elements from food.

These few considerations make the list that follows worth its weight in gold.

These entries are merely a sampling of botanical sources of elements, essential or otherwise. A full inventory will eventually be assembled. For more details consult the Jim Duke phytochemical database online at *www.ars-grin.gov/duke*. Bibliographic data for the entries exhibited here is given there as well.

Natural Sources of Elements

Listed by: Botanical name (AUTHOR NAME, if applicable) — Common name — Part analyzed — Parts per million (in descending order). T = toxic; E = edible; M = medicinal properties.

Aluminum

Cucumis sativus L. — Cucumber — Fruit — 21,000 ppm. E

Echinacea spp. — Coneflower, Echinacea — Root — 12,900 ppm. M

Juniperus virginiana L. — Red Cedar — Shoot — 8,800 ppm. TEM

Carya glabra (MILLER) SWEET — Pignut Hickory — Shoot — 7,700 ppm. E

Symphoricarpos orbiculatus MOENCH. — Buckbush — Stem — 4,400 ppm. M

Pinus echinata MILLER — Shortleaf Pine — Shoot — 4,200 ppm. M

Phaseolus lunatus L. — Butter Bean, Lima Bean — Seed — 3,000 ppm. E

Nyssa sylvatica MARSHALL — Black Gum, Black Tupelo — Leaf — 2,730 ppm. EM

Centella asiatica (L.) URBAN — Gotu Kola, Pennywort — Leaf — 2,060 ppm. EM

Stellaria media (L.) VILLARS — Chickweed, Common Chickweed — Plant — 1,960 ppm. E

Rhus copallina L. — Dwarf Sumac, Winged Sumac — Leaf — 1,920 ppm. EM

Mentha pulegium L. — European Pennyroyal — Plant — 1,850 ppm. TEM

Liquidambar styraciflua L. — American Styrax, Sweetgum — Stem — 1,800 ppm. EM

Lycopersicon esculentum MILLER — Tomato — Fruit — 1,700 ppm. TEM

Prunus serotina subsp. serotina — Black Cherry, Wild Cherry — Leaf — 1,440 ppm. TEM

Agathosma betulina (P.P. BERGIUS) PILLANS — Buchu, Honey Buchu, Mountain Buchu — Leaf — 1,360 ppm. M

Sassafras albidum (NUTT.) NEES — Sassafras — Leaf — 1,360 ppm. TEM

Ruscus aculeatus L. — Box-Holly, Butcher's Broom — Root — 1,310 ppm. EM

Liquidambar styraciflua L. — American Styrax, Sweetgum — Leaf — 1,230 ppm. EM

Verbascum thapsus L. — Flannelleaf, Flannelplant, Great Mullein, Mullein, Velvetplant — Leaf — 1,090 ppm. M

Quercus alba L. — White Oak — Stem — 1,064 ppm. EM

Daucus carota L. — Carrot — Root — 1,050 ppm. E

Phaseolus vulgaris var. vulgaris — Black Bean, Dwarf Bean, Field Bean, Flageolet Bean, French Bean, Garden Bean, Green Bean, Haricot, Haricot Bean, Haricot Vert, Kidney Bean, Navy Bean, Pop Bean, Popping Bean, Snap Bean, String Bean, Wax Bean — Fruit — 1,050 ppm. E

Prunus persica (L.) BATSCH — Peach — Fruit — 1,050 ppm. TEM

Vitis vinifera L. — European Grape, Grape, Grapevine, Parra (Sp.), Vid (Sp.), Vigne Vinifere (Fr.), Weinrebe (Ger.), Wine Grape — Stem — 1,030 ppm. EM

Rhus glabra L. — Smooth Sumac — Stem — 1,005 ppm. EM

Harpagophytum procumbens (BURCH.) DC. EX MEISN. — Devil's Claw, Grapple — Plant — Root — 939 ppm. M

Thymus vulgaris L. — Common Thyme, Garden Thyme, Thyme — Leaf — 920 ppm. EM

Quercus stellata WANGENH. — Post Oak — Stem — 840 ppm. EM

Vigna unguiculata subsp. sesquipedalis (L.) VERDC. — Asparagus Bean, Pea Bean, Yardlong Bean — Seed — 840 ppm. E

Caulophyllum thalictroides (L.) MICHX. — Blue Cohosh — Root — 762 ppm. M

Smilax spp. — Sarsaparilla — Root — 745 ppm. EM

Sassafras albidum (NUTT.) NEES — Sassafras — Stem — 740 ppm. TEM

Aluminum, cont.

Arctostaphylos uva-ursi (L.) SPRENGEL — Bearberry, Uva Ursi — Leaf — 719 ppm. M

Viburnum opulus — Crampbark, European Cranberry Bush, Guelder Rose, Snowball Bush — Bark — 702 ppm. TEM

Asparagus officinalis L. — Asparagus — Shoot — 700 ppm. E

Camellia sinensis (L.) KUNTZE — Tea — Leaf — 690 ppm. E

Althaea officinalis L. — Marshmallow, White Mallow — Root — 680 ppm. M

Zingiber officinale ROSCOE — Ginger — Rhizome — 663 ppm. EM

Nyssa sylvatica MARSHALL — Black Gum, Black Tupelo — Stem — 660 ppm. EM

Quercus rubra L. — Northern Red Oak — Stem — 660 ppm. EM

Taraxacum officinale WEBER EX F.F. WIGG. — Dandelion — Root — 656 ppm. EM

Fucus vesiculosus L. — Bladderwrack, Kelp — Plant — 631 ppm. EM

Rhodymenia palmata — Dulse — Plant — 615 ppm. E

Rhus copallina L. — Dwarf Sumac, Winged Sumac — Stem — 610 ppm. EM

Turnera diffusa WILLD. EX SCHULT. — Damiana — Leaf — 605 ppm. M

Prunus serotina subsp. serotina — Black Cherry, Wild Cherry — Stem — 540 ppm. TEM

Cymbopogon citratus (DC. ex NEES) STAPF — Lemongrass, West Indian Lemongrass — Plant — 515 ppm. EM

Berberis vulgaris L. — Barberry — Root — 489 ppm. M

Quercus velutina LAM. — Black Oak — Stem — 434 ppm. EM

Angelica sinensis (OLIV.) DIELS — Chinese Angelica, Dang Gui, Dang Quai, Dang Qui, Dong Gui, Dong Quai — Root — 422 ppm. M

Valeriana officinalis L. — Common Valerian, Garden-Heliotrope, Valerian — Root — 422 ppm. M

Beta vulgaris subsp. vulgaris — Beet, Beetroot, Garden Beet, Sugar Beet — Root — 420 ppm. E

Erythroxylum coca var. coca — Coca — Leaf — 420 ppm. EM

Quercus phellos L. — Willow Oak — Stem — 420 ppm. EM

Rubus idaeus L. — Raspberry, Red Raspberry — Leaf — 392 ppm. EM

Petroselinum crispum (MILLER) NYMAN EX A.A. HILLL — Parsley — Plant — 390 ppm. E

Rumex crispus L. — Curly Dock, Lengua De Vaca, Sour Dock, Yellow Dock — Root — 390 ppm. TEM

Allium cepa L. — Onion, Shallot Bulb — 385 ppm. E

Diospyros virginiana L. — American Persimmon — Stem — 378 ppm. EM

Equisetum arvense L. — Field Horsetail, Horsetail — Plant — 378 ppm. M

Chondrus crispus (L.) STACKH. — Irish Moss — Plant — 355 ppm. E

Trigonella foenum-graecum L. — Alholva (Sp.), Bockshornklee (Ger.), Fenugreek, Greek Clover, Greek Hay — Seed — 350 ppm. EM

Urtica dioica L. — European Nettle, Stinging Nettle — Leaf — 345 ppm. EM

Elytrigia repens (L.) DESV. EX NEVSKI — Couchgrass, Doggrass, Quackgrass, Twitchgrass, Wheatgrass — Plant — 331 ppm. EM

Citrus paradisi MacFAD. — Grapefruit — Fruit — 330 ppm. E

Hydrastis canadensis L. — Goldenseal — Root — 325 ppm. M

Gentiana lutea L. — Gentian, Yellow Gentian — Root — 291 ppm. M

Larrea tridentata (SESSE & MOC. ex DC.) COV. — Chaparral, Creosote Bush — Plant — 290 ppm. M

Panax quinquefolius L. — American Ginseng, Ginseng — Plant — 285 ppm. M

Viscum album L. — European Mistletoe — Leaf — 283 ppm. TM

Zea mays L. — Corn — Seed — 275 ppm. E

Spinacia oleracea L. — Spinach — Leaf — 270 ppm. E

Silybum marianum (L.) GAERTN. — Lady's Thistle, Milk Thistle — Plant — 267 ppm. M

Scutellaria lateriflora L. — Mad-Dog, Skullcap, Scullcap — Plant — 258 ppm. M

Antimony

Anacardium occidentale L. — Cashew — Seed. E

Carya illinoensis (WANGENH.) K. KOCHC — Pecan — Seed. E

Quercus rubra L. — Northern Red Oak — Seed. EM

Bertholletia excelsa BONPL. — Brazilnut, Brazilnut-Tree, Creamnut, Paranut — Seed. E

Carya ovata (MILL.) K. KOCH — Shagbark Hickory — Seed. E

Cocos nucifera L. — Coconut, Coconut Palm, Cocotero (Sp.), Copra, Koko-spalme (Ger.), Nariyal — Seed. E

Corylus avellana L. — Cobnut, English Filbert, European Filbert, European Hazel, Hazel — Seed. E

Juglans nigra L. — Black Walnut — Seed. E

Prunus dulcis (MILLER) D.D. WEBB — Almond — Seed. TEM

Juglans cinerea L. — Butternut — Seed. E

Pistacia vera L. — Pistachio — Seed. E

Vigna unguiculata subsp. sesquipedalis (L.) VERDC. — Asparagus Bean, Pea Bean, Yardlong Bean — Seed. E

Arsenic

Isatis tinctoria L. — Dyer's Woad — Root — 132 ppm. M

Fucus vesiculosus L. — Bladder-wrack, Kelp — Plant — 68 ppm. EM

Rhodymenia palmata — Dulse — Plant — 33 ppm. E

Chondrus crispus (L.) STACKH. — Irish Moss — Plant — 10 ppm. E

Cynanchum atratum BUNGE — Bai-Wei, Pai-Wei — Root — 4.85 ppm. EM

Citrus paradisi MacFAD. — Grapefruit — Fruit — 4.4 ppm. E

Nardostachys chinensis BATALIN — Chinese Spikenard — Rhizome — 2.11 ppm. M

Taraxacum mongolicum HAND.-MAZZ. — Mongoloid Dandelion — Plant — 1.95 ppm. EM

Plantago asiatica L. — Asian Plantain — Plant — 1.71 ppm. EM

Citrus medica L. — Citron — Fruit — 1.64 ppm. E

Vicia faba L. — Broadbean, Faba Bean, Habas — Seed — 1.4 ppm. E

Bletilla striata (THUNB.) REICHB. f. — Bletilla, Chinese Ground Orchid, Dai Chi (Chin.), Hardy Orchid, Hyacinth Bletilla, Hyacinth Orchid, Shiran (Jap.) — Tuber — 1.35 ppm. M

Lygodium japonicum (THUNB.) SW. — Climbing Fern Pollen or Spore — 1.17 ppm. M

Pulsatilla chinensis (BUNGE) REGEL — Chinese Anemone — Root — 1.14 ppm. M

Acorus calamus L. — Calamus, Flagroot, Myrtle Flag, Sweet Calamus, Sweetflag, Sweetroot — Rhizome — 1.13 ppm. M

Rubia cordifolia L. — Madder — Root — 1.1 ppm. M

Gentiana scabra BUNGE — Japanese Gentian, — Root — 1.06 ppm. M

Daucus carota L. — Carrot, — Root — 1 ppm. E

Jussiaea repens L. — Jussiaeae Herba, Pond Dragon, — Plant — 1 ppm. M

Boron

Valerianella locusta (L.) LATERRADE — Corn Salad, Lamb's Lettuce — Plant — 350 ppm. E

Prunus domestica L. — Plum — Fruit — 255 ppm. TEM

Cydonia oblonga MILLER — Quince — Fruit — 160 ppm. E

Fragaria spp. — Strawberry — Fruit — 160 ppm. E

Prunus persica (L.) BATSCH — Peach — Fruit — 150 ppm. TEM

Brassica oleracea var. capitata L. — Cabbage, Red Cabbage, White Cabbage — Leaf — 145 ppm. E

Nyssa sylvatica MARSHALL — Black Gum, Black Tupelo — Leaf — 136 ppm. EM

Taraxacum officinale WEBER EX F.F. WIGG. — Dandelion — Leaf — 125 ppm. EM

Malus domestica BORKH. — Apple — Fruit — 110 ppm. E

Annona squamosa L. — Sugar-Apple, Sweetsop — Leaf — 107 ppm. E

Boron, cont.

Asparagus officinalis L. — Asparagus — Shoot — 104 ppm. E

Apium graveolens L. — Celery — Root — 103 ppm. E

Ficus carica L. — Echte Feige (Ger.), Feigenbaum (Ger.), Fico (Ital.), Fig, Figueira (Port.), Figuier Commun (Fr.), Higo (Sp.), Higuera Comun (Sp.) — Fruit — 100 ppm. E

Lycopersicon esculentum MILLER — Tomato — Fruit — 96 ppm. TEM

Panax quinquefolius L. — American Ginseng, Ginseng — Plant — 96 ppm. M

Papaver somniferum L. — Opium Poppy, Poppyseed Poppy — Seed — 95 ppm. E

Lactuca sativa L. — Lettuce — Leaf — 87 ppm. E

Brassica oleracea var. botrytis L. — Cauliflower — Leaf — 85 ppm. E

Liquidambar styraciflua L. — American Styrax, Sweetgum — Leaf — 84 ppm. EM

Rhizophora mangle L. — Red Mangrove — Leaf — 83 ppm. M

Pyrus communis L. — Pear — Fruit — 82 ppm. E

Beta vulgaris subsp. vulgaris — Beet, Beetroot, Garden Beet, Sugar Beet — Root — 80 ppm. E

Prunus cerasus L. — Sour Cherry — Fruit — 80 ppm. TEM

Ribes rubrum L. — Red Currant, White Currant — Fruit — 80 ppm. E

Carya glabra (MILLER) SWEET — Pignut Hickory — Shoot — 77 ppm. E

Brassica oleracea var. botrytis L. — Cauliflower — Flower — 76 ppm. E

Prunus armeniaca L. — Apricot — Fruit — 70 ppm. TEM

Rhus copallina L. — Dwarf Sumac, Winged Sumac — Leaf — 67 ppm. EM

Quercus rubra L. — Northern Red Oak — Stem — 66 ppm. EM

Raphanus sativus L. — Radish — Root — 64 ppm. E

Ribes nigrum L. — Black Currant — Fruit — 64 ppm. E

Carya ovata (MILL.) K. KOCH — Shagbark Hickory — Shoot — 63 ppm. E

Apium graveolens L. — Celery — Seed — 61 ppm. E

Liquidambar styraciflua L. — American Styrax, Sweetgum — Stem — 60 ppm. EM

Vigna unguiculata subsp. sesquipedalis (L.) VERDC. — Asparagus Bean, Pea Bean, Yardlong Bean — Seed — 60 ppm. E

Brassica oleracea var. gemmifera DC — Brussel-Sprout, Brussels-Sprouts — Leaf — 57 ppm. E

Erythroxylum coca var. coca — Coca — Leaf — 57 ppm. EM

Petroselinum crispum (MILLER) NYMAN EX A.A. HILLL — Parsley — Plant — 54 ppm. E

Prunus serotina subsp. serotina — Black Cherry, Wild Cherry — Stem — 54 ppm. TEM

Bromine

Fucus vesiculosus L. — Bladderwrack, Kelp — Plant — 150 ppm. EM

Capsicum annuum L. — Bell Pepper, Cherry Pepper, Cone Pepper, Green Pepper, Paprika, Sweet Pepper — Fruit — 111 ppm. E

Urtica dioica L. — European Nettle, Stinging Nettle — Leaf — 110 ppm. EM

Bertholletia excelsa BONPL. — Brazilnut, Brazilnut-Tree, Creamnut, Paranut — Seed — 87 ppm. E

Polygonum cuspidatum SIEBOLD & ZUCC. — Giant Knotweed, Hu-Zhang, Japanese Knotweed, Mexican Bamboo — Plant — 80 ppm. TEM

Taraxacum officinale WEBER EX F.F. WIGG. — Dandelion — Leaf — 80 ppm. EM

Petasites japonicus (SIEBOLD & ZUCC.) MAXIM. — Butterbur — Plant — 40 ppm. T

Artemisia vulgaris L. — Mugwort — Plant — 38 ppm. M

Brassica oleracea var. capitata L. — Cabbage, Red Cabbage, White Cabbage — Leaf — 37 ppm. E

Solanum tuberosum L. — Potato — Tuber — 30 ppm. E

Musa x paradisiaca L. — Banana, Plantain — Fruit — 27 ppm. E

Peucedanum decursivum (MIQ.) MAX. — Qian Hu — Plant — 23 ppm. M

Petroselinum crispum (MILLER) NYMAN EX A.A. HILLL — Parsley — Plant — 21 ppm. E

Cinnamomum burmannii (NEES) BLUME — Java Cinnamon, Padang Cassia — Bark — 20 ppm. TEM

Phaseolus vulgaris var. vulgaris — Black Bean, Dwarf Bean, Field Bean, Flageolet Bean, French Bean, Garden Bean, Green Bean, Haricot, Haricot Bean, Haricot Vert, Kidney Bean, Navy Bean, Pop Bean, Popping Bean, Snap Bean, String Bean, Wax Bean — Fruit — 20 ppm. E

Prunus dulcis (MILLER) D.D. WEBB — Almond — Seed — 20 ppm. TEM

Rheum rhabarbarum L. — Rhubarb — Plant — 20 ppm. E

Armoracia rusticana GAERTN. ET AL. — Horseradish — Root — 19 ppm. E

Glechoma hederacea L. — Alehoof — Plant — 19 ppm. M

Beta vulgaris subsp. vulgaris — Beet, Beetroot, Garden Beet, Sugar Beet — Root — 16 ppm. E

Pistacia vera L. — Pistachio — Seed — 16 ppm. E

Allium cepa L. — Onion, Shallot Bulb — 15 ppm. E

Boehmeria nivea (L.) GAUDICH. — Ramie — Plant — 14 ppm. M

Pisum sativum L. — Pea — Seed — 12 ppm. E

Cinnamomum aromaticum NEES — Canela de la China (Sp.), Canelero chino (Sp.), Canelle de Cochinchine (Fr.), Cannelier Casse (Fr.), Cannelier de Chine (Fr.), Cassia, Cassia Bark, Cassia Lignea, China Junk Cassia, Chinazimt (Ger.), Chinese Cassia, Chinese Cinnamon, Chinesischer Zimtbaum (Ger.), Kashia-Keihi (Jap.), Saigon Cinnamon, Zimtcassie (Ger.) — Bark — 10 ppm. TEM

Cinnamomum verum J. PRESL — Ceylon Cinnamon, Cinnamon — Bark — 10 ppm. TEM

Polystichum polyblepharum (ROEM.) PRESL — Chinese Polystichum — Plant — 10 ppm. T

Daucus carota L. — Carrot — Root — 9 ppm. E

Anethum graveolens L. — Dill, Garden Dill — Plant — 6 ppm. E

Cinnamomum sieboldii — Japanese Cinnamon Root — Bark — 5 ppm. TEM

Rosa canina L. — Dog Rose, Dogbrier, Rose — Fruit — 5 ppm. EM

Cocos nucifera L. — Coconut, Coconut Palm, Cocotero (Sp.), Copra, Kokospalme (Ger.), Nariyal — Seed — 4 ppm. E

Sorbus aucuparia L. — Rowan Berry, Mountain Ash — Fruit — 4 ppm. TEM

Spinacia oleracea L. — Spinach — Leaf — 4 ppm. E

Juglans nigra L. — Black Walnut — Seed — 2.5 ppm. E

Carya ovata (MILL.) K. KOCH — Shagbark Hickory — Seed — 1.8 ppm. E

Corylus avellana L. — Cobnut, English Filbert, European Filbert, European Hazel, Hazel — Seed — 1.8 ppm. E

Quercus rubra L. — Northern Red Oak — Seed — 1.6 ppm. EM

Carya illinoensis (WANGENH.) K. KOCH — Pecan — Seed — 1.5 ppm. E

Juglans cinerea L. — Butternut — Seed — 1.5 ppm. E

Anacardium occidentale L. — Cashew — Seed — 1.2 ppm. E

Citrus reticulata BLANCO — Mandarin, Tangerine — Fruit — 1 ppm. E

Cadmium

Phoenix dactylifera L. — Date Palm — Seed — 9 ppm. E

Hypericum perforatum L. — Common St. Johnswort, Goatweed, Hypericum, Klamath Weed, St. John's-wort — Leaf — 7 ppm. — Plant — 5 ppm. TM

Spinacia oleracea L. — Spinach — Leaf — 5 ppm. E

Symphoricarpos orbiculatus MOENCH. — Buckbush — Stem — 5 ppm. TM

Lactuca sativa L. — Lettuce — Leaf — 4 ppm. E

Rhus glabra L. — Smooth Sumac — Stem — 4 ppm. EM

Carya ovata (MILL.) K. KOCH — Shagbark Hickory — Shoot — 3 ppm. E

Cadmium, cont.

Hypericum perforatum L. — Common St. Johnswort, Goatweed, Hypericum, Klamath Weed, St. John's-wort — Root — 3 ppm. TM

Quercus phellos L. — Willow Oak — Stem — 3 ppm. EM

Pinus echinata MILLER — Shortleaf Pine — Shoot — 2 ppm. EM

Lycopersicon esculentum MILLER — Tomato — Fruit — 1.7 ppm. TEM

Anethum graveolens L. — Dill, Garden Dill — Plant — 1 ppm. E

Juniperus virginiana L. — Red Cedar — Shoot — 1 ppm. TEM

Quercus alba L. — White Oak — Stem — 1 ppm. EM

Quercus stellata WANGENH. — Post Oak — Stem — 1 ppm. EM

Zea mays L. — Corn — Seed — 1 ppm. E

Calcium

Lycopersicon esculentum MILLER — Tomato — Leaf — 60,800 ppm. TEM

Ephedra nevadensis S. WATS. — Brigham Tea, Mormon Tea — Plant — 58,100 ppm. M

Luffa aegyptiaca MILLER — Luffa, Smooth Loofah, Vegetable Sponge — Leaf — 55,000 ppm. E

Mimulus glabratus HBK. — Huaca-Mullo — Shoot — 54,300 ppm. M

Brassica oleracea var. botrytis L. — Cauliflower — Leaf — 54,247 ppm. E

Lycium chinense MILL. — Chinese Boxthorn, Chinese Matrimony Vine, Chinese Wolfberry, Chinesischer Bocksdorn (Ger.), Daun Koki (Indones.), Gou Qi (Chin.), Kaukichai (Malays.), Kuko (Jap.), Lyciet de Chine (Fr.), Spina Santa Cinese (Ital.), Wolfberry Root — Bark — 53,900 ppm. EM

Amaranthus sp. — Pigweed — Leaf — 53,333 ppm. EM

Achyranthes bidentata BLUME — Chaff — Flower — Root — 52,200 ppm. M

Boehmeria nivea (L.) GAUDICH. — Ramie — Shoot — 46,000 ppm. M

Justicia pectoralis JACQ. — Angel Of Death, Bolek Hena, Curia — Leaf — 44,200 ppm. M

Liquidambar styraciflua L. — American Styrax, Sweetgum — Stem — 42,000 ppm. EM

Valeriana officinalis L. — Common Valerian, Garden-Heliotrope, Valerian — Root — 42,000 ppm. M

Carya glabra (MILLER) SWEET — Pignut Hickory — Shoot — 40,700 ppm. E

Paeonia lactiflora PALL. — Bai Shao (Chinese), Chih-Shao, Common Garden Peony, Peony, White Peony — Root — 40,600 ppm. M

Boehmeria nivea (L.) GAUDICH. — Ramie — Plant — 39,000 ppm. M

Agathosma betulina (P.P. BERGIUS) PILLANS — Buchu, Honey Buchu, Mountain Buchu — Leaf — 38,800 ppm. M

Cucurbita foetidissima HBK. — Buffalo Gourd — Leaf — 0-77,600 ppm. TEM

Fraxinus rhynchophylla HANCE — Chinese Ash — Bark — 38,600 ppm. M

Rubia cordifolia L. — Madder — Root — 37,800 ppm. M

Quercus alba L. — White Oak — Bark — 37,000 ppm. EM

Albizia julibrissin DURAZZ. — Mimosa — Bark — 35,500 ppm. EM

Chenopodium album L. — Lamb's Quarters — Leaf — 33,800 ppm. TEM

Carya ovata (MILL.) K. KOCH — Shagbark Hickory — Shoot — 33,300 ppm. E

Urtica dioica L. — European Nettle, Stinging Nettle — Leaf — 33,000 ppm. EM

Prunus serotina subsp. serotina — Black Cherry, Wild Cherry Leaf — 32,640 ppm. TEM

Tabebuia heptaphylla (VELL.) TOLEDO — Pau D'Arco — Bark — 32,600 ppm. M

Bupleurum chinense DC. — Chai-Hu — Root — 32,100 ppm. M

Quercus stellata WANGENH. — Post Oak — Stem — 31,920 ppm. EM

Juniperus virginiana L. — Red Cedar — Shoot — 31,680 ppm. TEM

Ficus carica L. — Echte Feige (Ger.), Feigenbaum (Ger.), Fico (Ital.), Fig, Figueira (Port.), Figuier Commun (Fr.), Higo (Sp.), Higuera Comun (Sp.) — Leaf — 31,600 ppm. E

Arachis hypogaea L. — Groundnut, Peanut — Plant — 31,500 ppm. EM

Vicia faba L. — Broadbean, Faba Bean, Habas — Seed — 31,160 ppm. E

Calendula officinalis L. — Calendula, Pot-Marigold — Leaf — 30,400 ppm. EM

Fucus vesiculosus L. — Bladderwrack, Kelp — Plant — 30,400 ppm. EM

Anogeissus latifolia WALL. — Gum Ghatti — Leaf — 30,300 ppm. E

Peucedanum decursivum (MIQ.) MAX. — Qian Hu — Plant — 30,000 ppm. M

Mangifera indica L. — Mango — Leaf — 29,300 ppm. EM

Cassia tora L. — Sickle Senna — Sprout — Seedling — 28,100 ppm. M

Acacia catechu (L. f.) WILLD. — Black Cutch, Catechu — Leaf — 27,400 ppm. M

Morus alba L. — Sang-Pai-Pi, White Mulberry — Leaf — 27,400 ppm. EM

Quercus alba L. — White Oak — Stem — 27,360 ppm. EM

Vigna mungo (L.) HEPPER — Black Gram — Fruit — 27,100 ppm. E

Broussonetia papyrifera (L.) VENT — Paper Mulberry — Fruit — 26,900 ppm. EM

Ricinus communis L. — Castor Bean — Leaf — 26,700 ppm. T

Amaranthus spinosus L. — Spiny pigweed — Leaf — 4,760-53,335 ppm. EM

Azadirachta indica A. JUSS. — Neem — Leaf — 26,500 ppm. M

Melia azedarach L. — Chinaberry — Leaf — 25,500 ppm. T

Rhus copallina L. — Dwarf Sumac, Winged Sumac — Leaf — 24,960 ppm. EM

Rhus glabra L. — Smooth Sumac — Stem — 24,790 ppm. EM

Equisetum arvense L. — Field Horsetail, Horsetail — Plant — 24,000 ppm. M

Nasturtium officinale R. BR. — Berro, Watercress — Plant — 24,000 ppm. E

Carica papaya L. — Papaya — Leaf — 23,800 ppm. EM

Mimosa pudica L. — Sensitive — Plant — Leaf — 23,800 ppm. M

Quercus rubra L. — Northern Red Oak — Stem — 23,760 ppm. EM

Vigna aconitifolia (JACQ.) MARECHAL — Mat Bean, Moth Bean — Plant — 23,700 ppm. E

Malva parviflora L. — Cheeseweed — Plant — 23,650 ppm. EM

Origanum majorana L. — Marjoram, Sweet Marjoram — Plant — 23,625 ppm. E

Viburnum opulus— Crampbark, European Cranberry Bush, Guelder Rose, Snowball Bush — Bark — 23,540 ppm. TEM

Sida rhombifolia L. — Broomweed, Teaplant — Leaf — 23,535 ppm. EM

Glycyrrhiza uralensis FISCH. EX DC. — Chinese Licorice, Gan-Cao, Kan-Tsao — Root — 23,500 ppm. M

Satureja hortensis L. — Summer Savory — Plant — 23,429 ppm. E

Oenothera biennis L. — Evening-Primrose — Plant — 23,400 ppm. EM

Vigna aconitifolia (JACQ.) MARECHAL — Mat Bean, Moth Bean — Leaf — 23,400 ppm. E

Glechoma hederacea L. — Alehoof — Plant — 23,000 ppm. M

Tamarindus indica L. — Indian Tamarind, Kilytree, Tamarind — Leaf — 23,000 ppm. M

Quercus velutina LAM. — Black Oak — Stem — 22,940 ppm. EM

Trifolium pratense L. — Cowgrass, Peavine Clover, Purple Clover, Red Clover — Shoot — 22,900 ppm. EM

Symphoricarpos orbiculatus MOENCH. — Buckbush — Stem — 22,880 ppm. TM

Nyssa sylvatica MARSHALL — Black Gum, Black Tupelo — Leaf — 22,750 ppm. EM

Acacia tortilis (FORSSK.) HAYNE — Umbrella Thorn — Leaf — 22,700 ppm. M

Thymus vulgaris L. — Common Thyme, Garden Thyme, Thyme — Plant — 22,534 ppm. EM

Brassica chinensis L. — Bok-Choy, Celery Cabbage, Celery Mustard, Chinese Cabbage, Chinese Mustard, Chinese White Cabbage, Pak-Choi — Leaf — 22,440 ppm. E

Ocimum basilicum L. — Basil, Cuban Basil, Sweet Basil — Leaf — 22,112 ppm. E

Calcium, cont.

Eriobotrya japonica (THUNB.) LINDL. — Loquat — Leaf — 21,900 ppm. E

Zizyphus jujuba MILL. — Da-Zao, Jujube, Ta-Tsao — Shoot — 21,600 ppm. EM

Arachis hypogaea L. — Groundnut, Peanut — Leaf — 21,500 ppm. EM

Anethum graveolens L. — Dill, Garden Dill — Plant — 21,453 ppm. E

Rhus copallina L. — Dwarf Sumac, Winged Sumac — Stem — 21,350 ppm. EM

Annona squamosa L. — Sugar-Apple, Sweetsop — Leaf — 21,200 ppm. E

Cnidoscolus chayamansa McVAUGH — Chaya — Leaf — 21,050 ppm. E

Chenopodium ambrosioides L. — Epazote, Wormseed — Leaf — 21,000 ppm. TEM

Taraxacum officinale WEBER EX F.F. WIGG. — Dandelion — Plant — 21,000 ppm. EM

Portulaca oleracea L. — Purslane, Verdolaga — Plant — 20,800 ppm. E

Prosopis juliflora (SW.) DC. — Mesquite — Leaf — 20,800 ppm. M

Apium graveolens L. — Celery — Seed — 20,776 ppm. E

Phaseolus vulgaris var. vulgaris — Black Bean, Dwarf Bean, Field Bean, Flageolet Bean, French Bean, Garden Bean, Green Bean, Haricot, Haricot Bean, Haricot Vert, Kidney Bean, Navy Bean, Pop Bean, Popping Bean, Snap Bean, String Bean, Wax Bean — Leaf — 20,758 ppm. E

Plectranthus amboinicus (LOUR.) SPRENGEL — Amboini Coleus, Country Borage, Cuban Oregano, French Thyme, Indian Borage, Mexican Mint, Soup Mint, Spanish Thyme — Leaf — 2,320-41,430 ppm. E

Eryngium floridanum L. — Florida Eryngium — Shoot — 20,600 ppm. M

Coffea arabica L. — Coffee — Leaf — 20,406 ppm. EM

Lepidium sativum L. — Garden Cress — Leaf — 20,340 ppm. E

Vigna aconitifolia (JACQ.) MARECHAL — Mat Bean, Moth Bean — Fruit — 20,100 ppm. E

Zizyphus jujuba MILL. — Da-Zao, Jujube, Ta-Tsao — Leaf — 19,700 ppm. EM

Sonchus oleraceus L. — Cerraja, Sow Thistle — Leaf — 19,265 ppm. EM

Rhynchosia minima DC. — Burn Mouth Vine — Shoot — 19,200 ppm. TM

Brassica oleracea var. viridis l. L. — Collards, Cow Cabbage, Spring-Heading Cabbage, Tall Kale, Tree Kale — Leaf — 19,180 ppm. E

Lactuca sativa L. — Lettuce — Leaf — 19,140 ppm. E

Raphanus sativus L. — Radish — Leaf — 19,130 ppm. E

Berberis vulgaris L. — Barberry — Root — 19,100 ppm. M

Akebia quinata (THUNB.) DECNE — Chocolate Vine — Stem — 19,000 ppm. M

Robinia pseudoacacia L. — Black Locust — Seed — 19,000 ppm. T

Vanilla planifolia JACKS. — Bourbon Vanilla, Vanilla — Fruit — 19,000 ppm. E

Cichorium intybus L. — Chicory, Succory, Witloof — Leaf — 18,900 ppm. ES

Liquidambar styraciflua L. — American Styrax, Sweetgum Leaf — 18,860 ppm. EM

Chondrus crispus (L.) STACKH. — Irish Moss — Plant — 18,820 ppm. E

Origanum vulgare L. — Common Turkish Oregano, European Oregano, Oregano, Pot Marjoram, Wild Marjoram, Wild Oregano — Plant — 18,794 ppm. E

Petasites japonicus (SIEBOLD & ZUCC.) MAXIM. — Butterbur Plant — 18,725 ppm. T

Momordica charantia L. — Bitter Melon, Sorosi — Leaf — 18,701 ppm. E

Solanum melongena L. — Aubergine, Eggplant — Leaf — 18,676 ppm. E

Sophora subprostrata CHUN & CHEN — Shan Dou Gen — Root — 18,600 ppm. TM

Rheum rhabarbarum L. — Rhubarb — Plant — 18,462 ppm. E

Corchorus olitorius L. — Jew's Mallow, Mulukiya, Nalta Jute — Leaf — 18,365 ppm. EM

Prunus serotina subsp. serotina — Black Cherry, Wild Cherry — Stem — 18,360 ppm. TEM

Tetrapanax papyrifera (HOOK.) K.KOCH
— Rice Paper Tree, Tong-Cao, Tung-Tsao — Pith — 18,300 ppm. M

Turnera diffusa WILLD. EX SCHULT. —
Damiana — Leaf — 18,100 ppm. M

Oenothera biennis L. — Evening-Primrose
— Seed — 18,000 ppm. EM

Phaseolus vulgaris var. vulgaris — Black
Bean, Dwarf Bean, Field Bean, Flageolet
Bean, French Bean, Garden Bean, Green
Bean, Haricot, Haricot Bean, Haricot
Vert, Kidney Bean, Navy Bean, Pop
Bean, Popping Bean, Snap Bean, String
Bean, Wax Bean — Fruit — 18,000
ppm. E

Plantago asiatica L. — Asian Plantain —
Plant — 18,000 ppm. EM

Salvia officinalis L. — Sage — Leaf —
17,957 ppm. EM

Ipomoea batatas (L.) LAM — Sweet Potato
— Leaf — 17,900 ppm. E

Brassica nigra (L.) W.W. J. KOCH — Black
Mustard — Leaf — 17,867 ppm. E

Diospyros virginiana L. — American Per-simmon — Stem — 17,820 ppm. EM

Xanthosoma sagittifolium (L.) SCHOTT
— Malanga, Tannia, Yautia — Leaf —
17,800 ppm. E

Vitis vinifera L. — European Grape, Grape,
Grapevine, Parra (Sp.), Vid (Sp.), Vigne
Vinifere (Fr.), Weinrebe (Ger.), Wine
Grape — Stem — 17,700 ppm. EM

Sassafras albidum (NUTT.) NEES —
Sassafras — Leaf — 17,680 ppm. TEM

Anethum graveolens L. — Dill, Garden Dill
— Fruit — 17,671 ppm. E

Cesium

Bertholletia excelsa BONPL. — Brazilnut,
Brazilnut-Tree, Creamnut, Paranut —
Seed — 1.3 ppm. E

Carya illinoensis (WANGENH.) K. KOCH
— Pecan — Seed. E

Vigna unguiculata subsp. sesquipedalis (L.)
VERDC. — Asparagus Bean, Pea Bean,
Yardlong Bean — Seed. E

Anacardium occidentale L. — Cashew —
Seed. E

Carya ovata (MILL.) K. KOCH — Shagbark
Hickory — Seed. E

Cocos nucifera L. — Coconut, Coconut
Palm, Cocotero (Sp.), Copra, Koko-spalme (Ger.), Nariyal — Seed. E

Juglans nigra L. — Black Walnut — Seed. E

Pistacia vera L. — Pistachio — Seed. E

Prunus dulcis (MILLER) D.D. WEBB —
Almond — Seed. TEM

Juglans cinerea L. — Butternut — Seed. E

Corylus avellana L. — Cobnut, English Fil-bert, European Filbert, European Hazel,
Hazel — Seed. E

Chlorine

Taraxacum officinale WEBER EX F.F. WIGG.
— Dandelion — Leaf — 22,000 ppm.
EM

Stellaria media (L.) VILLARS — Chickweed,
Common Chickweed — Plant —
12,936 ppm. E

Boehmeria nivea (L.) GAUDICH. — Ramie
— Plant — 12,000 ppm. M

Artemisia vulgaris L. — Mugwort — Plant
— 11,000 ppm. M

Petasites japonicus (SIEBOLD & ZUCC.)
MAXIM. — Butterbur — Plant —
11,000 ppm. T

Portulaca oleracea L. — Purslane, Verdolaga
— Plant — 7,300 ppm. E

Spinacia oleracea L. — Spinach — Plant —
6,835 ppm. E

Glechoma hederacea L. — Alehoof — Plant
— 1,100 ppm. M

Polygonum cuspidatum SIEBOLD & ZUCC.
— Giant Knotweed, Hu-Zhang, Japa-nese Knotweed, Mexican Bamboo —
Plant — 6,000 ppm. TEM

Avena sativa L. — Oats — Plant — 5,700
ppm. EM

Piper nigrum L. — Black Pepper, Pepper,
White Pepper — Fruit — 5,100 ppm.
EM

Polystichum polyblepharum (ROEM.)
PRESL — Chinese Polystichum —
Plant — 4,700 ppm. T

Peucedanum decursivum (MIQ.) MAX. —
Qian Hu — Plant — 4,000 ppm. M

Trichosanthes anguina L. — Snakegourd —
Fruit — 3,890 ppm. E

Triticum aestivum L. — Wheat — Plant —
3,400 ppm. EM

Chlorine, cont.

Vicia faba L. — Broadbean, Faba Bean, Habas — Seed — 2,945 ppm. E

Panicum maximum JACQ. — Guinea grass — Leaf — 0-5,600 ppm. M

Urtica dioica L. — European Nettle, Stinging Nettle — Leaf — 2,700 ppm. EM

Avena sativa L. — Oats — Seed — 1,900 ppm. EM

Triticum aestivum L. — Wheat — Seed — 1,800 ppm. EM

Trigonella foenum-graecum L. — Alholva (Sp.), Bockshornklee (Ger.), Fenugreek, Greek Clover, Greek Hay — Leaf — 1,650 ppm. EM

Musa x paradisiaca L. — Banana, Plantain — Fruit — 1,250 ppm. E

Cocos nucifera L. — Coconut, Coconut Palm, Cocotero (Sp.), Copra, Kokospalme (Ger.), Nariyal — Seed — 1,007 ppm. E

Tamarindus indica L. — Indian Tamarind, Kilytree, Tamarind — Leaf — 940 ppm. M

Ribes rubrum L. — Red Currant, White Currant — Fruit — 910 ppm. E

Larrea tridentata (SESSE & MOC. ex DC.) COV. — Chaparral, Creosote Bush — Plant — 900 ppm. M

Ribes uva-crispa L. — Gooseberry — Fruit — 882 ppm. E

Ipomoea batatas (L.) LAM — Sweet Potato — Root — 850 ppm. E

Lens culinaris MEDIK. — Lentil — Seed — 636 ppm. E

Pisum sativum L. — Pea — Seed — 590 ppm. E

Solanum melongena L. — Aubergine, Eggplant — Fruit — 520 ppm. E

Lycopersicon esculentum MILLER — Tomato — Fruit — 510 ppm. TEM

Trigonella foenum-graecum L. — Alholva (Sp.), Bockshornklee (Ger.), Fenugreek, Greek Clover, Greek Hay — Seed — 500 ppm. EM

Ananas comosus (L.) MERR. — Pineapple — Fruit — 460 ppm. E

Tragopogon porrifolius L. — Salsify — Root — 460 ppm. E

Pistacia vera L. — Pistachio — Seed — 408 ppm. E

Gossypium sp — Cotton — Seed — 400 ppm. T

Lactuca sativa L. — Lettuce — Leaf — 395 ppm. E

Zea mays L. — Corn — Fruit — 330 ppm. E

Rosa canina L. — Dog Rose, Dogbrier, Rose — Fruit — 313 ppm. EM

Phoenix dactylifera L. — Date Palm — Fruit — 310 ppm. E

Cinnamomum sieboldii — Japanese Cinnamon Root — Bark — 300 ppm. TEM

Cinnamomum verum J. PRESL — Ceylon Cinnamon, Cinnamon — Bark — 300 ppm. TEM

Vigna radata (L.) WILCZEK — Green Gram, Mungbean — Seed — 278 ppm. E

Bertholletia excelsa BONPL. — Brazilnut, Brazilnut-Tree, Creamnut, Paranut — Seed — 246 ppm. E

Syzygium cumini SKEELS — Aceituna Dulce, Jambolan, Java Plum — Fruit — 80-490 ppm. E

Juglans regia L. — English Walnut — Seed — 230 ppm. E

Mangifera indica L. — Mango — Fruit — 205 ppm. EM

Cinnamomum burmannii (NEES) BLUME — Java Cinnamon, Padang Cassia — Bark — 200 ppm. TEM

Cinnamomum sieboldii — Japanese Cinnamon — Bark — 200 ppm. TEM

Glycine max (L.) MERR. — Soybean — Seed — 200 ppm. E

Anacardium occidentale L. — Cashew — Seed — 184 ppm. E

Fagopyrum esculentum MOENCH. — Buckwheat — Seed — 138 ppm. E

Syzygium jambos ALSTON — Pomarrosa, Rose Apple — Fruit — 40-258 ppm. E

Vigna aconitifolia (JACQ.) MARECHAL — Mat Bean, Moth Bean — Seed — 101 ppm. E

Vigna mungo (L.) HEPPER — Black Gram — Seed — 101 ppm. E

Vigna unguiculata subsp. sesquipedalis (L.) VERDC. — Asparagus Bean, Pea Bean, Yardlong Bean — Seed — 100 ppm. E

Juglans cinerea L. — Butternut — Seed — 78 ppm. E

Linum usitatissimum L. — Flax, Linseed — Seed — 78 ppm. E

Carya ovata (MILL.) K. KOCH — Shagbark Hickory — Seed — 71 ppm. E

Cinnamomum aromaticum NEES — Canela de la China (Sp.), Canelero chino (Sp.), Canelle de Cochinchine (Fr.), Cannelier Casse (Fr.), Cannelier de Chine (Fr.), Cassia, Cassia Bark, Cassia Lignea, China Junk Cassia, Chinazimt (Ger.), Chinese Cassia, Chinese Cinnamon, Chinesischer Zimtbaum (Ger.), Kashia-Keihi (Jap.), Saigon Cinnamon, Zimtcassie (Ger.) — Bark — 70 ppm. TEM

Juglans nigra L. — Black Walnut — Seed — 54 ppm. E

Quercus rubra L. — Northern Red Oak — Seed — 49 ppm. EM

Carya illinoensis (WANGENH.) K. KOCH — Pecan — Seed — 46 ppm. E

Corylus avellana L. — Cobnut, English Filbert, European Filbert, European Hazel, Hazel — Seed — 41 ppm. E

Psidium guajava L. — Guava — Fruit — 40 ppm. E

Citrus sinensis (L.) OSBECK — Orange — Fruit — 32 ppm. E

Prunus dulcis (MILLER) D.D. WEBB — Almond — Seed — 28 ppm. TEM

Citrus reticulata BLANCO — Mandarin, Tangerine — Fruit — 24 ppm. E

Punica granatum L. — Granado (Sp.), Granatapfelbaum (Ger.), Granatapfelstrauch (Ger.), Grenadier (Fr.), Mangrano (Sp.), Pomegranate, Romanzeiro (Port.), Zakuro (Jap.) — Fruit — 20 ppm. E

Solanum tuberosum L. — Potato — Tuber — 16 ppm. E

Citrus paradisi MacFAD. — Grapefruit — Plant — 6 ppm. E

Chromium

Hibiscus sabdariffa L. — Acedera de Guinea (Sp.), Indian Sorrel, Jamaica Sorrel, Kharkadi, Malventee (Ger.), Red Sorrel, Rosa de Jamaica (Sp.), Rosella (Ger.), Roselle, Sereni (Sp.), Sorrel — Flower — 54 ppm. E

Taraxacum officinale WEBER EX F. H. WIGG. — Dandelion — Leaf — 50 ppm. EM

Avena sativa L. — Oats — Plant — 39 ppm. EM

Stevia rebaudiana (BERTONI) BERTONI — Ca-A-E, Stevia, Sweet Leaf of Paraguay — Leaf — 39 ppm. E

Cymbopogon citratus (DC. ex NEES) STAPF — Lemongrass, West Indian Lemongrass — Plant — 37 ppm. EM

Elytrigia repens (L.) DESV. EX NEVSKI — Couchgrass, Doggrass, Quackgrass, Twitchgrass, Wheatgrass — Plant — 37 ppm. EM

Prunus persica (L.) BATSCH — Peach — Bark — 35 ppm. TEM

Juniperus communis L. — Common Juniper, Juniper — Fruit — 32 ppm. TEM

Trifolium pratense L. — Cowgrass, Peavine Clover, Purple Clover, Red Clover — Flower — 32 ppm. EM

Carthamus tinctorius L. — Safflower — Flower — 31 ppm. M

Hordeum vulgare L. — Barley, Barleygrass — Stem — 31 ppm. EM

Trachyspermum ammi (L.) SPRAGUE ex TURRILL — Ajwan — Fruit — 31 ppm. EM

Turnera diffusa WILLD. EX SCHULT. — Damiana — Leaf — 31 ppm. M

Elettaria cardamomum (L.) MATON — Cardamom — Fruit — 29.5 ppm. EM

Agathosma betulina (P. J. BERGIUS) PILLANS — Buchu, Honey Buchu, Mountain Buchu — Leaf — 29 ppm. M

Coriandrum sativum L. — Chinese Parsley, Cilantro, Coriander — Seed — 28.8 ppm. E

Nepeta cataria L. — Catnip — Plant — 27 ppm. M

Rhodymenia palmata — Dulse — Plant — 27 ppm. E

Dioscorea sp. — Wild Yam — Root — 26 ppm. E

Achillea millefolium L. — Milfoil, Yarrow — Plant — 25 ppm. M

Hydrangea arborescens L. — Hydrangea, Smooth Hydrangea — Root — 25 ppm. EM

Ruscus aculeatus L. — Box-Holly, Butcher's Broom — Root — 25 ppm. EM

Petasites japonicus (SIEBOLD & ZUCC.) MAXIM. — Butterbur — Plant — 23 ppm. T

Chromium, cont.

Artemisia vulgaris L. — Mugwort — Plant — 22 ppm. M

Equisetum arvense L. — Field Horsetail, Horsetail — Plant — 22 ppm. M

Silybum marianum (L.) GAERTN. — Lady's Thistle, Milk Thistle — Plant — 22 ppm. M

Viburnum opulus — Crampbark, European Cranberry Bush, Guelder Rose, Snowball Bush — Bark — 21 ppm. TEM

Arctium lappa L. — Burdock, Gobo, Great Burdock — Root — 20 ppm. EM

Lactuca sativa L. — Lettuce — Leaf — 20 ppm. E

Polystichum polyblepharum (ROEM.) PRESL — Chinese Polystichum — Plant — 20 ppm. T

Thymus vulgaris L. — Common Thyme, Garden Thyme, Thyme — Leaf — 20 ppm. EM

Zingiber officinale ROSCOE — Ginger — Rhizome — 20 ppm. EM

Echinacea spp. — Coneflower, Echinacea — Root — 19 ppm. M

Viscum album L. — European Mistletoe — Leaf — 19 ppm. TM

Sinapis alba L. — White Mustard — Seed — 18.6 ppm. TEM

Cimicifuga racemosa (L.) NUTT. — Black Cohosh, Black Snakeroot — Root — 18 ppm. M

Schisandra chinensis (TURCZ.) BAILL. — Chinese Magnolia Vine, Five-Flavor-Fruit, Magnolia Vine, Schizandra, Wu Wei Zi, Wu Wei Zu — Fruit — 18 ppm. M

Valeriana officinalis L. — Common Valerian, Garden-Heliotrope, Valerian — Root — 18 ppm. M

Chrysanthemum parthenium (L.) BERNH. — Feverfew — Plant — 17 ppm. M

Crataegus laevigata (POIR.) DC — English Hawthorn, Hawthorn, Whitethorn, Woodland Hawthorn — Fruit — 17 ppm. M

Cucurbita pepo L. — Pumpkin — Seed — 17 ppm. E

Glycyrrhiza glabra L. — Commom Licorice, Licorice, Licorice-Root, Smooth Licorice — Root — 17 ppm. M

Mentha pulegium L. — European Pennyroyal — Plant — 17 ppm. TEM

Smilax spp. — Sarsaparilla — Root — 17 ppm. EM

Myristica fragrans HOUTT. — Mace, Muskatnussbaum (Ger.), Nutmeg, nogal moscado (Sp.), nuez moscada (Sp.) — Seed — 16.4 ppm. E

Boehmeria nivea (L.) GAUDICH. — Ramie — Plant — 16 ppm. M

Cnicus benedictus L. — Blessed Thistle — Plant — 16 ppm. M

Peucedanum decursivum (MIQ.) MAX. — Qian Hu — Plant — 16 ppm. M

Carum carvi L. — Caraway, Carum, Comino (Sp.), Comino de prado (Sp.), Kummel (Ger.) — Fruit — 15.5 ppm. E

Allium sativum var. sativum L. — Garlic — Bulb — 15 ppm. E

Althaea officinalis L. — Marshmallow, White Mallow — Root — 15 ppm. M

Myrica cerifera L. — Bayberry, Candle-Berry, Southern Bayberry, Wax Myrtle — Bark — 15 ppm. EM

Cinnamomum verum J. PRESL — Ceylon Cinnamon, Cinnamon — Leaf — 14.4 ppm. TEM

Polygonum cuspidatum SIEBOLD & ZUCC. — Giant Knotweed, Hu-Zhang, Japanese Knotweed, Mexican Bamboo — Plant — 14 ppm. TEM

Verbascum thapsus L. — Flannelleaf, Flannelplant, Great Mullein, Mullein, Velvetplant — Leaf — 14 ppm. M

Papaver somniferum L. — Opium Poppy, Poppyseed Poppy — Seed — 13.4 ppm. E

Myristica fragrans HOUTT. — Mace, Muskatnussbaum (Ger.), Nutmeg, nogal moscado (Sp.), nuez moscada (Sp.) — Aril — 13.2 ppm. E

Gentiana lutea L. — Gentian, Yellow Gentian — Root — 13 ppm. M

Rubus idaeus L. — Raspberry, Red Raspberry — Leaf — 13 ppm. EM

Zea mays L. — Corn — Silk Stigma — Style — 13 ppm. E

Arctostaphylos uva-ursi (L.) SPRENGEL — Bearberry, Uva Ursi — Leaf — 12 ppm. M

Berberis vulgaris L. — Barberry — Root — 12 ppm. M

Caulophyllum thalictroides (L.) MICHX. —
Blue Cohosh — Root — 12 ppm. M

Chondrus crispus (L.) STACKH. — Irish
Moss — Plant — 12 ppm. E

Harpagophytum procumbens (BURCH.)
DC. EX MEISN. — Devil's Claw,
Grapple — Plant — Root — 12 ppm. M

Panax ginseng C. A. MEYER — Chinese
Ginseng, Ginseng, Korean Ginseng,
Oriental Ginseng — Root — 11 ppm. M

Stellaria media (L.) VILLARS — Chickweed,
Common Chickweed — Plant —
11 ppm. E

Rhus glabra L. — Smooth Sumac — Stem
— 10.05 ppm. EM

Centella asiatica (L.) URBAN — Gotu Kola,
Pennywort — Leaf — 10 ppm. EM

Cinnamomum verum J. PRESL — Ceylon
Cinnamon, Cinnamon — Bark —
10 ppm. TEM

Cypripedium pubescens WILLD. — Yellow
Ladyslipper — Root — 10 ppm. M

Ulmus rubra MUHLENB. — Red Elm,
Slippery Elm — Bark — 10 ppm. M

Angelica sinensis (OLIV.) DIELS — Chinese
Angelica, Dang Gui, Dang Quai, Dang
Qui, Dong Gui, Dong Quai — Root —
9 ppm. M

Hydrastis canadensis L. — Goldenseal —
Root — 9 ppm. M

Juglans nigra L. — Black Walnut — Hull
Husk — 9 ppm. E

Medicago sativa subsp. sativa — Alfalfa,
Lucerne — Plant — 9 ppm. E

Tabebuia heptaphylla (VELL.) TOLEDO —
Pau D'Arco — Bark — 9 ppm. M

Taraxacum officinale WEBER EX F. H.
WIGG. — Dandelion — Root —
9 ppm. EM

Vitis vinifera L. — European Grape, Grape,
Grapevine, Parra (Sp.), Vid (Sp.), Vigne
Vinifere (Fr.), Weinrebe (Ger.), Wine
Grape — Stem — 9 ppm. EM

Cobalt

Nyssa sylvatica MARSHALL — Black Gum,
Black Tupelo — Leaf — 910 ppm. EM

Hydrastis canadensis L. — Goldenseal —
Root — 153 ppm. M

Smilax spp.. — Sarsaparilla — Root —
152 ppm. EM

Angelica sinensis (OLIV.) DIELS — Chinese
Angelica, Dang Gui, Dang Quai, Dang
Qui, Dong Gui, Dong Quai — Root —
151 ppm. M

Tabebuia heptaphylla (VELL.) TOLEDO —
Pau D'Arco — Bark — 151 ppm. M

Rhodymenia palmata — Dulse — Plant —
150 ppm. E

Echinacea spp.. — Coneflower, Echinacea —
Root — 148 ppm. M

Dioscorea sp. — Wild Yam — Root —
147 ppm. E

Euphrasia officinalis L. — Eyebright —
Plant — 147 ppm. M

Harpagophytum procumbens (BURCH.)
DC. EX MEISN. — Devil's Claw,
Grapple — Plant — Root — 145 ppm. M

Polygonum multiflorum THUNB. —
Chinese Cornbind, Chinese Knotweed,
Fleeceflower, Fo Ti, He Shou Wu —
Root — 145 ppm. TEM

Cucurbita pepo L. — Pumpkin — Seed —
143 ppm. E

Symphytum officinale L. — Comfrey —
Root — 129 ppm. TM

Turnera diffusa WILLD. EX SCHULT. —
Damiana — Leaf — 129 ppm. M

Ruscus aculeatus L. — Box-Holly, Butcher's
Broom — Root — 128 ppm. EM

Verbascum thapsus L. — Flannelleaf,
Flannelplant, Great Mullein, Mullein,
Velvetplant — Leaf — 128 ppm. M

Amorphophallus konjac K. KOCH —
Devil's Tongue, Elephant Yam, Konjac,
Leopard Palm, Snake Palm, Umbrella
Arum — Root — 125 ppm. TEM

Juniperus communis L. — Common Juniper,
Juniper — Fruit — 123 ppm. TEM

Stellaria media (L.) VILLARS — Chickweed,
Common Chickweed — Plant —
121 ppm. E

Arctium lappa L. — Burdock, Gobo, Great
Burdock — Root — 120 ppm. EM

Nepeta cataria L. — Catnip — Plant —
118 ppm. M

Frangula purshiana (DC.) J. G. COOPER —
Cascara Buckthorn, Cascara Sagrada —
Bark — 116 ppm. M

Medicago sativa subsp. sativa — Alfalfa,
Lucerne — Plant — 115 ppm. E

Viburnum opulus — Crampbark, European Cranberry Bush, Guelder Rose, Snowball Bush — Bark — 115 ppm. TEM

Thymus vulgaris L. — Common Thyme, Garden Thyme, Thyme — Leaf — 113 ppm. EM

Schisandra chinensis (TURCZ.) BAILL. — Chinese Magnolia Vine, Five-Flavor-Fruit, Magnolia Vine, Schizandra, Wu Wei Zi, Wu Wei Zu — Fruit — 104 ppm. M

Glycyrrhiza glabra L. — Commom Licorice, Licorice, Licorice-Root, Smooth Licorice — Root — 101 ppm. M

Allium sativum var. sativum L. — Garlic Bulb — 100 ppm. E

Diospyros virginiana L. — American Persimmon — Leaf — 100 ppm. EM

Salix alba L. — White Willow — Bark — 98 ppm. M

Larrea tridentata (SESSE & MOC. ex DC.) COV. — Chaparral, Creosote Bush — Bark — 93 ppm. M

Mentha x piperita subsp. nothosubsp. piperita — Peppermint — Leaf — 93 ppm. TEM

Viscum album L. — European Mistletoe — Leaf — 92 ppm. TM

Agathosma betulina (P. J. BERGIUS) PILLANS — Buchu, Honey Buchu, Mountain Buchu — Leaf — 87 ppm. M

Taraxacum officinale WEBER EX F. H. WIGG. — Dandelion — Root — 80 ppm. EM

Centella asiatica (L.) URBAN — Gotu Kola, Pennywort — Leaf — 73 ppm. EM

Chondrus crispus (L.) STACKH. — Irish Moss — Plant — 70 ppm. E

Nyssa sylvatica MARSHALL — Black Gum, Black Tupelo — Stem — 66 ppm. EM

Zea mays L. — Corn — Silk Stigma — Style — 64 ppm. E

Chamaemelum nobile (L.) ALL. — Garden Camomile, Perennial Camomile, Roman Camomile — Flower — 58 ppm. M

Diospyros virginiana L. — American Persimmon — Stem — 54 ppm. EM

Equisetum arvense L. — Field Horsetail, Horsetail — Plant — 53 ppm. M

Hordeum vulgare L. — Barley, Barleygrass — Stem — 49 ppm. EM

Cymbopogon citratus (DC. ex NEES) STAPF — Lemongrass, West Indian Lemongrass — Plant — 48 ppm. EM

Valeriana officinalis L. — Common Valerian, Garden-Heliotrope, Valerian — Root — 48 ppm. M

Berberis vulgaris L. — Barberry — Root — 42 ppm. M

Zingiber officinale ROSCOE — Ginger — Rhizome — 42 ppm. EM

Silybum marianum (L.) GAERTN. — Lady's Thistle, Milk Thistle — Plant — 41 ppm. M

Ephedra sinica STAPF — Chinese Ephedra, Ma Huang — Plant — 40 ppm. M

Copper

Prunus serotina subsp. serotina — Black Cherry, Wild Cherry — Stem — 378 ppm. TEM

Liquidambar styraciflua L. — American Styrax, Sweetgum — Stem — 360 ppm. EM

Nyssa sylvatica MARSHALL — Black Gum, Black Tupelo — Leaf — 182 ppm. EM

Liquidambar styraciflua L. — American Styrax, Sweetgum — Leaf — 164 ppm. EM

Symphoricarpos orbiculatus MOENCH. — Buckbush — Stem — 132 ppm. TM

Diospyros virginiana L. — American Persimmon — Stem — 108 ppm. EM

Sassafras albidum (NUTT.) NEES — Sassafras — Leaf — 102 ppm. TEM

Lycopersicon esculentum MILLER — Tomato — Fruit — 100 ppm. TEM

Brassica oleracea var. capitata L. — Cabbage, Red Cabbage, White Cabbage — Leaf — 87 ppm. E

Corylus avellana L. — Cobnut, English Filbert, European Filbert, European Hazel, Hazel — Seed — 82 ppm. E

Sassafras albidum (NUTT.) NEES — Sassafras — Stem — 56 ppm. TEM

Sesamum indicum L. — Ajonjoli (Sp.), Beni, Benneseed, Sesame, Sesamo (Sp.) — Plant — 56 ppm. EM

Carya glabra (MILLER) SWEET — Pignut Hickory — Shoot — 55 ppm. E

Brassica oleracea var. botrytis L. — Cauliflower — Leaf — 52 ppm. E

Carya ovata (MILL.) K. KOCH — Shagbark Hickory — Shoot — 45 ppm. E

Phaseolus vulgaris var. vulgaris — Black Bean, Dwarf Bean, Field Bean, Flageolet Bean, French Bean, Garden Bean, Green Bean, Haricot, Haricot Bean, Haricot Vert, Kidney Bean, Navy Bean, Pop Bean, Popping Bean, Snap Bean, String Bean, Wax Bean — Fruit — 45 ppm. E

Brassica oleracea var. viridis l. L. — Collards, Cow Cabbage, Spring-Heading Cabbage, Tall Kale, Tree Kale — Leaf — 43 ppm. E

Cucumis sativus L. — Cucumber — Fruit — 42 ppm. E

Quercus stellata WANGENH. — Post Oak — Stem — 42 ppm. EM

Anacardium occidentale L. — Cashew — Seed — 37 ppm. E

Rosa canina L. — Dog Rose, Dogbrier, Rose — Fruit — 36 ppm. EM

Rhizophora mangle L. — Red Mangrove — Leaf — 35 ppm. M

Prunus domestica L. — Plum — Fruit — 34 ppm. TEM

Cocos nucifera L. — Coconut, Coconut Palm, Cocotero (Sp.), Copra, Kokospalme (Ger.), Nariyal — Seed — 33 ppm. E

Pistacia vera L. — Pistachio — Seed — 33 ppm. E

Psophocarpus tetragonolobus (L.) DC. — Asparagus Pea, Goa Bean, Winged Bean — Seed — 33 ppm. E

Senna obtusifolia (L.) H.IRWIN & BARNE-BY — Sicklepod — Seed — 32 ppm. TE

Nyssa sylvatica MARSHALL — Black Gum, Black Tupelo — Stem — 31 ppm. EM

Quercus velutina LAM. — Black Oak — Stem — 31 ppm. EM

Cucurbita maxima DUCH. — Pumpkin — Leaf — 30 ppm. E

Helianthus tuberosus L. — Jerusalem Artichoke — Plant — 30 ppm. E

Momordica charantia L. — Bitter Melon, Sorosi — Fruit — 30 ppm. E

Prunus persica (L.) BATSCH — Peach — Fruit — 30 ppm. TEM

Rhus copallina L. — Dwarf Sumac, Winged Sumac — Stem — 30 ppm. EM

Rumex acetosa L. — Garden Sorrel — Leaf — 30 ppm. TEM

Arctium lappa L. — Burdock, Gobo, Great Burdock — Root — 29 ppm. EM

Lactuca sativa L. — Lettuce — Leaf — 29 ppm. E

Prunus serotina subsp. serotina — Black Cherry, Wild Cherry — Leaf — 29 ppm. TEM

Quercus phellos L. — Willow Oak — Stem — 29 ppm. EM

Carthamus tinctorius L. — Safflower — Flower — 26 ppm. M

Houttuynia cordata THUNB. — Dokudami, Fishwort, Yu Xing Cao — Plant — 26 ppm. EM

Hyoscyamus niger L. — Henbane — Seed — 26 ppm. T

Avena sativa L. — Oats — Seed — 25.7 ppm. EM

Myristica fragrans HOUTT. — Mace, Muskatnussbaum (Ger.), Nutmeg, nogal moscado (Sp.), nuez moscada (Sp.) — Aril — 25 ppm. E

Pachyrhizus erosus RICH. ex DC. — Yambean, Jicama — Tuber — 25 ppm. E

Asparagus officinalis L. — Asparagus — Shoot — 24 ppm. E

Chaenomeles lagenaria KOIDZ. — Chinese Quince, Mu-Kua — Fruit — 24 ppm. E

Cynara cardunculus subsp. cardunculus — Artichoke — Flower — 24 ppm. E

Foeniculum vulgare MILLER — Fennel — Fruit — 24 ppm. M

Spinacia oleracea L. — Spinach — Plant — 24 ppm. E

Theobroma cacao L. — Cacao, Chocolate — Seed — 24 ppm. E

Geranium thunbergii SIEB. & ZUCC — Gennoshiouko, Oriental Geranium — Plant — 23 ppm. EM

Papaver somniferum L. — Opium Poppy, Poppyseed Poppy — Seed — 23 ppm. E

Schizonepeta tenuifolia BRIQ. — Ching-Chieh, Jing-Jie — Plant — 23 ppm. M

Vigna radata (L.) WILCZEK — Green Gram, Mungbean — Sprout Seedling — 23 ppm. E

Abelmoschus manihot (L.) MEDIK. — Manioc Hibiscus — Leaf — 21.5 ppm. EM

Copper, cont.

Myristica fragrans HOUTT. — Mace, Muskatnussbaum (Ger.), Nutmeg, nogal moscado (Sp.), nuez moscada (Sp.) — Seed — 21 ppm. E

Tamarindus indica L. — Indian Tamarind, Kilytree, Tamarind — Leaf — 21 ppm. M

Artemisia vulgaris L. — Mugwort — Plant — 20 ppm. M

Brassica oleracea var. acephala DC — Curly Kale, Kale, Kitchen Kale, Scotch Kale — Leaf — 20 ppm. E

Camellia sinensis (L.) KUNTZE — Tea — Leaf — 20 ppm. E

Capsicum annuum L. — Bell Pepper, Cherry Pepper, Cone Pepper, Green Pepper, Paprika, Sweet Pepper — Fruit — 20 ppm. E

Hordeum vulgare L. — Barley, Barleygrass — Seed — 20 ppm. EM

Mentha arvensis var. piperascens MALINV. EX L. H. BAILEY — Cornmint, Field Mint, Japanese Mint — Plant — 20 ppm. TEM

Piper nigrum L. — Black Pepper, Pepper, White Pepper — Fruit — 20 ppm. EM

Rhus glabra L. — Smooth Sumac — Stem — 20 ppm. EM

Solanum melongena L. — Aubergine, Eggplant — Fruit — 20 ppm. E

Trichosanthes anguina L. — Snakegourd — Fruit — 20 ppm. E

Tussilago farfara L. — Coltsfoot — Flower — 20 ppm. TM

Zea mays L. — Corn — Fruit — 20 ppm. E

Fluorine

Lactuca sativa L. — Lettuce — Leaf — 8 ppm. E

Petroselinum crispum (MILLER) NYMAN EX A. W. HILLL — Parsley — Plant — 7.8 ppm. E

Urtica dioica L. — European Nettle, Stinging Nettle — Leaf — 7.8 ppm. EM

Spinacia oleracea L. — Spinach — Leaf — 5.7 ppm. E

Anethum graveolens L. — Dill, Garden Dill — Plant — 5.3 ppm. E

Pimenta dioica (L.) MERR. — Allspice, Clover-Pepper, Jamaica-Pepper, Pimenta, Pimento — Plant — 5 ppm. E

Momordica charantia L. — Bitter Melon, Sorosi — Fruit — 4.8 ppm. E

Rheum rhabarbarum L. — Rhubarb — Plant — 4 ppm. E

Pistacia vera L. — Pistachio — Seed — 3.8 ppm. E

Ribes nigrum L. — Black Currant — Fruit — 2.8 ppm. E

Cocos nucifera L. — Coconut, Coconut Palm, Cocotero (Sp.), Copra, Kokospalme (Ger.), Nariyal — Seed — 2.7 ppm. E

Brassica oleracea var. botrytis L. — Cauliflower — Flower — 2.5 ppm. E

Brassica oleracea var. capitata L. — Cabbage, Red Cabbage, White Cabbage — Leaf — 2.5 ppm. E

Malus domestica BORKH. — Apple — Fruit — 2.1 ppm. E

Moringa oleifera LAM. — Ben Nut, Benzolive Tree, Drumstick Tree, Horseradish Tree, Jacinto (Sp.), Moringa, West Indian Ben — Leaf — 0-4 ppm. E

Phaseolus vulgaris var. vulgaris — Black Bean, Dwarf Bean, Field Bean, Flageolet Bean, French Bean, Garden Bean, Green Bean, Haricot, Haricot Bean, Haricot Vert, Kidney Bean, Navy Bean, Pop Bean, Popping Bean, Snap Bean, String Bean, Wax Bean — Fruit — 2 ppm. E

Zingiber officinale ROSCOE — Ginger — Rhizome — 2 ppm. EM

Rubus chamaemorus L. — Cloudberry — Fruit — 1.9 ppm. EM

Daucus carota L. — Carrot — Root — 1.8 ppm. E

Ribes rubrum L. — Red Currant, White Currant — Fruit — 1.8 ppm. E

Bertholletia excelsa BONPL. — Brazilnut, Brazilnut-Tree, Creamnut, Paranut — Seed — 1.7 ppm. E

Lycopersicon esculentum MILLER — Tomato — Fruit — 1.7 ppm. TEM

Carya illinoensis (WANGENH.) K. KOCH — Pecan — Seed — 1.6 ppm. E

Juglans nigra L. — Black Walnut — Seed — 1.6 ppm. E

Rosa canina L. — Dog Rose, Dogbrier, Rose — Fruit — 1.5 ppm. EM

Sorbus aucuparia L. — Rowan Berry,
Mountain Ash — Fruit — 1.5 ppm. TEM

Anacardium occidentale L. — Cashew —
Seed — 1.4 ppm. E

Carya ovata (MILL.) K. KOCH — Shagbark
Hickory — Seed — 1.3 ppm. E

Prunus dulcis (MILLER) D. A. WEBB —
Almond — Seed — 1.3 ppm. TEM

Quercus rubra L. — Northern Red Oak —
Seed — 1.3 ppm. EM

Corylus avellana L. — Cobnut, English Filbert, European Filbert, European Hazel,
Hazel — Seed — 1.2 ppm. E

Juglans cinerea L. — Butternut — Seed —
1.1 ppm. E

Capsicum annuum L. — Bell Pepper, Cherry
Pepper, Cone Pepper, Green Pepper,
Paprika, Sweet Pepper — Fruit — 1
ppm. E

Pisum sativum L. — Pea — Seed — 1 ppm. E

Germanium

Zingiber officinale ROSCOE — Ginger —
Rhizome — 169 ppm. EM

Gold

Corylus avellana L. — Cobnut, English Filbert, European Filbert, European Hazel,
Hazel — Seed. E

Pistacia vera L. — Pistachio — Seed. E

Carya illinoensis (WANGENH.) K. KOCH
— Pecan — Seed. E

Carya ovata (MILL.) K. KOCH — Shagbark
Hickory — Seed. E

Juglans cinerea L. — Butternut — Seed. E

Juglans nigra L. — Black Walnut — Seed. E

Prunus dulcis (MILLER) D. A. WEBB —
Almond — Seed. TEM

Quercus rubra L. — Northern Red Oak —
Seed. EM

Hafnium

Carya illinoensis (WANGENH.) K. KOCH
— Pecan — Seed. E

Carya ovata (MILL.) K. KOCH — Shagbark
Hickory — Seed. E

Corylus avellana L. — Cobnut, English
Filbert, European Filbert, European
Hazel, Hazel — Seed. E

Juglans nigra L. — Black Walnut — Seed. E

Quercus rubra L. — Northern Red Oak —
Seed. EM

Prunus dulcis (MILLER) D. A. WEBB —
Almond — Seed. TEM

Anacardium occidentale L. — Cashew —
Seed. E

Iodine

Fucus vesiculosus L. — Bladderwrack, Kelp
— Plant — 5,400 ppm. EM

Pistacia vera L. — Pistachio — Seed —
51 ppm. E

Glycine max (L.) MERR. — Soybean —
Seed — 16 ppm. E

Juniperus virginiana L. — Red Cedar —
Shoot — 10 ppm. TEM

Liquidambar styraciflua L. — American
Styrax, Sweetgum — Stem — 6 ppm.
EM

Pinus echinata MILLER — Shortleaf Pine
— Shoot — 6 ppm. M

Quercus alba L. — White Oak — Stem —
6 ppm. EM

Quercus phellos L. — Willow Oak — Stem
— 6 ppm. EM

Rhus glabra L. — Smooth Sumac — Stem
— 6 ppm. EM

Symphoricarpos orbiculatus MOENCH. —
Buckbush — Stem — 6 ppm. TM

Carya glabra (MILLER) SWEET — Pignut
Hickory — Shoot — 5 ppm. E

Carya ovata (MILL.) K. KOCH — Shagbark
Hickory — Shoot — 5 ppm. E

Quercus rubra L. — Northern Red Oak —
Stem — 5 ppm. EM

Quercus stellata WANGENH. — Post Oak
— Stem — 5 ppm. EM

Quercus velutina LAM. — Black Oak —
Stem — 5 ppm. EM

Cinnamomum sieboldii — Japanese Cinnamon — Root — Bark — 4 ppm. TEM

Cinnamomum verum J. PRESL — Ceylon
Cinnamon, Cinnamon — Bark —
3 ppm. TEM

Rumex acetosa L. — Garden Sorrel —
Leaf — 2 ppm. TEM

Iodine, cont.

Ipomoea aquatica FORSSKAL — Swamp Cabbage, Water Spinach — Leaf — 1.5 ppm. E

Lagenaria siceraria (MOLINA) STANDLEY. — Calabash Gourd, White-Flowered Gourd — Fruit — 1.12 ppm. E

Ananas comosus (L.) MERR. — Pineapple — Fruit — 1 ppm. E

Cinnamomum aromaticum NEES — Canela de la China (Sp.), Canelero chino (Sp.), Canelle de Cochinchine (Fr.), Cannelier Casse (Fr.), Cannelier de Chine (Fr.), Cassia, Cassia Bark, Cassia Lignea, China Junk Cassia, Chinazimt (Ger.), Chinese Cassia, Chinese Cinnamon, Chinesischer Zimtbaum (Ger.), Kashia-Keihi (Jap.), Saigon Cinnamon, Zimtcassie (Ger.) — Bark — 1 ppm. TEM

Pteridium aquilinum (L.) KUHN — Bracken, Bracken Fern — Leaf. TEM

Spondias pinnata L. — Yellow Mombin, Yellow Plum — Fruit. E

Vicia faba L. — Broadbean, Faba Bean, Habas — Seed. E

Trachyspermum ammi (L.) SPRAGUE ex TURRILL — Ajwan — Fruit. EM

Momordica charantia L. — Bitter Melon, Sorosi — Fruit. E

Moringa oleifera LAM. — Ben Nut, Benzolive Tree, Drumstick Tree, Horseradish Tree, Jacinto (Sp.), Moringa, West Indian Ben — Leaf. E

Cocos nucifera L. — Coconut, Coconut Palm, Cocotero (Sp.), Copra, Kokospalme (Ger.), Nariyal — Seed. E

Fragaria spp.. — Strawberry — Plant. E

Bertholletia excelsa BONPL. — Brazilnut, Brazilnut-Tree, Creamnut, Paranut — Seed. E

Prunus dulcis (MILLER) D. A. WEBB — Almond — Seed. TEM

Spinacia oleracea L. — Spinach — Plant. E

Trichosanthes anguina L. — Snakegourd — Fruit. E

Fagopyrum esculentum MOENCH. — Buckwheat — Seed. E

Panicum maximum JACQ. — Guinea grass — Leaf. M

Avena sativa L. — Oats — Plant. EM

Lepidium sativum L. — Garden Cress — Leaf. E

Anacardium occidentale L. — Cashew — Seed. E

Carya illinoensis (WANGENH.) K. KOCH — Pecan — Seed. E

Carya ovata (MILL.) K. KOCH — Shagbark Hickory — Seed. E

Juglans cinerea L. — Butternut — Seed. E

Juglans nigra L. — Black Walnut — Seed. E

Quercus rubra L. — Northern Red Oak — Seed. EM

Piper nigrum L. — Black Pepper, Pepper, White Pepper — Fruit. EM

Phoenix dactylifera L. — Date Palm — Fruit. E

Erythroxylum coca var. coca — Coca — Leaf. EM

Prunus armeniaca L. — Apricot — Fruit. TEM

Ipomoea batatas (L.) LAM — Sweet Potato — Root. E

Helianthus annuus L. — Girasol, Sunflower — Seed. E

Secale cereale L. — Rye — Seed. E

Vigna radata (L.) WILCZEK — Green Gram, Mungbean — Seed. E

Vigna mungo (L.) HEPPER — Black Gram — Seed. E

Corylus avellana L. — Cobnut, English Filbert, European Filbert, European Hazel, Hazel — Seed. E

Lens culinaris MEDIK. — Lentil — Seed. E

Sesamum indicum L. — Ajonjoli (Sp.), Beni, Benneseed, Sesame, Sesamo (Sp.) — Seed. EM

Mangifera indica L. — Mango — Fruit. EM

Hyssopus officinalis L. — Hyssop — Plant. EM

Helianthus tuberosus L. — Jerusalem Artichoke — Tuber. E

Zea mays L. — Corn — Seed. E

Solanum tuberosum L. — Potato — Plant. E

Pisum sativum L. — Pea — Seed. E

Papaver somniferum L. — Opium Poppy, Poppyseed Poppy — Seed. E

Foeniculum vulgare MILLER — Fennel — Fruit. M

Iron

Taraxacum officinale WEBER EX F. H.
WIGG. — Dandelion — Leaf — 5,000
ppm. EM

Echinacea spp.. — Coneflower, Echinacea —
Root — 4,800 ppm. M

Symphoricarpos orbiculatus MOENCH. —
Buckbush — Stem — 4,400 ppm. TM

Artemisia vulgaris L. — Mugwort — Plant
— 3,900 ppm. M

Boehmeria nivea (L.) GAUDICH. — Ramie
— Plant — 3,500 ppm. M

Physalis ixocarpa BROT. — Tomatillo —
Fruit — 2,974 ppm. E

Harpagophytum procumbens (BURCH.)
DC. EX MEISN. — Devil's Claw, Grapple — Plant — Root — 2,900 ppm. M

Asarum heterotropoides MAEK. — Asian
Wild Ginger — Root — 2,800 ppm. M

Asarum sieboldii (MIQ.) MAEK. — Siebold's Wild Ginger — Root — 2,800
ppm. M

Stellaria media (L.) VILLARS — Chickweed,
Common Chickweed — Plant — 2,530
ppm. E

Verbascum thapsus L. — Flannelleaf, Flannelplant, Great Mullein, Mullein, Velvetplant — Leaf — 2,360 ppm. M

Mentha pulegium L. — European Pennyroyal — Plant — 2,310 ppm. TEM

Carthamus tinctorius L. — Safflower —
Flower — 2,200 ppm. M

Petasites japonicus (SIEBOLD & ZUCC.)
MAXIM. — Butterbur — Plant —
2,100 ppm. T

Valerianella locusta (L.) LATERRADE —
Corn Salad, Lamb's Lettuce — Plant —
3,519-4,143 ppm. E

Polystichum polyblepharum (ROEM.)
PRESL — Chinese Polystichum — Plant
— 1,900 ppm. T

Trifolium pratense L. — Cowgrass, Peavine
Clover, Purple Clover, Red Clover —
Shoot — 1,850 ppm. EM

Nyssa sylvatica MARSHALL — Black Gum,
Black Tupelo — Leaf — 1,820 ppm. EM

Angelica dahurica BENTH & HOOK. — Bai
Zhi — Root — 1,800 ppm. M

Schizonepeta tenuifolia BRIQ. — Ching-
Chieh, Jing-Jie — Plant — 1,700 ppm. M

Caulophyllum thalictroides (L.) MICHX. —
Blue Cohosh — Root — 1,640 ppm. M

Ruscus aculeatus L. — Box-Holly, Butcher's
Broom — Root — 1,640 ppm. EM

Diospyros virginiana L. — American Persimmon — Stem — 1,620 ppm. EM

Amaranthus sp. — Pigweed — Leaf —
1,527 ppm. EM

Thymus vulgaris L. — Common Thyme,
Garden Thyme, Thyme — Plant —
1,508 ppm. EM

Camellia sinensis (L.) KUNTZE — Tea —
Leaf — 1,500 ppm. E

Manihot esculenta CRANTZ — Cassava,
Tapioca, Yuca — Leaf — 1,500 ppm. E

Arctium lappa L. — Burdock, Gobo, Great
Burdock — Root — 1,470 ppm. EM

Prunus serotina subsp. serotina — Black
Cherry, Wild Cherry — Leaf — 1,440
ppm. TEM

Berberis vulgaris L. — Barberry — Root —
1,410 ppm. M

Anemarrhena asphodeloides BUNGE —
Chih-Mu, Zhi-Mu — Rhizome —
1,400 ppm. M

Peucedanum decursivum (MIQ.) MAX. —
Qian Hu — Plant — 1,400 ppm. M

Nepeta cataria L. — Catnip — Plant —
1,380 ppm. M

Cynanchum atratum BUNGE — Bai-Wei,
Pai-Wei — Root — 1,350 ppm. EM

Juniperus virginiana L. — Red Cedar —
Shoot — 1,320 ppm. TEM

Polygonum cuspidatum SIEBOLD & ZUCC.
— Giant Knotweed, Hu-Zhang, Japa-
nese Knotweed, Mexican Bamboo —
Plant — 1,300 ppm. TEM

Senna occidentalis (L.) H. IRWIN &
BARNEBY — Coffee Senna — Seed —
1,300 ppm. TE

Equisetum arvense L. — Field Horsetail,
Horsetail — Plant — 1,230 ppm. M

Nardostachys chinensis BATALIN —
Chinese Spikenard — Rhizome —
1,210 ppm. M

Bupleurum chinense DC. — Chai-Hu —
Root — 1,200 ppm. M

Luffa aegyptiaca MILLER — Luffa, Smooth
Loofah, Vegetable Sponge — Leaf —
1,162 ppm. E

Iron, cont.

Althaea officinalis L. — Marshmallow, White Mallow — Root — 1,150 ppm. M

Solanum melongena L. — Aubergine, Eggplant — Leaf — 1,140 ppm. E

Lygodium japonicum (THUNB.) SW. — Climbing Fern — Pollen or Spore — 1,090 ppm. M

Silybum marianum (L.) GAERTN. — Lady's Thistle, Milk Thistle — Plant — 1,060 ppm. M

Arctostaphylos uva-ursi (L.) SPRENGEL — Bearberry, Uva Ursi — Leaf — 1,050 ppm. M

Phaseolus vulgaris var. vulgaris — Black Bean, Dwarf Bean, Field Bean, Flageolet Bean, French Bean, Garden Bean, Green Bean, Haricot, Haricot Bean, Haricot Vert, Kidney Bean, Navy Bean, Pop Bean, Popping Bean, Snap Bean, String Bean, Wax Bean — Fruit — 1,050 ppm. E

Pulsatilla chinensis (BUNGE) REGEL — Chinese Anemone — Root — 1,050 ppm. M

Coffea arabica L. — Coffee — Leaf — 1,032 ppm. EM

Sassafras albidum (NUTT.) NEES — Sassafras — Leaf — 1,020 ppm. TEM

Rubus idaeus L. — Raspberry, Red Raspberry — Leaf — 1,010 ppm. EM

Phaseolus lunatus L. — Butter Bean, Lima Bean — Seed — 1,000 ppm. E

Avena sativa L. — Oats — Plant — 990 ppm. EM

Amaranthus spinosus L. — Spiny pigweed — Leaf — 22-1,965 ppm. EM

Origanum majorana L. — Marjoram, Sweet Marjoram — Plant — 975 ppm. E

Taraxacum officinale WEBER EX F. H. WIGG. — Dandelion — Root — 960 ppm. EM

Rehmannia glutinosa (GAERTN.) LIBOSCH. — Chinese Foxglove — Root — 920 ppm. M

Mentha spicata L. — Hortela da Folha Miuda, Spearmint — Plant — 918 ppm. TEM

Amomum xanthioides WALL. — Bastard Cardamom, Chin Kousha, Malabar Cardamom, Tavoy Cardamom — Seed — 910 ppm. E

Gentiana scabra BUNGE — Japanese Gentian — Root — 910 ppm. M

Taraxacum mongolicum HAND.-MAZZ. — Mongoloid Dandelion — Plant — 910 ppm. EM

Smilax spp.. — Sarsaparilla — Root — 905 ppm. EM

Vitis vinifera L. — European Grape, Grape, Grapevine, Parra (Sp.), Vid (Sp.), Vigne Vinifere (Fr.), Weinrebe (Ger.), Wine Grape — Stem — 900 ppm. EM

Plantago asiatica L. — Asian Plantain — Plant — 890 ppm. EM

Angelica sinensis (OLIV.) DIELS — Chinese Angelica, Dang Gui, Dang Quai, Dang Qui, Dong Gui, Dong Quai — Root — 880 ppm. M

Glycyrrhiza glabra L. — Commom Licorice, Licorice, Licorice-Root, Smooth Licorice — Root — 880 ppm. M

Turnera diffusa WILLD. EX SCHULT. — Damiana — Leaf — 880 ppm. M

Viburnum opulus — Crampbark, European Cranberry Bush, Guelder Rose, Snowball Bush — Bark — 880 ppm. TEM

Chondrus crispus (L.) STACKH. — Irish Moss — Plant — 874 ppm. E

Agathosma betulina (P. J. BERGIUS) PILLANS — Buchu, Honey Buchu, Mountain Buchu — Leaf — 867 ppm. M

Sophora angustifolia AIT. — Narrowleaf Sophora — Root — 860 ppm. TM

Juncus effusus L. — Rush — Pith — 840 ppm. TEM

Phaseolus lunatus L. — Butter Bean, Lima Bean — Leaf — 821 ppm. E

Artemisia herba-alba ASSO. — Desert Wormwood — Plant — 820 ppm. M

Glehnia littoralis F. SCHMIDT & MIQUEL — Bei Sha Shen — Root — 820 ppm. EM

Prunus serotina subsp. serotina — Black Cherry, Wild Cherry — Stem — 810 ppm. TEM

Symphytum officinale L. — Comfrey — Root — 810 ppm. TM

Lycopersicon esculentum MILLER — Tomato — Fruit — 800 ppm. TEM

Rhodymenia palmata — Dulse — Plant — 792 ppm. E

Atractylodes ovata DC. — Bai-Zhu, Pai-Chu — Rhizome — 780 ppm. M

Triticum aestivum L. — Wheat — Plant — 770 ppm. EM

Rumex crispus L. — Curly Dock, Lengua De Vaca, Sour Dock, Yellow Dock — Root — 760 ppm. TEM

Anethum graveolens L. — Dill, Garden Dill — Plant — 755 ppm. E

Cuminum cyminum L. — Cumin — Fruit — 748 ppm. EM

Sassafras albidum (NUTT.) NEES — Sassafras — Stem — 740 ppm. TEM

Rubia cordifolia L. — Madder — Root — 720 ppm. M

Spirulina pratensis — Spirulina — Plant — 713 ppm. E

Jussiaea repens L. — Jussiaeae Herba, Pond Dragon — Plant — 700 ppm. M

Phaseolus vulgaris var. vulgaris — Black Bean, Dwarf Bean, Field Bean, Flageolet Bean, French Bean, Garden Bean, Green Bean, Haricot, Haricot Bean, Haricot Vert, Kidney Bean, Navy Bean, Pop Bean, Popping Bean, Snap Bean, String Bean, Wax Bean — Leaf — 697 ppm. E

Chamissoa altissima (JACQ.) HBK — Guanique — Leaf — 137-1,370 ppm. M

Cimicifuga dahurica (TURCZ. EX FISCH. & C. A. MEY.) MAXIM. — Sheng Ma — Rhizome — 680 ppm. M

Lycium chinense MILL. — Chinese Boxthorn, Chinese Matrimony Vine, Chinese Wolfberry, Chinesischer Bocksdorn (Ger.), Daun Koki (Indones.), Gou Qi (Chin.), Kaukichai (Malays.), Kuko (Jap.), Lyciet de Chine (Fr.), Spina Santa Cinese (Ital.), Wolfberry — Root — Bark — 670 ppm. EM

Mimulus glabratus HBK. — Huaca-Mullo — Shoot — 660 ppm. M

Solanum nigrum L. — Black Nightshade — Leaf — 660 ppm. E

Lycopodium clavatum L. — Antler Herb, Clubmoss — Plant — 650 ppm. TM

Prunella vulgaris L. — Heal-All, Self-Heal — Flower — 640 ppm.

Pinus echinata MILLER — Shortleaf Pine — Shoot — 630 ppm. M

Hydrastis canadensis L. — Goldenseal — Root — 610 ppm. M

Arisaema consanguineum SCHOTT — Chinese Jack-In-The-Pulpit — Rhizome — 600 ppm. TEM

Cnidoscolus chayamansa McVAUGH — Chaya — Leaf — 600 ppm. E

Ephedra spp.. — Ma-Huang — Plant — 600 ppm. M

Mentha x piperita subsp. nothosubsp. piperita — Peppermint — Leaf — 600 ppm. TEM

Origanum vulgare L. — Common Turkish Oregano, European Oregano, Oregano, Pot Marjoram, Wild Marjoram, Wild Oregano — Plant — 598 ppm. E

Larrea tridentata (SESSE & MOC. ex DC.) COV. — Chaparral, Creosote Bush — Plant — 580 ppm. M

Apium graveolens L. — Celery — Seed — 571 ppm. E

Broussonetia papyrifera (L.) VENT — Paper Mulberry — Fruit — 560 ppm. EM

Momordica charantia L. — Bitter Melon, Sorosi — Fruit — 560 ppm. E

Trigonella foenum-graecum L. — Alholva (Sp.), Bockshornklee (Ger.), Fenugreek, Greek Clover, Greek Hay — Seed — 560 ppm. EM

Linum usitatissimum L. — Flax, Linseed — Seed — 549 ppm. E

Cymbopogon citratus (DC. ex NEES) STAPF — Lemongrass, West Indian Lemongrass — Plant — 543 ppm. EM

Ipomoea aquatica FORSSKAL — Swamp Cabbage, Water Spinach — Leaf — 540 ppm. E

Hibiscus sabdariffa L. — Acedera de Guinea (Sp.), Indian Sorrel, Jamaica Sorrel, Kharkadi, Malventee (Ger.), Red Sorrel, Rosa de Jamaica (Sp.), Rosella (Ger.), Roselle, Sereni (Sp.), Sorrel — Flower — 536 ppm. E

Coriandrum sativum L. — Chinese Parsley, Cilantro, Coriander — Leaf — 528 ppm. E

Lycium chinense MILL. — Chinese Boxthorn, Chinese Matrimony Vine, Chinese Wolfberry, Chinesischer Bocksdorn (Ger.), Daun Koki (Indones.), Gou Qi (Chin.), Kaukichai (Malays.), Kuko (Jap.), Lyciet de Chine (Fr.), Spina Santa Cinese (Ital.), Wolfberry — Leaf — 519 ppm. EM

Zea mays L. — Corn — Silk Stigma — Style — 504 ppm. E

Cinnamomum sieboldii — Japanese Cinnamon — Root — Bark — 500 ppm. TEM

Diospyros virginiana L. — American Persimmon — Leaf — 500 ppm. EM

Glechoma hederacea L. — Alehoof — Plant — 500 ppm. M

Houttuynia cordata THUNB. — Dokudami, Fishwort, Yu Xing Cao — Plant — 500 ppm. EM

Justicia pectoralis JACQ. — Angel Of Death, Bolek Hena, Curia — Leaf — 495 ppm. M

Erythroxylum coca var. coca — Coca — Leaf — 490 ppm. EM

Corchorus olitorius L. — Jew's Mallow, Mulukiya, Nalta Jute — Leaf — 485 ppm. EM

Valeriana officinalis L. — Common Valerian, Garden-Heliotrope, Valerian — Root — 480 ppm. M

Perilla frutescens (L.) BRITTON — Perilla — Leaf — 479 ppm. TEM

Ocimum basilicum L. — Basil, Cuban Basil, Sweet Basil — Leaf — 478 ppm. E

Borago officinalis L. — Beebread, Beeplant, Borage, Talewort — Leaf — 472 ppm. TEM

Myrica cerifera L. — Bayberry, Candle-Berry, Southern Bayberry, Wax Myrtle — Bark — 470 ppm. EM

Curcuma longa L. — Indian Saffron, Turmeric — Rhizome — 467 ppm. E

Portulaca oleracea L. — Purslane, Verdolaga — Plant — 467 ppm. E

Astragalus membranaceus (FISCH. EX LINK) BUNGE — Huang Qi, Huang-Chi — Root — 460 ppm. M

Perilla frutescens (L.) BRITTON — Perilla — Plant — 460 ppm. TEM

Viscum album L. — European Mistletoe — Leaf — 460 ppm. TM

Juglans nigra L. — Black Walnut — Fruit — 455 ppm. E

Sonchus oleraceus L. — Cerraja, Sow Thistle — Leaf — 455 ppm. EM

Forsythia suspensa VAHL — Lian-Jiao, Lien-Chiao — Fruit — 440 ppm. M

Malva sylvestris L. — High Mallow — Leaf — 440 ppm. EM

Nyssa sylvatica MARSHALL — Black Gum, Black Tupelo — Stem — 440 ppm. EM

Allium cepa L. — Onion, Shallot — Leaf — 436 ppm. E

Cyperus rotundus L. — Nutsedge — Rhizome — 430 ppm. EM

Carya glabra (MILLER) SWEET — Pignut Hickory — Shoot — 429 ppm. E

Cinnamomum aromaticum NEES — Canela de la China (Sp.), Canelero chino (Sp.), Canelle de Cochinchine (Fr.), Cannelier Casse (Fr.), Cannelier de Chine (Fr.), Cassia, Cassia Bark, Cassia Lignea, China Junk Cassia, Chinazimt (Ger.), Chinese Cassia, Chinese Cinnamon, Chinesischer Zimtbaum (Ger.), Kashia-Keihi (Jap.), Saigon Cinnamon, Zimtcassie (Ger.) — Bark — 421 ppm. TEM

Cinnamomum verum J. PRESL — Ceylon Cinnamon, Cinnamon — Bark — 421 ppm. TEM

Chrysanthemum coronarium L. — Garland Chrysanthemum — Bud — 420 ppm. M

Cucumis sativus L. — Cucumber — Fruit — 420 ppm. E

Quercus stellata WANGENH. — Post Oak — Stem — 420 ppm. EM

Urtica dioica L. — European Nettle, Stinging Nettle — Leaf — 418 ppm. EM

Satureja hortensis L. — Summer Savory — Plant — 416 ppm. E

Pimpinella anisum L. — Anise, Sweet Cumin — Fruit — 409 ppm. EM

Capsella bursa-pastoris (L.) MEDICUS — Shepherd's Purse — Plant — 407 ppm. EM

Panax quinquefolius L. — American Ginseng, Ginseng — Plant — 407 ppm. M

Piper nigrum L. — Black Pepper, Pepper, White Pepper — Fruit — 407 ppm. EM

Eryngium floridanum L. — Florida Eryngium — Shoot — 400 ppm. M

Geranium thunbergii SIEB. & ZUCC — Gennoshiouko, Oriental Geranium — Plant — 400 ppm. EM

Mentha arvensis var. piperascens MALINV. EX L. H. BAILEY — Cornmint, Field Mint, Japanese Mint — Plant — 400 ppm. TEM

Pisum sativum L. — Pea — Plant — 400 ppm. E

Rosmarinus officinalis L. — Rosemary — Plant — 400 ppm. EM

Spondias pinnata L. — Yellow Mombin, Yellow Plum — Fruit — 400 ppm. E

Beta vulgaris subsp. vulgaris — Beet, Beetroot, Garden Beet, Sugar Beet — Leaf — 392 ppm. E

Oenothera biennis L. — Evening-Primrose — Seed — 390 ppm. EM

Chrysanthemum coronarium L. — Garland Chrysanthemum — Leaf — 385 ppm. M

Spinacia oleracea L. — Spinach — Plant — 384 ppm. E

Cimicifuga racemosa (L.) NUTT. — Black Cohosh, Black Snakeroot — Root — 380 ppm. M

Quercus alba L. — White Oak — Stem — 380 ppm. EM

Phyllanthus acidus (L.) SKEELS — Indian Gooseberry, Otaheite Gooseberry — Fruit — 372 ppm. E

Gentiana lutea L. — Gentian, Yellow Gentian — Root — 370 ppm. M

Sinapis alba L. — White Mustard — Seed — 370 ppm. TEM

Tussilago farfara L. — Coltsfoot — Flower — 370 ppm. TM

Ipomoea batatas (L.) LAM — Sweet Potato — Leaf — 365 ppm. E

Xanthosoma sagittifolium (L.) SCHOTT — Malanga, Tannia, Yautia — Leaf — 365 ppm. E

Cichorium endivia L. — Endive, Escarole — Leaf — 360 ppm. E

Panax japonicus C.A.MEYER — Japanese Ginseng — Rhizome — 360 ppm. M

Momordica charantia L. — Bitter Melon, Sorosi — Leaf — 357 ppm. E

Raphanus sativus L. — Radish — Leaf — 357 ppm. E

Acorus calamus L. — Calamus, Flagroot, Myrtle Flag, Sweet Calamus, Sweetflag, Sweetroot — Rhizome — 350 ppm. M

Artemisia dracunculus L. — Tarragon — Plant — 350 ppm. M

Lonicera japonica THUNB. — Japanese Honeysuckle — Flower — 350 ppm. M

Schisandra chinensis (TURCZ.) BAILL. — Chinese Magnolia Vine, Five-Flavor-Fruit, Magnolia Vine, Schizandra, Wu Wei Zi, Wu Wei Zu — Fruit — 350 ppm. M

Plectranthus amboinicus (LOUR.) SPRENGEL — Amboini Coleus, Country Borage, Cuban Oregano, French Thyme, Indian Borage, Mexican Mint, Soup Mint, Spanish Thyme — Leaf — 39-695 ppm. E

Apium graveolens L. — Celery — Plant — 347 ppm. E

Anthriscus cerefolium (L.) HOFFM. — Chervil — Leaf — 345 ppm. E

Quercus rubra L. — Northern Red Oak — Stem — 343 ppm. EM

Ophiopogon japonicus KER-GAWL. — Mai-Men-Dong, Mai-Men-Tung — Tuber — 340 ppm. M

Hibiscus sabdariffa L. — Acedera de Guinea (Sp.), Indian Sorrel, Jamaica Sorrel, Kharkadi, Malventee (Ger.), Red Sorrel, Rosa de Jamaica (Sp.), Rosella (Ger.), Roselle, Sereni (Sp.), Sorrel — Leaf — 333 ppm. E

Medicago sativa subsp. sativa — Alfalfa, Lucerne — Plant — 333 ppm. E

Coptis chinensis FRANCH. — Chinese Goldthread, Huang-Lian, Huang-Lien — Rhizome — 320 ppm. M

Coptis japonica (THUNB.) MAKINO — Huang-Lia, Huang-Lian, Huang-Lien, Japanese Goldthread — Rhizome — 320 ppm. M

Coptis spp.. — Generic Goldthread — Rhizome — 320 ppm. M

Magnolia denudata DESR. — Hsin-I, Xin-Yi — Flower — 320 ppm. EM

Magnolia fargesii CHENG — Hsin-I, Xin-Yi — Flower — 320 ppm. EM

Magnolia kobus DC. — Hsin-I, Xin-Yi — Flower — 320 ppm. EM

Morinda sp — Morinda — Root — 320 ppm. M

Dioscorea sp. — Wild Yam — Root — 315 ppm. E

Piper auritum HBK. — Cordoncillo, Hierba Santa, Hoja Santa — Leaf — 315 ppm. EM

Solanum torvum SW. — Susumba, Wild Eggplant — Fruit — 315 ppm. E

Elytrigia repens (L.) DESV. EX NEVSKI — Couchgrass, Doggrass, Quackgrass, Twitchgrass, Wheatgrass — Plant — 311 ppm. EM

Iron, cont.

Aconitum carmichaelii DEBX. — Aconite, Fu-Tsu — Tuber — 310 ppm. TM

Euphrasia officinalis L. — Eyebright — Plant — 310 ppm. M

Lobelia inflata L. — Indian Tobacco, Lobelia — Leaf — 310 ppm. TM

Asimina triloba (L.) DUNAL — Pawpaw — Fruit — 308 ppm. E

Salvia officinalis L. — Sage — Leaf — 305 ppm. EM

Aloe vera (L.) BURM. f. — Aloe, Bitter Aloes — Leaf — 300 ppm. EM

Avena sativa L. — Oats — Seed — 300 ppm. EM

Daucus carota L. — Carrot — Root — 300 ppm. E

Eucommia ulmoides OLIV. — Du Zhong, Gutta-Percha Tree, Tu Chung — Bark — 300 ppm. M

Trachyspermum ammi (L.) SPRAGUE ex TURRILL — Ajwan — Fruit — 299 ppm. EM

Raphanus sativus L. — Radish — Fruit — 295 ppm. E

Quercus phellos L. — Willow Oak — Stem — 294 ppm. EM

Atractylodes lancea DC. — Cang Zhu — Rhizome — 290 ppm. M

Centella asiatica (L.) URBAN — Gotu Kola, Pennywort — Leaf — 290 ppm. EM

Morus alba L. — Sang-Pai-Pi, White Mulberry — Root — Bark — 290 ppm. EM

Polygala tenuifolia WILLD. — Chinese Senega — Root — 290 ppm. M

Capsicum annuum L. — Bell Pepper, Cherry Pepper, Cone Pepper, Green Pepper, Paprika, Sweet Pepper — Fruit — 286 ppm. E

Carum carvi L. — Caraway, Carum, Comino (Sp.), Comino de prado (Sp.), Kummel (Ger.) — Fruit — 286 ppm. E

Lepidium sativum L. — Garden Cress — Leaf — 286 ppm. E

Abelmoschus manihot (L.) MEDIK. — Manioc Hibiscus — Leaf — 284 ppm. EM

Glycyrrhiza uralensis FISCH. EX DC. — Chinese Licorice, Gan-Cao, Kan-Tsao — Root — 280 ppm. M

Notopterygium incisum TING. — Qiang Huo — Rhizome — 280 ppm. M

Annona cherimola MILL. — Cherimoya — Seed — 270 ppm. E

Foeniculum vulgare MILLER — Fennel — Plant — 270 ppm. M

Panicum maximum JACQ. — Guinea grass — Leaf — 0-525 ppm. M

Nasturtium officinale R. BR. — Berro, Watercress — Herb — 262 ppm. E

Sechium edule (JACQ.) SW. — Chayote — Leaf — 262 ppm. EM

Citrus aurantium L. — Bitter Orange, Petitgrain — Fruit — 260 ppm. E

Psophocarpus tetragonolobus (L.) DC. — Asparagus Pea, Goa Bean, Winged Bean — Leaf — 259 ppm. E

Allium ampeloprasum L. — Elephant Garlic, Kurrat — Leaf — 255 ppm. E

Sida rhombifolia L. — Broomweed, Teaplant — Leaf — 253 ppm. M

Acanthopanax gracilistylis W.W.SMITH — Wu Chia Pi — Root — Bark — 250 ppm. M

Chenopodium album L. — Lamb's Quarters — Leaf — 250 ppm. TEM

Petroselinum crispum (MILLER) NYMAN EX A. W. HILLL — Parsley — Plant — 250 ppm. E

Rheum rhabarbarum L. — Rhubarb — Leaf — 250 ppm. E

Scutellaria lateriflora L. — Mad-Dog, Skullcap, Scullcap — Plant — 250 ppm. M

Vaccinium myrtillus L. — Bilberry, Dwarf Bilberry, Whortleberry — Leaf — 250 ppm. EM

Vaccinium vitis-idaea var. minus LODD. — Cowberry, Lingen, Lingonberry — Leaf — 250 ppm. EM

Morus alba L. — Sang-Pai-Pi, White Mulberry — Fruit — 247 ppm. EM

Cichorium intybus L. — Chicory, Succory, Witloof — Leaf — 246 ppm. E

Cenchrus biflorus ROXB — Two-Flowered Sandspur — Seed — 245 ppm. E

Mangifera indica L. — Mango — Fruit — 243 ppm. EM

Asparagus officinalis L. — Asparagus — Shoot — 240 ppm. E

Cnicus benedictus L. — Blessed Thistle — Plant — 240 ppm. M

Cnidium officinale MAKINO — Jih-Chiung — Rhizome — 240 ppm. EM

Foeniculum vulgare MILLER — Fennel — Fruit — 240 ppm. M

Lophatherum gracile BROGN. — Dan Zhu Ye — Plant — 240 ppm. M

Piper betel L. — Betel Pepper — Leaf — 240 ppm. EM

Quercus velutina LAM. — Black Oak — Stem — 236 ppm. EM

Allium cepa L. — Onion, Shallot — Seed — 235 ppm. E

Anethum graveolens L. — Dill, Garden Dill — Fruit — 230 ppm. E

Angelica laxiflora DIELS — Tu Huo — Root — 230 ppm. M

Frangula purshiana (DC.) J. G. COOPER — Cascara Buckthorn, Cascara Sagrada — Bark — 230 ppm. M

Salvia miltiorrhiza BUNGE — Dan-Shen, Red Sage, Tan-Shen — Root — 230 ppm. EM

Phaseolus lunatus L. — Butter Bean, Lima Bean — Sprout Seedling — 228 ppm. E

Coriandrum sativum L. — Chinese Parsley, Cilantro, Coriander — Fruit — 227 ppm. E

Scutellaria baicalensis GEORGI — Baikal Skullcap, Chinese Skullcap, Huang Qin — Root — 220 ppm. M

Valerianella radata — Plant — 349-425 ppm. E

Crataegus cuneata SIEB. & ZUCC. — Hawthorn — Fruit — 210 ppm. M

Cyclanthera pedata (L.) SCHRADER — Achocha — Fruit — 210 ppm. EM

Ephedra sinica STAPF — Chinese Ephedra, Ma Huang — Plant — 210 ppm. M

Glycine max (L.) MERR. — Soybean — Plant — 210 ppm. E

Phellodendron amurense RUPR. — Amur Cork Tree, Huang Bai, Huang Po, Po Mu — Bark — 210 ppm. M

Salix alba L. — White Willow — Bark — 210 ppm. M

Brassica nigra (L.) W. D. J. KOCH — Black Mustard — Leaf — 209 ppm. E

Pisum sativum L. — Pea — Fruit — 206 ppm. E

Peperomia pelucida — Pepper elder, Yerba de la plata — Leaf — 30-410 ppm.

Phytolacca americana L. — Pokeweed — Shoot — 202 ppm. TEM

Allium schoenoprasum L. — Chives — Leaf — 200 ppm. E

Artemisia capillaris THUNB. — Capillary Wormwood — Plant — 200 ppm. M

Colocasia esculenta (L.) SCHOTT — Taro — Leaf — 200 ppm. — Root — 200 ppm. E

Eriobotrya japonica (THUNB.) LINDL. — Loquat — Leaf — 200 ppm. E

Macadamia spp.. — Macadamia — Seed — 200 ppm. E

Mucuna pruriens (L.) DC. — Cowage, Velvetbean — Seed — 200 ppm. EM

Plantago psyllium L. — Psyllium — Seed — 200 ppm. EM

Platycodon grandiflorum (JACQ.) A.DC. — Balloon Flower, Chieh-Keng, Jie-Geng — Root — 200 ppm. TEM

Trichosanthes anguina L. — Snakegourd — Fruit — 200 ppm. E

Acacia farnesiana (L.) WILLD. — Cassie, Huisache, Opopanax, Popinac, Sweet Acacia — Leaf — 199 ppm. M

Anacardium occidentale L. — Cashew — Seed — 195 ppm. E

Arachis hypogaea L. — Groundnut, Peanut — Leaf — 195 ppm. EM

Malva parviflora L. — Cheeseweed — Plant — 195 ppm. EM

Aristolochia debilis SIEB. & ZUCC. — Chinese Birthwort — Fruit — 190 ppm. TEM

Peperomia pereskiifolia — Perejil — Leaf — 57-380 ppm.

Siegesbeckia orientalis L. — Hsi Chien, Saint Paul's Wort — Plant — 190 ppm. M

Raphanus sativus L. — Radish — Root — 189 ppm. E

Vigna unguiculata subsp. sesquipedalis (L.) VERDC. — Asparagus Bean, Pea Bean, Yardlong Bean — Shoot — 188 ppm. E

Catha edulis VAHL — Khat — Leaf — 185 ppm. E

Plantago psyllium L. — Psyllium — Hull Husk — 183 ppm. EM

Achyranthes bidentata BLUME — Chaff Flower — Root — 180 ppm. M

Amphicarpaea bracteata (L.) FERNALD — Hog Peanut — Shoot — 0-360 ppm. EM

Iron, cont.

Celosia cristata L. — Cockscomb — Flower — 180 ppm. M

Glycine max (L.) MERR. — Soybean — Seed — 180 ppm. E

Hyoscyamus niger L. — Henbane — Seed — 180 ppm. T

Panax ginseng C. A. MEYER — Chinese Ginseng, Ginseng, Korean Ginseng, Oriental Ginseng — Root — 180 ppm. M

Rheum palmatum L. — Chinese Rhubarb — Rhizome — 180 ppm. E

Hydrangea arborescens L. — Hydrangea, Smooth Hydrangea — Root — 179 ppm. EM

Lactuca sativa L. — Lettuce — Leaf — 176 ppm. E

Basella alba L. — Vinespinach — Leaf — 175 ppm. EM

Canavalia ensiformis (L.) DC. — Jack Bean — Fruit — 175 ppm. E

Brassica juncea (L.) CZERNJ. & COSSON — Mustard Greens — Leaf — 174 ppm. E

Blighia sapida KOENIG — Akee, Seso Vegetal — Seed — 173 ppm. M

Cucurbita pepo L. — Pumpkin — Seed — 172 ppm. E

Brassica chinensis L. — Bok-Choy, Celery Cabbage, Celery Mustard, Chinese Cabbage, Chinese Mustard, Chinese White Cabbage, Pak-Choi — Leaf — 171 ppm. E

Chamaemelum nobile (L.) ALL. — Garden Camomile, Perennial Camomile, Roman Camomile — Flower — 170 ppm. M

Zizyphus jujuba MILL. — Da-Zao, Jujube, Ta-Tsao — Fruit — 170 ppm. EM

Sesamum indicum L. — Ajonjoli (Sp.), Beni, Benneseed, Sesame, Sesamo (Sp.) — Seed — 169 ppm. EM

Helianthus tuberosus L. — Jerusalem Artichoke — Tuber — 168 ppm. E

Beta vulgaris subsp. vulgaris — Beet, Beetroot, Garden Beet, Sugar Beet — Root — 165 ppm. E

Phyllanthus emblica L. — Emblic, Myrobalan — Fruit — 163 ppm. E

Zingiber officinale ROSCOE — Ginger — Rhizome — 162 ppm. EM

Genipa americana L. — Genipap, Jagua — Fruit — 160 ppm. EM

Hordeum vulgare L. — Barley, Barleygrass — Stem — 160 ppm. EM

Rumex acetosa L. — Garden Sorrel — Leaf — 160 ppm. TEM

Psophocarpus tetragonolobus (L.) DC. — Asparagus Pea, Goa Bean, Winged Bean — Seed — 158 ppm. E

Limonia acidissima L. — Elephant Apple, Manzana De Elefante, Wood-Apple — Seed — 300-312 ppm. EM

Polygonum multiflorum THUNB. — Chinese Cornbind, Chinese Knotweed, Fleeceflower, Fo Ti, He Shou Wu — Root — 156 ppm. TEM

Rheum rhabarbarum L. — Rhubarb — Plant — 154 ppm. E

Vitis vinifera L. — European Grape, Grape, Grapevine, Parra (Sp.), Vid (Sp.), Vigne Vinifere (Fr.), Weinrebe (Ger.), Wine Grape — Fruit — 154 ppm. EM

Elettaria cardamomum (L.) MATON — Cardamom — Seed — 153 ppm. EM

Rhizophora mangle L. — Red Mangrove — Leaf — 152 ppm. M

Brassica oleracea var. capitata L. — Cabbage, Red Cabbage, White Cabbage — Leaf — 151 ppm. E

Phoenix dactylifera L. — Date Palm — Fruit — 151 ppm. E

Abelmoschus esculentus (L.) MOENCH — Okra — Fruit — 150 ppm. EM

Akebia quinata (THUNB.) DECNE — Chocolate Vine — Stem — 150 ppm. M

Belamcanda chinensis (L.) DC. — Blackberry Lily, Iris Tigre (Fr.), Leopard Lily, Leopardenblume (Ger.), Maravilla (Sp.), Mariposa (Sp.), Shenan — Rhizome — 150 ppm. M

Citrus mitis BLANCO — Calamansi, Calamondin — Fruit — 30-300 ppm. E

Fucus vesiculosus L. — Bladderwrack, Kelp — Plant — 150 ppm. EM

Isatis tinctoria L. — Dyer's Woad — Root — 150 ppm. M

Juniperus communis L. — Common Juniper, Juniper — Fruit — 150 ppm. TEM

Polygonum multiflorum THUNB. — Chinese Cornbind, Chinese Knotweed, Fleeceflower, Fo Ti, He Shou Wu — Rhizome — 150 ppm. TEM

Sinomenium acutum (THUNB.) REHD. & WILS. — Ching-Feng-Teng — Rhizome — 150 ppm. EM

Syzygium aromaticum (L.) MERR. & L. M. PERRY — Clove, Clovetree — Flower — 150 ppm. E

Alpinia galanga (L.) SW. — Greater Galangal, Languas, Siamese Ginger — Rhizome — 149 ppm. M

Areca catechu L. — Betel Nut, Pin-Lang — Shoot — 147 ppm. EM

Phaseolus vulgaris var. vulgaris — Black Bean, Dwarf Bean, Field Bean, Flageolet Bean, French Bean, Garden Bean, Green Bean, Haricot, Haricot Bean, Haricot Vert, Kidney Bean, Navy Bean, Pop Bean, Popping Bean, Snap Bean, String Bean, Wax Bean — Seed — 147 ppm. E

Cucurbita maxima DUCH. — Pumpkin — Leaf — 145 ppm. E

Cucurbita pepo L. — Pumpkin — Flower — 144 ppm. E

Citrullus lanatus (THUNB.) MATSUM. & NAKAI — Watermelon — Fruit — 143 ppm. E

Papaver somniferum L. — Opium Poppy, Poppyseed Poppy — Seed — 143 ppm. E

Passiflora quadrangularis L. — Granadilla — Fruit — 143 ppm. E

Vigna aconitifolia (JACQ.) MARECHAL — Mat Bean, Moth Bean — Seed — 143 ppm. E

Catalpa ovata G. DON — Hsin-Pa-Pi, Kisasage — Fruit — 140 ppm. EM

Equisetum hyemale L. — Horsetail, Scouring Rush — Plant — 140 ppm. M

Erythrina berteroana URB. — Pito — Shoot — 140 ppm. E

Lycium chinense MILL. — Chinese Boxthorn, Chinese Matrimony Vine, Chinese Wolfberry, Chinesischer Bocksdorn (Ger.), Daun Koki (Indones.), Gou Qi (Chin.), Kaukichai (Malays.), Kuko (Jap.), Lyciet de Chine (Fr.), Spina Santa Cinese (Ital.), Wolfberry — Fruit — 140 ppm. EM

Moringa oleifera LAM. — Ben Nut, Benzolive Tree, Drumstick Tree, Horseradish Tree, Jacinto (Sp.), Moringa, West Indian Ben — Leaf — 70-280 ppm. E

Myristica fragrans HOUTT. — Mace, Muskatnussbaum (Ger.), Nutmeg, nogal moscado (Sp.), nuez moscada (Sp.) — Aril — 140 ppm. E

Nigella sativa L. — Black Caraway, Black Cumin, Fennel-Flower, Nutmeg-Flower, Roman Coriander — Seed — 140 ppm. EM

Scrophularia buergeriana MIQ. — Hsuan-Shen, Yuan-Shen — Root — 140 ppm. M

Cannabis sativa L. — Hemp, Indian Hemp, Marihuana, Marijuana — Seed — 139 ppm. M

Pistacia vera L. — Pistachio — Seed — 137 ppm. E

Solanum melongena L. — Aubergine, Eggplant — Fruit — 137 ppm. E

Brassica oleracea var. gemmifera DC — Brussel-Sprout, Brussels-Sprouts — Leaf — 136 ppm. E

Vigna subterranea (L.) VERDC. — Bambarra Groundnut, Groundbean — Seed — 136 ppm. E

Allium cepa L. — Onion, Shallot — Bulb — 135 ppm. E

Capsicum frutescens L. — Cayenne, Chili, Hot Pepper, Red Chili, Spur Pepper, Tabasco — Fruit — 135 ppm. E

Perilla frutescens (L.) BRITTON — Perilla — Seed — 135 ppm. TEM

Passiflora quadrangularis L. — Granadilla — Seed — 134 ppm. E

Tetragonia tetragonioides (PALLAS) KUNTZE — New Zealand Spinach — Leaf — 133 ppm. E

Fagopyrum esculentum MOENCH. — Buckwheat — Seed — 132 ppm. E

Vigna radata (L.) WILCZEK — Green Gram, Mungbean — Sprout Seedling — 132 ppm. E

Blighia sapida KOENIG — Akee, Seso Vegetal — Aril — 130 ppm. M

Gardenia jasminoides J. ELLIS — Cape Jasmine, Gardenia, Jasmin, Shan-Chih-Tzu, Shan-Zhi-Zi, Zhi Zi — Fruit — 130 ppm. M

Sophora subprostata CHUN & CHEN — Shan Dou Gen — Root — 130 ppm. TM

Allium sativum var. sativum L. — Garlic — Bulb — 129 ppm. E

Iron, cont.

Gliricidia sepium STEUD. — Mata Raton — Flower — 129 ppm. M

Solanum tuberosum L. — Potato — Tuber — 128 ppm. E

Spondias mombin L. — Yellow Mombin, Yellow Plum — Fruit — 127 ppm. E

Benincasa hispida (THUNB.) COGN. — Waxgourd — Fruit — 125 ppm.

Pereskia aculeata MILL. — Barbados Gooseberry, Grosela Americana — Fruit — 0-250 ppm. EM

Boehmeria nivea (L.) GAUDICH. — Ramie — Leaf — 123 ppm. M

Malus domestica BORKH. — Apple — Fruit — 123 ppm. E

Brassica oleracea var. botrytis L. — Cauliflower — Flower — 122 ppm. E

Fraxinus rhynchophylla HANCE — Chinese Ash — Bark — 120 ppm. M

Ligustrum japonicum THUNB. — Japanese Privet, Ligustri Fructus — Fruit — 120 ppm. M

Ligustrum lucidum W. T. AITON — Chinese Privet, Glossy Privet, Ligustri Fructus, Privet, White Waxtree — Fruit — 120 ppm. M

Magnolia officinalis REHDER & E. H. WILSON — Chinese Magnolia, Hou Pu, Magnolia-Bark — Bark — 120 ppm. EM

Paeonia suffruticosa ANDREWS — Moutan, Moutan Peony, Tree Peony — Root — Bark — 120 ppm. M

Raphanus sativus L. — Radish — Seed — 120 ppm. E

Triticum aestivum L. — Wheat — Seed — 120 ppm. EM

Artemisia vulgaris L. — Mugwort — Leaf — 118 ppm. M

Cypripedium pubescens WILLD. — Yellow Ladyslipper — Root — 117 ppm. M

Prunus persica (L.) BATSCH — Peach — Bark — 117 ppm. TEM

Lens culinaris MEDIK. — Lentil — Sprout Seedling — 116 ppm. E

Amorphophallus konjac K. KOCH — Devil's Tongue, Elephant Yam, Konjac, Leopard Palm, Snake Palm, Umbrella Arum — Leaf — 115 ppm. TEM

Physalis peruviana L. — Cape Gooseberry, Ground Cherry — Fruit — 115 ppm. E

Manihot esculenta CRANTZ — Cassava, Tapioca, Yuca — Root — 114 ppm. E

Amorphophallus campanulatus BLUME — Elephant-Foot Yam — Root — 112 ppm. TEM

Pastinaca sativa L. — Parsnip — Root — 112 ppm. E

Alisma plantago-aquatica L. — Mud Plantain, Tse-Hsieh, Water Plantain, Ze-Xie — Rhizome — 110 ppm. M

Brassica oleracea var. acephala DC — Curly Kale, Kale, Kitchen Kale, Scotch Kale — Leaf — 110 ppm. E

Chaenomeles lagenaria KOIDZ. — Chinese Quince, Mu-Kua — Fruit — 110 ppm. E

Rubus chingii HU — Chinese Raspberry — Fruit — 110 ppm. EM

Brassica oleracea var. botrytis L. — Cauliflower — Leaf — 109 ppm. E

Tamarindus indica L. — Indian Tamarind, Kilytree, Tamarind — Fruit — 109 ppm. M

Ribes nigrum L. — Black Currant — Fruit — 108 ppm. E

Armoracia rusticana GAERTN. ET AL. — Horseradish — Root — 106 ppm. E

Lens culinaris MEDIK. — Lentil — Seed — 106 ppm. E

Phaseolus coccineus L. — Scarlet Runner Bean — Seed — 103 ppm. E

Brassica oleracea var. viridis l. L. — Collards, Cow Cabbage, Spring-Heading Cabbage, Tall Kale, Tree Kale — Leaf — 102 ppm. E

Carthamus tinctorius L. — Safflower — Seed — 102 ppm. M

Vigna mungo (L.) HEPPER — Black Gram — Seed — 102 ppm. E

Cynara cardunculus subsp. cardunculus — Artichoke — Flower — 101 ppm. E

Albizia julibrissin DURAZZ. — Mimosa — Bark — 100 ppm. EM

Bletilla striata (THUNB.) REICHB. f. — Bletilla, Chinese Ground Orchid, Dai Chi (Chin.), Hardy Orchid, Hyacinth Bletilla, Hyacinth Orchid, Shiran (Jap.) — Tuber — 100 ppm. M

Cinnamomum burmannii (NEES) BLUME — Java Cinnamon, Padang Cassia — Bark — 100 ppm. TEM

Fragaria spp.. — Strawberry — Fruit — 100 ppm. E

Genipa americana L. — Genipap, Jagua — Seed — 100 ppm. EM

Hordeum vulgare L. — Barley, Barleygrass — Seed — 100 ppm.

— Sprout Seedling — 100 ppm. EM

Morinda citrifolia L. — Indian Mulberry, Noni — Leaf — 100 ppm. M

Opuntia ficus-indica (L.) MILL. — Indian Fig, Nopal, Nopalito, Prickly Pear — Seed — 100 ppm. EM

Vicia faba L. — Broadbean, Faba Bean, Habas — Seed — 100 ppm. E

Lanthanum

Carya glabra (MILLER) SWEET — Pignut Hickory — Shoot — 220 ppm. E

Carya ovata (MILL.) K. KOCH — Shagbark Hickory — Shoot — 90 ppm. E

Rhus copallina L. — Dwarf Sumac, Winged Sumac — Leaf — 29 ppm. EM

Quercus alba L. — White Oak — Stem — 23.6 ppm. EM

Brassica oleracea var. capitata L. — Cabbage, Red Cabbage, White Cabbage — Leaf — 20.3 ppm. E

Lactuca sativa L. — Lettuce — Leaf — 20.3 ppm. E

Quercus rubra L. — Northern Red Oak — Stem — 19.8 ppm. EM

Prunus serotina subsp. serotina — Black Cherry, Wild Cherry — Leaf — 19 ppm. TEM

Liquidambar styraciflua L. — American Styrax, Sweetgum — Stem — 18 ppm. EM

Diospyros virginiana L. — American Persimmon — Stem — 16.2 ppm. EM

Prunus serotina subsp. serotina — Black Cherry, Wild Cherry — Stem — 16 ppm. TEM

Diospyros virginiana L. — American Persimmon — Leaf — 15 ppm. EM

Quercus velutina LAM. — Black Oak — Stem — 14.9 ppm. EM

Prunus domestica L. — Plum — Fruit — 12 ppm. TEM

Rhus copallina L. — Dwarf Sumac, Winged Sumac — Stem — 9.2 ppm. EM

Liquidambar styraciflua L. — American Styrax, Sweetgum — Leaf — 8.2 ppm. EM

Bertholletia excelsa BONPL. — Brazilnut, Brazilnut-Tree, Creamnut, Paranut — Seed. E

Quercus rubra L. — Northern Red Oak — Seed. EM

Carya ovata (MILL.) K. KOCH — Shagbark Hickory — Seed. E

Cocos nucifera L. — Coconut, Coconut Palm, Cocotero (Sp.), Copra, Kokospalme (Ger.), Nariyal — Seed. E

Juglans cinerea L. — Butternut — Seed. E

Juglans nigra L. — Black Walnut — Seed. E

Prunus dulcis (MILLER) D. A. WEBB — Almond — Seed. TEM

Anacardium occidentale L. — Cashew — Seed. E

Carya illinoensis (WANGENH.) K. KOCH — Pecan — Seed. E

Corylus avellana L. — Cobnut, English Filbert, European Filbert, European Hazel, Hazel — Seed. E

Pistacia vera L. — Pistachio — Seed. E

Lead

Nyssa sylvatica MARSHALL — Black Gum, Black Tupelo — Leaf — 182 ppm. EM

Symphoricarpos orbiculatus MOENCH. — Buckbush — Stem — 176 ppm. TM

Juniperus virginiana L. — Red Cedar — Shoot — 132 ppm. TEM

Nyssa sylvatica MARSHALL — Black Gum, Black Tupelo — Stem — 132 ppm. EM

Prunus serotina subsp. serotina — Black Cherry, Wild Cherry — Stem — 108 ppm. TEM

Carya glabra (MILLER) SWEET — Pignut Hickory — Shoot — 103 ppm. E

Rhus copallina L. — Dwarf Sumac, Winged Sumac — Stem — 92 ppm. EM

Fucus vesiculosus L. — Bladderwrack, Kelp — Plant — 91 ppm. EM

Diospyros virginiana L. — American Persimmon — Stem — 81 ppm. EM

Quercus alba L. — White Oak — Stem — 76 ppm. EM

Lead, cont.

Prunus serotina subsp. serotina — Black Cherry, Wild Cherry — Leaf — 67 ppm. TEM

Rhus copallina L. — Dwarf Sumac, Winged Sumac — Leaf — 67 ppm. EM

Malus domestica BORKH. — Apple — Fruit — 64 ppm. E

Pinus echinata MILLER — Shortleaf Pine — Shoot — 63 ppm. M

Lycopersicon esculentum MILLER — Tomato — Fruit — 60 ppm. TEM

Quercus stellata WANGENH. — Post Oak — Stem — 59 ppm. EM

Liquidambar styraciflua L. — American Styrax, Sweetgum — Stem — 57 ppm. EM

Carya ovata (MILL.) K. KOCH — Shagbark Hickory — Shoot — 46 ppm. E

Sassafras albidum (NUTT.) NEES — Sassafras — Stem — 37 ppm. TEM

Diospyros virginiana L. — American Persimmon — Leaf — 35 ppm. EM

Sassafras albidum (NUTT.) NEES — Sassafras — Leaf — 34 ppm. TEM

Quercus velutina LAM. — Black Oak — Stem — 31 ppm. EM

Asparagus officinalis L. — Asparagus — Shoot — 30 ppm. E

Liquidambar styraciflua L. — American Styrax, Sweetgum — Leaf — 25 ppm. EM

Quercus phellos L. — Willow Oak — Stem — 21 ppm. EM

Rhus glabra L. — Smooth Sumac — Stem — 20 ppm. EM

Hypericum perforatum L. — Common St. Johnswort, Goatweed, Hypericum, Klamath Weed, St. John's-wort — Leaf — 18 ppm. TM

Quercus rubra L. — Northern Red Oak — Stem — 17 ppm. EM

Zea mays L. — Corn — Seed — 14 ppm. E

Hypericum perforatum L. — Common St. Johnswort, Goatweed, Hypericum, Klamath Weed, St. John's-wort — Plant — 12 ppm. TM

Prunus domestica L. — Plum — Fruit — 11.9 ppm. TEM

Phaseolus vulgaris var. vulgaris — Black Bean, Dwarf Bean, Field Bean, Flageolet Bean, French Bean, Garden Bean, Green Bean, Haricot, Haricot Bean, Haricot Vert, Kidney Bean, Navy Bean, Pop Bean, Popping Bean, Snap Bean, String Bean, Wax Bean — Fruit — 10.5 ppm. E

Cinnamomum sieboldii — Japanese Cinnamon — Root — Bark — 9 ppm. TEM

Vitis vinifera L. — European Grape, Grape, Grapevine, Parra (Sp.), Vid (Sp.), Vigne Vinifere (Fr.), Weinrebe (Ger.), Wine Grape — Fruit — 9 ppm. EM

Vigna unguiculata subsp. sesquipedalis (L.) VERDC. — Asparagus Bean, Pea Bean, Yardlong Bean — Seed — 8.4 ppm. E

Cinnamomum sieboldii — Japanese Cinnamon — Bark — 8 ppm. TEM

Citrus paradisi MacFAD. — Grapefruit — Fruit — 7.7 ppm. E

Lactuca sativa L. — Lettuce — Leaf — 6 ppm. E

Urtica dioica L. — European Nettle, Stinging Nettle — Leaf — 6 ppm. EM

Brassica oleracea var. capitata L. — Cabbage, Red Cabbage, White Cabbage — Leaf — 5.8 ppm. E

Hypericum perforatum L. — Common St. Johnswort, Goatweed, Hypericum, Klamath Weed, St. John's-wort — Root — 5 ppm. TM

Momordica charantia L. — Bitter Melon, Sorosi — Fruit — 5 ppm. E

Phaseolus lunatus L. — Butter Bean, Lima Bean — Seed — 5 ppm. E

Cichorium endivia L. — Endive, Escarole — Leaf — 4.8 ppm. E

Brassica pekinensis (LOUR.) RUPR. — Chinese Cabbage — Leaf — 4.2 ppm. E

Solanum tuberosum L. — Potato — Tuber — 4.2 ppm. E

Petroselinum crispum (MILLER) NYMAN EX A. W. HILLL — Parsley — Plant — 4 ppm. E

Phoenix dactylifera L. — Date Palm — Seed — 4 ppm. E

Vigna mungo (L.) HEPPER — Black Gram — Seed — 3.832 ppm. E

Beta vulgaris subsp. vulgaris — Beet, Beetroot, Garden Beet, Sugar Beet — Root — 3.5 ppm. E

Rhodymenia palmata — Dulse — Plant — 3.5 ppm. E

Prunus persica (L.) BATSCH — Peach — Fruit — 3 ppm. TEM

Sorbus aucuparia L. — Rowan Berry, Mountain Ash — Fruit — 3 ppm. TEM

Spinacia oleracea L. — Spinach — Leaf — 3 ppm. E

Cucumis sativus L. — Cucumber — Fruit — 2.8 ppm. E

Cucumis melo subsp. melo var.cantalupensis NAUDIN — Cantaloupe, Melon, Muskmelon, Netted Melon, Nutmeg Melon, Persian Melon — Fruit — 2.2 ppm. E

Apium graveolens L. — Celery — Root — 2 ppm. E

Capsicum annuum L. — Bell Pepper, Cherry Pepper, Cone Pepper, Green Pepper, Paprika, Sweet Pepper — Fruit — 2 ppm. E

Daucus carota L. — Carrot — Root — 2 ppm. E

Vaccinium macrocarpon AITON — American Cranberry, Cranberry, Large Cranberry — Fruit — 2 ppm. E

Corylus avellana L. — Cobnut, English Filbert, European Filbert, European Hazel, Hazel — Seed — 1.7 ppm. E

Triticum aestivum L. — Wheat — Seed — 1.653 ppm. EM

Solanum melongena L. — Aubergine, Eggplant — Fruit — 1.6 ppm. E

Vigna radata (L.) WILCZEK — Green Gram, Mungbean — Seed — 1.57 ppm. E

Allium cepa L. — Onion, Shallot — Bulb — 1.4 ppm. E

Pyrus communis L. — Pear — Fruit — 1.11 ppm. E

Citrus sinensis (L.) OSBECK — Orange — Fruit — 1.1 ppm. E

Brassica oleracea var. botrytis L. — Cauliflower — Leaf — 1 ppm. E

Phaseolus vulgaris var. vulgaris — Black Bean, Dwarf Bean, Field Bean, Flageolet Bean, French Bean, Garden Bean, Green Bean, Haricot, Haricot Bean, Haricot Vert, Kidney Bean, Navy Bean, Pop Bean, Popping Bean, Snap Bean, String Bean, Wax Bean — Seed — 1 ppm. E

Rheum rhabarbarum L. — Rhubarb — Plant — 1 ppm. E

Rubus chamaemorus L. — Cloudberry — Fruit — 1 ppm. EM

Lithium

Chamissoa altissima (JACQ.) HBK — Guanique — Leaf — 13-132 ppm. M

Carya ovata (MILL.) K. KOCH — Shagbark Hickory — Shoot — 11.7 ppm. E

Carya glabra (MILLER) SWEET — Pignut Hickory — Shoot — 6.6 ppm. E

Quercus velutina LAM. — Black Oak — Stem — 5.2 ppm. EM

Quercus alba L. — White Oak — Stem — 4.94 ppm. EM

Thymus vulgaris L. — Common Thyme, Garden Thyme, Thyme — Plant — 4 ppm. EM

Quercus rubra L. — Northern Red Oak — Stem — 3.96 ppm. EM

Phaseolus vulgaris var. vulgaris — Black Bean, Dwarf Bean, Field Bean, Flageolet Bean, French Bean, Garden Bean, Green Bean, Haricot, Haricot Bean, Haricot Vert, Kidney Bean, Navy Bean, Pop Bean, Popping Bean, Snap Bean, String Bean, Wax Bean — Fruit — 2.7 ppm. E

Lactuca sativa L. — Lettuce — Leaf — 2.6 ppm. E

Phaseolus vulgaris var. vulgaris — Black Bean, Dwarf Bean, Field Bean, Flageolet Bean, French Bean, Garden Bean, Green Bean, Haricot, Haricot Bean, Haricot Vert, Kidney Bean, Navy Bean, Pop Bean, Popping Bean, Snap Bean, String Bean, Wax Bean — Seed — 2.45 ppm. E

Citrus paradisi MacFAD. — Grapefruit — Fruit — 2.31 ppm. E

Citrus sinensis (L.) OSBECK — Orange — Fruit — 1.54 ppm. E

Brassica oleracea var. capitata L. — Cabbage, Red Cabbage, White Cabbage — Leaf — 1.4 ppm. E

Symphoricarpos orbiculatus MOENCH. — Buckbush — Stem — 1.06 ppm. TM

Cichorium endivia L. — Endive, Escarole — Leaf. E

Brassica pekinensis (LOUR.) RUPR. — Chinese Cabbage — Leaf. E

Petroselinum crispum (MILLER) NYMAN EX A. W. HILLL — Parsley — Plant. E

Lithium, cont.

Lycopersicon esculentum MILLER — Tomato — Fruit. TEM

Prunus domestica L. — Plum — Fruit. TEM

Asparagus officinalis L. — Asparagus — Shoot. E

Beta vulgaris subsp. vulgaris — Beet, Beetroot, Garden Beet, Sugar Beet — Root. E

Daucus carota L. — Carrot — Root. E

Prunus persica (L.) BATSCH — Peach — Fruit. TEM

Cucumis sativus L. — Cucumber — Fruit. E

Cucumis melo subsp. melo var.cantalupensis NAUDIN — Cantaloupe, Melon, Muskmelon, Netted Melon, Nutmeg Melon, Persian Melon — Fruit. E

Pinus echinata MILLER — Shortleaf Pine — Shoot. M

Capsicum annuum L. — Bell Pepper, Cherry Pepper, Cone Pepper, Green Pepper, Paprika, Sweet Pepper — Fruit. E

Juniperus virginiana L. — Red Cedar — Shoot. TEM

Allium cepa L. — Onion, Shallot — Bulb. E

Solanum melongena L. — Aubergine, Eggplant — Fruit. E

Vitis vinifera L. — European Grape, Grape, Grapevine, Parra (Sp.), Vid (Sp.), Vigne Vinifere (Fr.), Weinrebe (Ger.), Wine Grape — Fruit. EM

Solanum tuberosum L. — Potato — Tuber. E

Zea mays L. — Corn — Seed. E

Pyrus communis L. — Pear — Fruit. E

Malus domestica BORKH. — Apple — Fruit. E

Magnesium

Carya glabra (MILLER) SWEET — Pignut Hickory — Shoot — 24,200 ppm. E

Carya ovata (MILL.) K. KOCH — Shagbark Hickory — Shoot — 21,600 ppm. E

Chondrus crispus (L.) STACKH. — Irish Moss — Plant — 19,600 ppm. E

Portulaca oleracea L. — Purslane, Verdolaga — Plant — 18,700 ppm. E

Phaseolus vulgaris var. vulgaris — Black Bean, Dwarf Bean, Field Bean, Flageolet Bean, French Bean, Garden Bean, Green Bean, Haricot, Haricot Bean, Haricot Vert, Kidney Bean, Navy Bean, Pop Bean, Popping Bean, Snap Bean, String Bean, Wax Bean — Fruit — 18,000 ppm. E

Papaver somniferum L. — Opium Poppy, Poppyseed Poppy — Seed — 15,600 ppm. E

Avena sativa L. — Oats — Plant — 14,800 ppm. EM

Spinacia oleracea L. — Spinach — Plant — 11,000 ppm. E

Tephrosia purpurea PERS. — Purple Tephrosia, Wild Indigo — Leaf — 10,300 ppm. TM

Trichosanthes anguina L. — Snakegourd — Fruit — 9,815 ppm. E

Glycyrrhiza glabra L. — Commom Licorice, Licorice, Licorice-Root, Smooth Licorice — Root — 9,650 ppm. M

Prunus serotina subsp. serotina — Black Cherry, Wild Cherry — Leaf — 9,600 ppm. TEM

Rhus copallina L. — Dwarf Sumac, Winged Sumac — Leaf — 9,600 ppm. EM

Nyssa sylvatica MARSHALL — Black Gum, Black Tupelo — Leaf — 9,100 ppm. EM

Juniperus virginiana L. — Red Cedar — Shoot — 8,800 ppm. TEM

Rhizophora mangle L. — Red Mangrove — Leaf — 8,800 ppm. M

Symphoricarpos orbiculatus MOENCH. — Buckbush — Stem — 8,800 ppm. TM

Arachis hypogaea L. — Groundnut, Peanut — Plant — 8,700 ppm. EM

Lactuca sativa L. — Lettuce — Leaf — 8,700 ppm. E

Fucus vesiculosus L. — Bladderwrack, Kelp — Plant — 8,670 ppm. EM

Urtica dioica L. — European Nettle, Stinging Nettle — Leaf — 8,600 ppm. EM

Quercus rubra L. — Northern Red Oak — Stem — 8,580 ppm. EM

Liquidambar styraciflua L. — American Styrax, Sweetgum — Stem — 8,400 ppm. EM

Trifolium pratense L. — Cowgrass, Peavine Clover, Purple Clover, Red Clover — Hay — 8,100 ppm. EM

Elytrigia repens (L.) DESV. EX NEVSKI — Couchgrass, Doggrass, Quackgrass,

Twitchgrass, Wheatgrass — Plant — 7,570 ppm. EM

Coriandrum sativum L. — Chinese Parsley, Cilantro, Coriander — Leaf — 7,488 ppm. E

Borago officinalis L. — Beebread, Beeplant, Borage, Talewort — Leaf — 7,436 ppm. TEM

Scutellaria baicalensis GEORGI — Baikal Skullcap, Chinese Skullcap, Huang Qin — Root — 7,220 ppm. M

Azadirachta indica A. JUSS. — Neem — Leaf — 7,100 ppm. M

Linum usitatissimum L. — Flax, Linseed — Seed — 7,002 ppm. E

Asparagus officinalis L. — Asparagus — Shoot — 7,000 ppm. E

Cucumis sativus L. — Cucumber — Fruit — 7,000 ppm. E

Phaseolus lunatus L. — Butter Bean, Lima Bean — Seed — 7,000 ppm. E

Triticum aestivum L. — Wheat — Plant — 7,000 ppm. EM

Erythroxylum coca var. coca — Coca — Leaf — 6,900 ppm. EM

Allium schoenoprasum L. — Chives — Leaf — 6,875 ppm. E

Quercus velutina LAM. — Black Oak — Stem — 6,820 ppm. EM

Sassafras albidum (NUTT.) NEES — Sassafras — Leaf — 6,800 ppm. TEM

Erythroxylum novogranatense var. truxillense (RUSBY) PLOWMAN — Coca — Leaf — 6,700 ppm. EM

Amaranthus sp. — Pigweed — Leaf — 6,616 ppm. EM

Mentha x piperita subsp. nothosubsp. piperita — Peppermint — Leaf — 6,610 ppm. TEM

Tetragonia tetragonioides (PALLAS) KUNTZE — New Zealand Spinach — Leaf — 6,500 ppm. E

Anethum graveolens L. — Dill, Garden Dill — Plant — 6,470 ppm. E

Celosia cristata L. — Cockscomb — Flower — 6,080 ppm. M

Abelmoschus esculentus (L.) MOENCH — Okra — Fruit — 6,000 ppm. EM

Lycopersicon esculentum MILLER — Tomato — Fruit — 6,000 ppm. TEM

Rhodymenia palmata — Dulse — Plant — 5,930 ppm. E

Quercus stellata WANGENH. — Post Oak — Stem — 5,880 ppm. EM

Brassica chinensis L. — Bok-Choy, Celery Cabbage, Celery Mustard, Chinese Cabbage, Chinese Mustard, Chinese White Cabbage, Pak-Choi — Leaf — 5,844 ppm. E

Cucurbita pepo L. — Pumpkin — Seed — 5,748 ppm. E

Liquidambar styraciflua L. — American Styrax, Sweetgum — Leaf — 5,740 ppm. EM

Achyranthes bidentata BLUME — Chaff — Flower — Root — 5,730 ppm. M

Erythroxylum coca var. coca — Coca — Leaf — 5,700 ppm. EM

Salix alba L. — White Willow — Bark — 5,600 ppm. M

Petroselinum crispum (MILLER) NYMAN EX A. W. HILLL — Parsley — Plant — 5,577 ppm. E

Lablab purpureus (L.) SWEET — Bonavist Bean, Hyacinth Bean, Lablab Bean — Seed — 5,505 ppm. TEM

Mentha pulegium L. — European Pennyroyal — Plant — 5,500 ppm. TEM

Harpagophytum procumbens (BURCH.) DC. EX MEISN. — Devil's Claw, Grapple — Plant — Root — 5,440 ppm. M

Diospyros virginiana L. — American Persimmon — Stem — 5,400 ppm. EM

Prunus serotina subsp. serotina — Black Cherry, Wild Cherry — Stem — 5,400 ppm. TEM

Arctium lappa L. — Burdock, Gobo, Great Burdock — Root — 5,370 ppm. EM

Plantago asiatica L. — Asian Plantain — Plant — 5,320 ppm. EM

Quercus alba L. — White Oak — Stem — 5,320 ppm. EM

Oenothera biennis L. — Evening-Primrose — Seed — 5,300 ppm. EM

Stellaria media (L.) VILLARS — Chickweed, Common Chickweed — Plant — 5,290 ppm. E

Hyoscyamus niger L. — Henbane — Seed — 5,250 ppm. T

Corchorus olitorius L. — Jew's Mallow, Mulukiya, Nalta Jute — Leaf — 5,200 ppm. EM

Althaea officinalis L. — Marshmallow, White Mallow — Root — 5,180 ppm. M

Helianthus annuus L. — Girasol, Sunflower — Seed — 5,176 ppm. E

Asimina triloba (L.) DUNAL — Pawpaw — Fruit — 5,128 ppm. E

Glycyrrhiza uralensis FISCH. EX DC. — Chinese Licorice, Gan-Cao, Kan-Tsao — Root — 5,070 ppm. M

Foeniculum vulgare MILLER — Fennel — Fruit — 5,012 ppm. M

Diospyros virginiana L. — American Persimmon — Leaf — 5,000 ppm. EM

Vigna aconitifolia (JACQ.) MARECHAL — Mat Bean, Moth Bean — Seed — 4,962 ppm. E

Cucurbita pepo L. — Pumpkin — Flower — 4,950 ppm. E

Euodia rutaecarpa BENTH. — Wou Chou Yu — Fruit — 4,950 ppm. E

Apium graveolens L. — Celery — Seed — 4,903 ppm. E

Benincasa hispida (THUNB.) COGN. — Waxgourd — Fruit — 4,870 ppm.

Abelmoschus manihot (L.) MEDIK. — Manioc Hibiscus — Leaf — 4,862 ppm. EM

Ephedra spp.. — Ma-Huang — Plant — 4,780 ppm. M

Sassafras albidum (NUTT.) NEES — Sassafras — Stem — 4,760 ppm. TEM

Rhus glabra L. — Smooth Sumac — Stem — 4,690 ppm. EM

Rumex acetosa L. — Garden Sorrel — Leaf — 4,600 ppm. TEM

Prunella vulgaris L. — Heal-All, Self-Heal — Flower — 4,560 ppm. M

Firmiana simplex (L.) W. F. WIGHT — Chinese Parasol — Seed — 4,480 ppm. EM

Isatis tinctoria L. — Dyer's Woad — Root — 4,410 ppm. M

Medicago sativa subsp. sativa — Alfalfa, Lucerne — Plant — 4,400 ppm. E

Nyssa sylvatica MARSHALL — Black Gum, Black Tupelo — Stem — 4,400 ppm. EM

Equisetum arvense L. — Field Horsetail, Horsetail — Plant — 4,370 ppm. M

Thymus vulgaris L. — Common Thyme, Garden Thyme, Thyme — Leaf — 4,360 ppm. EM

Vitis vinifera L. — European Grape, Grape, Grapevine, Parra (Sp.), Vid (Sp.), Vigne Vinifere (Fr.), Weinrebe (Ger.), Wine Grape — Stem — 4,360 ppm. EM

Ocimum basilicum L. — Basil, Cuban Basil, Sweet Basil — Leaf — 4,340 ppm. E

Lycopersicon esculentum MILLER — Tomato — Leaf — 4,300 ppm. TEM

Cynara cardunculus subsp. cardunculus — Artichoke — Flower — 4,275 ppm. E

Rhus copallina L. — Dwarf Sumac, Winged Sumac — Stem — 4,270 ppm. EM

Solanum tuberosum L. — Potato — Tuber — 4,250 ppm. E

Prunus persica (L.) BATSCH — Peach — Bark — 4,220 ppm. TEM

Vigna unguiculata subsp. sesquipedalis (L.) VERDC. — Asparagus Bean, Pea Bean, Yardlong Bean — Shoot — 4,207 ppm. E

Beta vulgaris subsp. vulgaris — Beet, Beetroot, Garden Beet, Sugar Beet — Root — 4,200 ppm. E

Nasturtium officinale R. BR. — Berro, Watercress — Herb — 4,200 ppm. E

Euphrasia officinalis L. — Eyebright — Plant — 4,160 ppm. M

Vigna unguiculata subsp. sesquipedalis (L.) VERDC. — Asparagus Bean, Pea Bean, Yardlong Bean — Fruit — 4,160 ppm. E

Drynaria fortunei (KUNZE) J. SMITH — Fortune's Fern — Rhizome — 4,140 ppm. M

Sesamum indicum L. — Ajonjoli (Sp.), Beni, Benneseed, Sesame, Sesamo (Sp.) — Seed — 4,082 ppm. EM

Taraxacum mongolicum HAND.-MAZZ. — Mongoloid Dandelion — Plant — 4,050 ppm. EM

Broussonetia papyrifera (L.) VENT — Paper Mulberry — Fruit — 4,030 ppm. EM

Silybum marianum (L.) GAERTN. — Lady's Thistle, Milk Thistle — Plant — 4,030 ppm. M

Coriandrum sativum L. — Chinese Parsley, Cilantro, Coriander — Fruit — 4,016 ppm. E

Azadirachta indica A. JUSS. — Neem — Fruit — 4,000 ppm. M

Raphanus sativus L. — Radish — Seed — 3,960 ppm. E

Vigna unguiculata subsp. sesquipedalis (L.) VERDC. — Asparagus Bean, Pea Bean, Yardlong Bean — Seed — 3,952 ppm. E

Oenothera biennis L. — Evening-Primrose — Herb — 3,900 ppm. EM

Origanum majorana L. — Marjoram, Sweet Marjoram — Plant — 3,900 ppm. E

Brassica juncea (L.) CZERNJ. & COSSON — Mustard Greens — Leaf — 3,837 ppm. E

Perilla frutescens (L.) BRITTON — Perilla — Plant — 3,830 ppm. TEM

Ipomoea aquatica FORSSKAL — Swamp Cabbage, Water Spinach — Leaf — 3,810 ppm. E

Prunus persica (L.) BATSCH — Peach — Seed — 3,810 ppm. TEM

Momordica charantia L. — Bitter Melon, Sorosi — Fruit — 3,800 ppm. E

Sechium edule (JACQ.) SW. — Chayote — Leaf — 3,785 ppm. EM

Sophora angustifolia AIT. — Narrowleaf Sophora — Root — 3,720 ppm. TM

Pisum sativum L. — Pea — Plant — 3,700 ppm. E

Pueraria pseudohirsuta TANG & WANG — Chinese Kudzu — Root — 3,690 ppm. EM

Cucurbita spp.. — Summer Squash — Fruit — 3,640 ppm. E

Jussiaea repens L. — Jussiaeae Herba, Pond Dragon — Plant — 3,590 ppm. M

Raphanus sativus L. — Radish — Root — 3,570 ppm. E

Amomum xanthioides WALL. — Bastard Cardamom, Chin Kousha, Malabar Cardamom, Tavoy Cardamom — Seed — 3,540 ppm. E

Triticum aestivum L. — Wheat — Seed — 3,500 ppm. EM

Stevia rebaudiana (BERTONI) BERTONI — Ca-A-E, Stevia, Sweet Leaf of Paraguay — Leaf — 3,490 ppm. E

Trifolium pratense L. — Cowgrass, Peavine Clover, Purple Clover, Red Clover — Flower — 3,490 ppm. EM

Artemisia dracunculus L. — Tarragon — Plant — 3,470 ppm. M

Moringa oleifera LAM. — Ben Nut, Benzolive Tree, Drumstick Tree, Horseradish Tree, Jacinto (Sp.), Moringa, West Indian Ben — Shoot — 1,470-6,890 ppm. E

Houttuynia cordata THUNB. — Dokudami, Fishwort, Yu Xing Cao — Plant — 3,430 ppm. EM

Phaseolus vulgaris var. vulgaris — Black Bean, Dwarf Bean, Field Bean, Flageolet Bean, French Bean, Garden Bean, Green Bean, Haricot, Haricot Bean, Haricot Vert, Kidney Bean, Navy Bean, Pop Bean, Popping Bean, Snap Bean, String Bean, Wax Bean — Seed — 3,430 ppm. E

Prunus domestica L. — Plum — Fruit — 3,400 ppm. TEM

Bupleurum chinense DC. — Chai-Hu — Root — 3,390 ppm. M

Schizonepeta tenuifolia BRIQ. — Ching-Chieh, Jing-Jie — Plant — 3,390 ppm. M

Bertholletia excelsa BONPL. — Brazilnut, Brazilnut-Tree, Creamnut, Paranut — Seed — 3,370 ppm. E

Cymbopogon citratus (DC. ex NEES) STAPF — Lemongrass, West Indian Lemongrass — Plant — 3,310 ppm. EM

Cucumis melo subsp. ssp melo var.cantalupensis NAUDIN — Cantaloupe, Melon, Muskmelon, Netted Melon, Nutmeg Melon, Persian Melon — Fruit — 3,300 ppm. E

Sinapis alba L. — White Mustard — Seed — 3,282 ppm. TEM

Salvia miltiorrhiza BUNGE — Dan-Shen, Red Sage, Tan-Shen — Root — 3,230 ppm. EM

Verbascum thapsus L. — Flannelleaf, Flannelplant, Great Mullein, Mullein, Velvetplant — Leaf — 3,230 ppm. M

Senna obtusifolia (L.) H.IRWIN & BARNEBY — Sicklepod — Seed — 3,220 ppm. TE

Centella asiatica (L.) URBAN — Gotu Kola, Pennywort — Leaf — 3,200 ppm. EM

Rumex crispus L. — Curly Dock, Lengua De Vaca, Sour Dock, Yellow Dock — Root — 3,200 ppm. TEM

Pulsatilla chinensis (BUNGE) REGEL — Chinese Anemone — Root — 3,190 ppm. M

Rubus idaeus L. — Raspberry, Red Raspberry — Leaf — 3,190 ppm. EM

Cassia tora L. — Sickle Senna — Seed — 3,180 ppm. M

Magnesium, cont.

Valeriana officinalis L. — Common Valerian, Garden-Heliotrope, Valerian — Root — 3,180 ppm. M

Xanthosoma sagittifolium (L.) SCHOTT — Malanga, Tannia, Yautia — Leaf — 3,170 ppm. E

Glycine max (L.) MERR. — Soybean — Seed — 3,160 ppm. E

Corylus avellana L. — Cobnut, English Filbert, European Filbert, European Hazel, Hazel — Seed — 3,156 ppm. E

Brassica pekinensis (LOUR.) RUPR. — Chinese Cabbage — Leaf — 3,150 ppm. E

Colocasia esculenta (L.) SCHOTT — Taro — Leaf — 3,140 ppm. E

Prunus dulcis (MILLER) D. A. WEBB — Almond — Seed — 3,126 ppm. TEM

Amorphophallus campanulatus BLUME — Elephant-Foot Yam — Root — 3,120 ppm. TEM

Viburnum opulus — Crampbark, European Cranberry Bush, Guelder Rose, Snowball Bush — Bark — 3,110 ppm. TEM

Viscum album L. — European Mistletoe — Leaf — 3,110 ppm. TM

Linum usitatissimum L. — Flax, Linseed — Hay — 3,100 ppm. E

Brassica oleracea var. botrytis L. — Cauliflower — Leaf — 3,072 ppm. E

Syzygium aromaticum (L.) MERR. & L. M. PERRY — Clove, Clovetree — Flower — 3,020 ppm. E

Origanum vulgare L. — Common Turkish Oregano, European Oregano, Oregano, Pot Marjoram, Wild Marjoram, Wild Oregano — Plant — 3,016 ppm. E

Thymus vulgaris L. — Common Thyme, Garden Thyme, Thyme — Plant — 2,992 ppm. EM

Lonicera japonica THUNB. — Japanese Honeysuckle — Flower — 2,990 ppm. M

Notopterygium incisum TING. — Qiang Huo — Rhizome — 2,980 ppm. M

Hydrastis canadensis L. — Goldenseal — Root — 2,940 ppm. M

Quercus phellos L. — Willow Oak — Stem — 2,940 ppm. EM

Chamaemelum nobile (L.) ALL. — Garden Camomile, Perennial Camomile, Roman Camomile — Flower — 2,920 ppm. M

Chenopodium album L. — Lamb's Quarters — Seed — 2,920 ppm. TEM

Avena sativa L. — Oats — Seed — 2,900 ppm. EM

Genipa americana L. — Genipap, Jagua — Fruit — 2,900 ppm. EM

Anethum graveolens L. — Dill, Garden Dill — Fruit — 2,893 ppm. E

Senna occidentalis (L.) H. IRWIN & BARNEBY — Coffee Senna — Seed — 2,880 ppm. TE

Carum carvi L. — Caraway, Carum, Comino (Sp.), Comino de prado (Sp.), Kummel (Ger.) — Fruit — 2,863 ppm. E

Acanthopanax gracilistylis W.W.SMITH — Wu Chia Pi — Root — Bark — 2,840 ppm. M

Mentha arvensis var. piperascens MALINV. EX L. H. BAILEY — Cornmint, Field Mint, Japanese Mint — Plant — 2,830 ppm. TEM

Rosa laevigata MICHX. — Cherokee Rose — Fruit — 2,830 ppm. EM

Salvia officinalis L. — Sage — Leaf — 2,830 ppm. EM

Luffa aegyptiaca MILLER — Luffa, Smooth Loofah, Vegetable Sponge — Fruit — 2,800 ppm. E

Brassica oleracea var. viridis l. L. — Collards, Cow Cabbage, Spring-Heading Cabbage, Tall Kale, Tree Kale — Leaf — 2,786 ppm. E

Trigonella foenum-graecum L. — Alholva (Sp.), Bockshornklee (Ger.), Fenugreek, Greek Clover, Greek Hay — Seed — 2,780 ppm. EM

Schisandra chinensis (TURCZ.) BAILL. — Chinese Magnolia Vine, Five-Flavor-Fruit, Magnolia Vine, Schizandra, Wu Wei Zi, Wu Wei Zu — Fruit — 2,760 ppm. M

Cucurbita maxima DUCH. — Pumpkin — Leaf — 2,752 ppm. E

Gentiana lutea L. — Gentian, Yellow Gentian — Root — 2,740 ppm. M

Rubus chingii HU — Chinese Raspberry — Fruit — 2,740 ppm. EM

Artemisia vulgaris L. — Mugwort — Shoot — 2,700 ppm. M

Zingiber officinale ROSCOE — Ginger — Rhizome — 2,690 ppm. EM

Juglans cinerea L. — Butternut — Seed — 2,676 ppm. E

Siegesbeckia orientalis L. — Hsi Chien, Saint Paul's Wort — Plant — 2,660 ppm. M

Cichorium intybus L. — Chicory, Succory, Witloof — Leaf — 2,652 ppm. E

Angelica sinensis (OLIV.) DIELS — Chinese Angelica, Dang Gui, Dang Quai, Dang Qui, Dong Gui, Dong Quai — Root — 2,650 ppm. M

Apium graveolens L. — Celery — Leaf — 2,650 ppm. E

Nelumbo nucifera L. — Water Lotus — Seed — 2,650 ppm. EM

Psophocarpus tetragonolobus (L.) DC. — Asparagus Pea, Goa Bean, Winged Bean — Seed — 2,623 ppm. E

Brassica napus var. napobrassica var. napobrassica (L.) REICHB. — Rutabaga, Swede, Swedish Turnip — Root — 2,610 ppm. E

Lycium chinense MILL. — Chinese Boxthorn, Chinese Matrimony Vine, Chinese Wolfberry, Chinesischer Bocksdorn (Ger.), Daun Koki (Indones.), Gou Qi (Chin.), Kaukichai (Malays.), Kuko (Jap.), Lyciet de Chine (Fr.), Spina Santa Cinese (Ital.), Wolfberry — Root — Bark — 2,610 ppm. EM

Asarum heterotropoides MAEK. — Asian Wild Ginger — Root — 2,600 ppm. M

Asarum sieboldii (MIQ.) MAEK. — Siebold's Wild Ginger — Root — 2,600 ppm. M

Pisum sativum L. — Pea — Fruit — 2,591 ppm. E

Nardostachys chinensis BATALIN — Chinese Spikenard — Rhizome — 2,590 ppm. M

Blechnum orientale L. — Kuan Chung, Shield Fern — Rhizome — 2,580 ppm. TEM

Rheum palmatum L. — Chinese Rhubarb — Rhizome — 2,560 ppm. E

Vigna radata (L.) WILCZEK — Green Gram, Mungbean — Sprout Seedling — 2,560 ppm. E

Spirulina pratensis — Spirulina — Plant — 2,550 ppm. E

Petasites japonicus (SIEBOLD & ZUCC.) MAXIM. — Butterbur — Plant — 2,545 ppm. T

Taraxacum officinale WEBER EX F. H. WIGG. — Dandelion — Leaf — 2,500 ppm. EM

Lophatherum gracile BROGN. — Dan Zhu Ye — Plant — 2,490 ppm. M

Rosmarinus officinalis L. — Rosemary — Plant — 2,483 ppm. EM

Eriobotrya japonica (THUNB.) LINDL. — Loquat — Leaf — 2,480 ppm. E

Brassica nigra (L.) W. D. J. KOCH — Black Mustard — Leaf — 2,471 ppm. E

Lagenaria siceraria (MOLINA) STANDLEY. — Calabash Gourd, White-Flowered Gourd — Fruit — 2,465 ppm. E

Morus alba L. — Sang-Pai-Pi, White Mulberry — Root — Bark — 2,450 ppm. EM

Coptis chinensis FRANCH. — Chinese Goldthread, Huang-Lian, Huang-Lien — Rhizome — 2,420 ppm. M

Coptis japonica (THUNB.) MAKINO — Huang-Lia, Huang-Lian, Huang-Lien, Japanese Goldthread — Rhizome — 2,420 ppm. M

Coptis spp.. — Generic Goldthread — Rhizome — 2,420 ppm. M

Annona muricata L. — Soursop — Fruit — 2,400 ppm. E

Chrysanthemum parthenium (L.) BERNH. — Feverfew — Plant — 2,400 ppm. M

Cichorium endivia L. — Endive, Escarole — Leaf — 2,400 ppm. E

Panax japonicus C.A.MEYER — Japanese Ginseng — Rhizome — 2,400 ppm. M

Humulus lupulus L. — Hops — Fruit — 2,380 ppm. TEM

Capsicum annuum L. — Bell Pepper, Cherry Pepper, Cone Pepper, Green Pepper, Paprika, Sweet Pepper — Fruit — 2,340 ppm. E

Lycopodium clavatum L. — Antler Herb, Clubmoss — Plant — 2,340 ppm. TM

Polygonum multiflorum THUNB. — Chinese Cornbind, Chinese Knotweed, Fleeceflower, Fo Ti, He Shou Wu — Root — 2,340 ppm. TEM

Ruscus aculeatus L. — Box-Holly, Butcher's Broom — Root — 2,340 ppm. EM

Magnesium, cont.

Piper nigrum L. — Black Pepper, Pepper, White Pepper — Fruit — 2,319 ppm. EM

Vitis vinifera L. — European Grape, Grape, Grapevine, Parra (Sp.), Vid (Sp.), Vigne Vinifere (Fr.), Weinrebe (Ger.), Wine Grape — Fruit — 2,310 ppm. EM

Hordeum vulgare L. — Barley, Barleygrass — Seed — 2,300 ppm. EM

Pinus edulis ENGELM — Pinyon Pine — Seed — 2,180-2,650 ppm. EM

Chrysanthemum coronarium L. — Garland Chrysanthemum — Bud — 2,285 ppm. M

Lygodium japonicum (THUNB.) SW. — Climbing Fern — Pollen or Spore — 2,270 ppm. M

Carthamus tinctorius L. — Safflower — Flower — 2,260 ppm. M

Vicia faba L. — Broadbean, Faba Bean, Habas — Seed — 2,260 ppm. E

Phaseolus vulgaris var. vulgaris — Black Bean, Dwarf Bean, Field Bean, Flageolet Bean, French Bean, Garden Bean, Green Bean, Haricot, Haricot Bean, Haricot Vert, Kidney Bean, Navy Bean, Pop Bean, Popping Bean, Snap Bean, String Bean, Wax Bean — Sprout Seedling — 2,258 ppm. E

Brassica oleracea var. botrytis L. — Cauliflower — Flower — 2,250 ppm. E

Hordeum vulgare L. — Barley, Barleygrass — Stem — 2,250 ppm. EM

Panicum maximum JACQ. — Guinea grass — Leaf — 0-4,500 ppm. M

Hibiscus sabdariffa L. — Acedera de Guinea (Sp.), Indian Sorrel, Jamaica Sorrel, Kharkadi, Malventee (Ger.), Red Sorrel, Rosa de Jamaica (Sp.), Rosella (Ger.), Roselle, Sereni (Sp.), Sorrel — Flower — 2,240 ppm. E

Brassica oleracea var. capitata L. — Cabbage, Red Cabbage, White Cabbage — Leaf — 2,228 ppm. E

Agathosma betulina (P. J. BERGIUS) PILLANS — Buchu, Honey Buchu, Mountain Buchu — Leaf — 2,210 ppm. M

Cynanchum atratum BUNGE — Bai-Wei, Pai-Wei — Root — 2,210 ppm. EM

Capsicum frutescens L. — Cayenne, Chili, Hot Pepper, Red Chili, Spur Pepper, Tabasco — Fruit — 2,203 ppm. E

Vigna radata (L.) WILCZEK — Green Gram, Mungbean — Seed — 2,203 ppm. E

Camellia sinensis (L.) KUNTZE — Tea — Leaf — 2,200 ppm. E

Lupinus albus L. — White Lupine — Seed — 2,200 ppm. TE

Oryza sativa L. — Rice — Plant — 2,200 ppm. E

Panax quinquefolius L. — American Ginseng, Ginseng — Plant — 2,200 ppm. M

Brassica oleracea var. acephala DC — Curly Kale, Kale, Kitchen Kale, Scotch Kale — Leaf — 2,190 ppm. E

Canavalia ensiformis (L.) DC. — Jack Bean — Seed — 2,190 ppm. E

Gardenia jasminoides J. ELLIS — Cape Jasmine, Gardenia, Jasmin, Shan-Chih-Tzu, Shan-Zhi-Zi, Zhi Zi — Fruit — 2,170 ppm. M

Physalis ixocarpa BROT. — Tomatillo — Fruit — 2,150 ppm. E

Magnolia denudata DESR. — Hsin-I, Xin-Yi — Flower — 2,120 ppm. EM

Magnolia fargesii CHENG — Hsin-I, Xin-Yi — Flower — 2,120 ppm. EM

Magnolia kobus DC. — Hsin-I, Xin-Yi — Flower — 2,120 ppm. EM

Tetrapanax papyrifera (HOOK.) K.KOCH — Rice Paper Tree, Tong-Cao, Tung-Tsao — Pith — 2,120 ppm. M

Arachis hypogaea L. — Groundnut, Peanut — Seed — 2,110 ppm. EM

Brassica oleracea var. gongylodes L. — Kohlrabi — Stem — 2,110 ppm. E

Ephedra sinica STAPF — Chinese Ephedra, Ma Huang — Plant — 2,110 ppm. M

Manihot esculenta CRANTZ — Cassava, Tapioca, Yuca — Root — 2,100 ppm. E

Pastinaca sativa L. — Parsnip — Root — 2,100 ppm. E

Pinus echinata MILLER — Shortleaf Pine — Shoot — 2,100 ppm. M

Xanthosoma sagittifolium (L.) SCHOTT — Malanga, Tannia, Yautia — Root — 2,100 ppm. E

Malpighia glabra L. — Acerola — Fruit — 2,095 ppm. EM

Rosa canina L. — Dog Rose, Dogbrier, Rose — Fruit — 2,090 ppm. EM

Eucommia ulmoides OLIV. — Du Zhong, Gutta-Percha Tree, Tu Chung — Bark — 2,080 ppm. M

Vigna mungo (L.) HEPPER — Black Gram — Seed — 2,076 ppm. E

Fraxinus rhynchophylla HANCE — Chinese Ash — Bark — 2,070 ppm. M

Nepeta cataria L. — Catnip — Plant — 2,070 ppm. M

Artemisia herba-alba ASSO. — Desert Wormwood — Plant — 2,060 ppm. M

Scrophularia buergeriana MIQ. — Hsuan-Shen, Yuan-Shen — Root — 2,060 ppm. M

Amphicarpaea bracteata (L.) FERNALD — Hog Peanut — Shoot — 0-4,100 ppm. EM

Turnera diffusa WILLD. EX SCHULT. — Damiana — Leaf — 2,040 ppm. M

Myristica fragrans HOUTT. — Mace, Muskatnussbaum (Ger.), Nutmeg, nogal moscado (Sp.), nuez moscada (Sp.) — Seed — 2,030 ppm. E

Brassica rapa var. rapa — Rapini, Seven-Top Turnip, Turnip — Root — 2,000 ppm. E

Sechium edule (JACQ.) SW. — Chayote — Fruit — 2,000 ppm. EM

Vicia faba L. — Broadbean, Faba Bean, Habas — Seed — 2,000 ppm. E

Daucus carota L. — Carrot — Root — 1,980 ppm. E

Rheum rhabarbarum L. — Rhubarb — Plant — 1,975 ppm. E

Catalpa ovata G. DON — Hsin-Pa-Pi, Kisasage — Fruit — 1,960 ppm. EM

Angelica laxiflora DIELS — Tu Huo — Root — 1,950 ppm. M

Panax ginseng C. A. MEYER — Chinese Ginseng, Ginseng, Korean Ginseng, Oriental Ginseng — Root — 1,950 ppm. M

Achillea millefolium L. — Milfoil, Yarrow — Plant — 1,920 ppm. M

Moringa oleifera LAM. — Ben Nut, Benzolive Tree, Drumstick Tree, Horseradish Tree, Jacinto (Sp.), Moringa, West Indian Ben — Fruit — 450-3,815 ppm. E

Valerianella locusta (L.) LATERRADE — Corn Salad, Lamb's Lettuce — Plant — 3,773-3,798 ppm. E

Bletilla striata (THUNB.) REICHB. f. — Bletilla, Chinese Ground Orchid, Dai Chi (Chin.), Hardy Orchid, Hyacinth Bletilla, Hyacinth Orchid, Shiran (Jap.) — Tuber — 1,890 ppm. M

Anacardium occidentale L. — Cashew — Seed — 1,886 ppm. E

Aristolochia debilis SIEB. & ZUCC. — Chinese Birthwort — Fruit — 1,880 ppm. TEM

Sophora subprostrata CHUN & CHEN — Shan Dou Gen — Root — 1,880 ppm. TM

Pimpinella anisum L. — Anise, Sweet Cumin — Fruit — 1,878 ppm. EM

Rubus chamaemorus L. — Cloudberry — Fruit — 1,875 ppm. EM

Rubia cordifolia L. — Madder — Root — 1,870 ppm. M

Astragalus membranaceus (FISCH. EX LINK) BUNGE — Huang Qi, Huang-Chi — Root — 1,860 ppm. M

Echinacea spp.. — Coneflower, Echinacea — Root — 1,860 ppm. M

Physalis peruviana L. — Cape Gooseberry, Ground Cherry — Fruit — 1,810 ppm. E

Helianthus tuberosus L. — Jerusalem Artichoke — Tuber — 1,800 ppm. E

Juglans nigra L. — Black Walnut — Seed — 1,794 ppm. E

Zea mays L. — Corn — Silk Stigma — Style — 1,790 ppm. E

Phaseolus coccineus L. — Scarlet Runner Bean — Seed — 1,780 ppm. E

Actinidia chinensis PLANCHON — Kiwi — Fruit — 1,770 ppm.

Cnicus benedictus L. — Blessed Thistle — Plant — 1,770 ppm. M

Alocasia macrorrhiza (L.) G. DON — Giant Taro — Root — 1,750 ppm. E

Prunus armeniaca L. — Apricot — Seed — 1,750 ppm. TEM

Alisma plantago-aquatica L. — Mud Plantain, Tse-Hsieh, Water Plantain, Ze-Xie — Rhizome — 1,740 ppm. M

Cimicifuga racemosa (L.) NUTT. — Black Cohosh, Black Snakeroot — Root — 1,740 ppm. M

Persea americana MILLER — Avocado — Fruit — 1,740 ppm. E

Magnesium, cont.

Citrus aurantium L. — Bitter Orange, Petit-grain — Fruit — 1,730 ppm. E

Larrea tridentata (SESSE & MOC. ex DC.) COV. — Chaparral, Creosote Bush — Plant — 1,720 ppm. M

Ribes nigrum L. — Black Currant — Fruit — 1,720 ppm. E

Pisum sativum L. — Pea — Seed — 1,700 ppm. E

Symphytum officinale L. — Comfrey — Root — 1,700 ppm. TM

Armoracia rusticana GAERTN. ET AL. — Horseradish — Root — 1,690 ppm. E

Cinnamomum aromaticum NEES — Canela de la China (Sp.), Canelero chino (Sp.), Canelle de Cochinchine (Fr.), Cannelier Casse (Fr.), Cannelier de Chine (Fr.), Cassia, Cassia Bark, Cassia Lignea, China Junk Cassia, Chinazimt (Ger.), Chinese Cassia, Chinese Cinnamon, Chinesischer Zimtbaum (Ger.), Kashia-Keihi (Jap.), Saigon Cinnamon, Zimtcassie (Ger.) — Bark — 1,680 ppm. TEM

Hordeum vulgare L. — Barley, Barleygrass — Sprout Seedling — 1,670 ppm. EM

Smilax spp.. — Sarsaparilla — Root — 1,670 ppm. EM

Geranium thunbergii SIEB. & ZUCC — Gennoshiouko, Oriental Geranium — Plant — 1,660 ppm. EM

Glehnia littoralis F. SCHMIDT & MIQUEL — Bei Sha Shen — Root — 1,650 ppm. EM

Pistacia vera L. — Pistachio — Seed — 1,644 ppm. E

Brassica oleracea var. gemmifera DC — Brussel-Sprout, Brussels-Sprouts — Leaf — 1,642 ppm. E

Apium graveolens L. — Celery — Root — 1,635 ppm. E

Dioscorea sp. — Wild Yam — Root — 1,630 ppm. E

Myristica fragrans HOUTT. — Mace, Muskatnussbaum (Ger.), Nutmeg, nogal moscado (Sp.), nuez moscada (Sp.) — Aril — 1,630 ppm. E

Hydrangea arborescens L. — Hydrangea, Smooth Hydrangea — Root — 1,620 ppm. EM

Lobelia inflata L. — Indian Tobacco, Lobelia — Leaf — 1,620 ppm. TM

Valerianella radata — Plant — 2,940-3,226 ppm. E

Eupatorium odoratum L. — Christmas bush — Leaf — 0-3,200 ppm. M

Zea mays L. — Corn — Seed — 1,600 ppm. E

Frangula purshiana (DC.) J. G. COOPER — Cascara Buckthorn, Cascara Sagrada — Bark — 1,590 ppm. M

Taraxacum officinale WEBER EX F. H. WIGG. — Dandelion — Root — 1,570 ppm. EM

Solanum melongena L. — Aubergine, Egg-plant — Fruit — 1,563 ppm. E

Fragaria spp.. — Strawberry — Fruit — 1,545 ppm. E

Castanea mollisima BLUME — Chinese Chestnut — Seed — 1,531 ppm. EM

Platycodon grandiflorum (JACQ.) A.DC. — Balloon Flower, Chieh-Keng, Jie-Geng — Root — 1,510 ppm. TEM

Citrullus lanatus (THUNB.) MATSUM. & NAKAI — Watermelon — Fruit — 1,500 ppm. E

Cyperus rotundus L. — Nutsedge — Rhizome — 1,500 ppm. EM

Genipa americana L. — Genipap, Jagua — Seed — 1,500 ppm. EM

Coix lacryma-jobi L. — Adlay, Adlay Millet, Job's Tears, Yi-Yi-Ren — Seed — 1,490 ppm. EM

Pimenta dioica (L.) MERR. — Allspice, Clover-Pepper, Jamaica-Pepper, Pimenta, Pimento — Fruit — 1,480 ppm. E

Pachyrhizus erosus RICH. ex DC. — Yam-bean, Jicama — Tuber — 1,475 ppm. E

Vigna angularis (WILLD.) OHWI & H. OHASHI — Adzuki Bean — Seed — 1,467 ppm. E

Musa x paradisiaca L. — Banana, Plantain — Fruit — 1,465 ppm. E

Lantana camara L. — Lantana, Wild Sage — Fruit — 1,460 ppm. M

Cimicifuga dahurica (TURCZ. EX FISCH. & C. A. MEY.) MAXIM. — Sheng Ma — Rhizome — 1,450 ppm. M

Berberis vulgaris L. — Barberry — Root — 1,430 ppm. M

Cucurbita pepo L. — Pumpkin — Fruit — 1,429 ppm. E

Opuntia ficus-indica (L.) MILL. — Indian Fig, Nopal, Nopalito, Prickly Pear — Bud — 1,420 ppm. EM

Citrus reticulata BLANCO — Mandarin, Tangerine — Fruit — 1,416 ppm. E

Simmondsia chinensis (LINK) C. SCHNEID. — Jojoba — Seed — 1,410 ppm.

Castanea dentata (MARSHALL) BORKH. — American Chestnut — Seed — 1,406 ppm. EM

Anthriscus cerefolium (L.) HOFFM. — Chervil — Leaf — 1,400 ppm. E

Psoralea esculenta PURSH. — Breadroot, Indian Bread-Root, Indian Turnip, Prairie Apple, Prairie Potato, Prairie Turnip — Root — 1,400 ppm. TEM

Artocarpus heterophyllus LAM. — Jackfruit — Fruit — 1,380 ppm. E

Citrus paradisi MacFAD. — Grapefruit — Fruit — 1,360 ppm. E

Colocasia esculenta (L.) SCHOTT — Taro — Root — 1,350 ppm. E

Cicer arietinum L. — Chickpea, Garbanzo — Seed — 1,348 ppm. E

Tamarindus indica L. — Indian Tamarind, Kilytree, Tamarind — Fruit — 1,341 ppm. M

Lens culinaris MEDIK. — Lentil — Sprout Seedling — 1,323 ppm. E

Juglans regia L. — English Walnut — Seed — 1,310 ppm. E

Caulophyllum thalictroides (L.) MICHX. — Blue Cohosh — Root — 1,300 ppm. M

Lens culinaris MEDIK. — Lentil — Seed — 1,280 ppm. E

Allium cepa L. — Onion, Shallot — Bulb — 1,230 ppm. E

Cyrtosperma chamissonis (SCHOTT) MERR. — Swamp Taro — Root — 1,215 ppm. E

Nelumbo nucifera L. — Water Lotus — Rhizome — 1,215 ppm. EM

Allium sativum var. sativum L. — Garlic — Bulb — 1,210 ppm. E

Arctostaphylos uva-ursi (L.) SPRENGEL — Bearberry, Uva Ursi — Leaf — 1,210 ppm. M

Anemarrhena asphodeloides BUNGE — Chih-Mu, Zhi-Mu — Rhizome — 1,200 ppm. M

Morinda sp — Morinda — Root — 1,200 ppm. M

Spondias dulcis FORST. — Ambarella — Seed — 1,200 ppm. E

Macadamia spp.. — Macadamia — Seed — 1,190 ppm. E

Rehmannia glutinosa (GAERTN.) LIBOSCH. — Chinese Foxglove — Root — 1,190 ppm. M

Sorbus aucuparia L. — Rowan Berry, Mountain Ash — Fruit — 1,190 ppm. TEM

Paeonia suffruticosa ANDREWS — Moutan, Moutan Peony, Tree Peony — Root — Bark — 1,180 ppm. M

Forsythia suspensa VAHL — Lian-Jiao, Lien-Chiao — Fruit — 1,160 ppm. M

Gentiana scabra BUNGE — Japanese Gentian — Root — 1,150 ppm. M

Scutellaria lateriflora L. — Mad-Dog, Skullcap, Scullcap — Plant — 1,130 ppm. M

Murraya sp. — Curry Leaf — Fruit — 1,118 ppm. EM

Pyrus communis L. — Pear — Fruit — 1,110 ppm. E

Acorus calamus L. — Calamus, Flagroot, Myrtle Flag, Sweet Calamus, Sweetflag, Sweetroot — Rhizome — 1,100 ppm. M

Cichorium intybus L. — Chicory, Succory, Witloof — Root — 1,100 ppm. E

Albizia julibrissin DURAZZ. — Mimosa — Bark — 1,090 ppm. EM

Cypripedium pubescens WILLD. — Yellow Ladyslipper — Root — 1,090 ppm. M

Tussilago farfara L. — Coltsfoot — Flower — 1,080 ppm. TM

Ananas comosus (L.) MERR. — Pineapple — Fruit — 1,075 ppm. E

Citrus sinensis (L.) OSBECK — Orange — Fruit — 1,075 ppm. E

Syzygium cumini SKEELS — Aceituna Dulce, Jambolan, Java Plum — Fruit — 350-2,145 ppm. E

Lycium chinense MILL. — Chinese Boxthorn, Chinese Matrimony Vine, Chinese Wolfberry, Chinesischer Bocksdorn (Ger.), Daun Koki (Indones.), Gou Qi (Chin.), Kaukichai (Malays.), Kuko (Jap.), Lyciet de Chine (Fr.), Spina Santa Cinese (Ital.), Wolfberry — Fruit — 1,060 ppm. EM

Carica papaya L. — Papaya — Fruit — 1,058 ppm. EM

Annona cherimola MILL. — Cherimoya — Seed — 1,045 ppm. E

Magnesium, cont.

Quisqualis indica L. — Rangoon Creeper — Fruit — 1,040 ppm. TE

Ligustrum japonicum THUNB. — Japanese Privet, Ligustri Fructus — Fruit — 1,020 ppm. M

Ligustrum lucidum W. T. AITON — Chinese Privet, Glossy Privet, Ligustri Fructus, Privet, White Waxtree — Fruit — 1,020 ppm. M

Equisetum hyemale L. — Horsetail, Scouring Rush — Plant — 1,010 ppm. M

Annona cherimola MILL. — Cherimoya — Fruit — 1,000 ppm. E

Artemisia capillaris THUNB. — Capillary Wormwood — Plant — 1,000 ppm. M

Tragopogon porrifolius L. — Salsify — Root — 1,000 ppm. E

Chaenomeles lagenaria KOIDZ. — Chinese Quince, Mu-Kua — Fruit — 990 ppm. E

Paeonia lactiflora PALL. — Bai Shao (Chinese), Chih-Shao, Common Garden Peony, Peony, White Peony — Root — 990 ppm. M

Carya illinoensis (WANGENH.) K. KOCH — Pecan — Seed — 980 ppm. E

Artocarpus altilis (PARKINS.) FOSBERG — Breadfruit — Fruit — 975 ppm. E

Belamcanda chinensis (L.) DC. — Blackberry Lily, Iris Tigre (Fr.), Leopard Lily, Leopardenblume (Ger.), Maravilla (Sp.), Mariposa (Sp.), Shenan — Rhizome — 970 ppm. M

Atractylodes ovata DC. — Bai-Zhu, Pai-Chu — Rhizome — 960 ppm. M

Polygala tenuifolia WILLD. — Chinese Senega — Root — 960 ppm. M

Citrus medica L. — Citron — Fruit — 950 ppm. E

Crataegus laevigata (POIR.) DC — English Hawthorn, Hawthorn, Whitethorn, Woodland Hawthorn — Fruit — 940 ppm. M

Ribes uva-crispa L. — Gooseberry — Fruit — 938 ppm. E

Ribes rubrum L. — Red Currant, White Currant — Fruit — 935 ppm. E

Aloe vera (L.) BURM. f. — Aloe, Bitter Aloes — Leaf — 930 ppm. EM

Juniperus communis L. — Common Juniper, Juniper — Fruit — 930 ppm. TEM

Juncus effusus L. — Rush — Pith — 920 ppm. TEM

Carya ovata (MILL.) K. KOCH — Shagbark Hickory — Seed — 900 ppm. E

Polygonum multiflorum THUNB. — Chinese Cornbind, Chinese Knotweed, Fleeceflower, Fo Ti, He Shou Wu — Rhizome — 890 ppm. TEM

Psidium cattleianum SABINE — Strawberry Guava — Fruit — 880 ppm. E

Mangifera indica L. — Mango — Fruit — 875 ppm. EM

Ficus carica L. — Echte Feige (Ger.), Feigenbaum (Ger.), Fico (Ital.), Fig, Figueira (Port.), Figuier Commun (Fr.), Higo (Sp.), Higuera Comun (Sp.) — Fruit — 872 ppm. E

Secale cereale L. — Rye — Seed — 1,185-1,740 ppm. E

Cnidium officinale MAKINO — Jih-Chiung — Rhizome — 850 ppm. EM

Prunus persica (L.) BATSCH — Peach — Fruit — 850 ppm. TEM

Pueraria montana var. lobata (WILLD.) MAESEN & S. M. ALMEIDA — Kudsu, Kudzu — Shoot — 850 ppm. EM

Akebia quinata (THUNB.) DECNE — Chocolate Vine — Stem — 840 ppm. M

Cornus officinalis SIEB. & ZUCC. — Chinese Dogwood — Fruit — 830 ppm. EM

Dioscorea alata L. — Greater Yam, Winged Yam — Root — 827 ppm. E

Cistanche salsa (C.A.MEYER) G. BECK — Broomrape, Cistanchis Herba, Jou Tsung Jung — Plant — 810 ppm. M

Tabebuia heptaphylla (VELL.) TOLEDO — Pau D'Arco — Bark — 810 ppm. M

Dioscorea pentaphylla L. — Mountain Yam — Root — 792 ppm. E

Atractylodes lancea DC. — Cang Zhu — Rhizome — 790 ppm. M

Opuntia ficus-indica (L.) MILL. — Indian Fig, Nopal, Nopalito, Prickly Pear — Seed — 790 ppm. EM

Phoenix dactylifera L. — Date Palm — Fruit — 790 ppm. E

Annona squamosa L. — Sugar-Apple, Sweetsop — Fruit — 785 ppm. E

Cocos nucifera L. — Coconut, Coconut Palm, Cocotero (Sp.), Copra, Kokospalme (Ger.), Nariyal — Seed — 770 ppm. E

Crataegus cuneata SIEB. & ZUCC. — Hawthorn — Fruit — 760 ppm. M

Phytelephas aequatorialis SPRUCE — Equatorial Ivory Palm — Flower — 440-1,505 ppm. EM

Psidium guajava L. — Guava — Fruit — 735 ppm. E

Ipomoea batatas (L.) LAM — Sweet Potato — Root — 710 ppm. E

Pinellia ternata BREITENBACH — Ban-Xia, Pan-Hsia — Tuber — 710 ppm. TEM

Tamarindus indica L. — Indian Tamarind, Kilytree, Tamarind — Leaf — 710 ppm. M

Castanea sativa MILLER — European Chestnut — Seed — 704 ppm. EM

Vaccinium myrtillus L. — Bilberry, Dwarf Bilberry, Whortleberry — Fruit — 700 ppm. E

Magnolia officinalis REHDER & E. H. WILSON — Chinese Magnolia, Hou Pu, Magnolia-Bark — Bark — 690 ppm. EM

Vaccinium macrocarpon AITON — American Cranberry, Cranberry, Large Cranberry — Fruit — 690 ppm. E

Eriocaulon sp — Oriental Pipewort — Leaf — 670 ppm. M

Phellodendron amurense RUPR. — Amur Cork Tree, Huang Bai, Huang Po, Po Mu — Bark — 650 ppm. M

Prunus cerasus L. — Sour Cherry — Fruit — 648 ppm. TEM

Annona reticulata L. — Custard Apple — Fruit — 630 ppm. E

Ipomoca batatas (L.) LAM — Sweet Potato — Leaf — 620 ppm. E

Zizyphus jujuba MILL. — Da-Zao, Jujube, Ta-Tsao — Fruit — 620 ppm. EM

Prunus armeniaca L. — Apricot — Fruit — 615 ppm. TEM

Ginkgo biloba L. — Ginkgo, Maidenhair Tree — Seed — 602 ppm. TEM

Averrhoa carambola L. — Carambola, Star — Fruit — Fruit — 80-1,200 ppm. E

Vaccinium vitis-idaea var. minus LODD. — Cowberry, Lingen, Lingonberry — Fruit — 600 ppm. E

Gastrodia elata BLUME — Tian Ma — Rhizome — 590 ppm.

Phyllanthus emblica L. — Emblic, Myrobalan — Fruit — 584 ppm. E

Ulmus rubra MUHLENB. — Red Elm, Slippery Elm — Bark — 580 ppm. M

Dendrobium nobile LINDL. — Noble Dendrobium — Stem — 520 ppm. M

Plantago psyllium L. — Psyllium — Seed — 510 ppm. EM

Yucca baccata TORR. — Banana Yucca, Blue Yucca, Spanish Bayonet, Yucca — Root — 510 ppm. TEM

Elaeagnus angustifolia — Russian Olive — Fruit — 170-1,010 ppm. EM

Phytelephas aequatorialis SPRUCE — Equatorial Ivory Palm — Mesocarp — 320-1,005 ppm. EM

Areca catechu L. — Betel Nut, Pin-Lang — Seed — 500 ppm. EM

Perideridia gairdneri (HOOK. & ARN.) MATHIAS — Squawroot — Root — 500 ppm. EM

Quercus rubra L. — Northern Red Oak — Seed — 500 ppm. EM

Aconitum carmichaelii DEBX. — Aconite, Fu-Tsu — Tuber — 490 ppm. TM

Myrica cerifera L. — Bayberry, Candle-Berry, Southern Bayberry, Wax Myrtle — Bark — 490 ppm. EM

Manganese

Quercus alba L. — White Oak — Stem — 3,800 ppm. EM

Carya glabra (MILLER) SWEET — Pignut Hickory — Shoot — 3,300 ppm. E

Quercus rubra L. — Northern Red Oak — Stem — 3,300 ppm. EM

Nyssa sylvatica MARSHALL — Black Gum, Black Tupelo — Leaf — 2,730 ppm. EM

Carya ovata (MILL.) K. KOCH — Shagbark Hickory — Shoot — 2,700 ppm. E

Juniperus virginiana L. — Red Cedar — Shoot — 2,640 ppm. TEM

Symphoricarpos orbiculatus MOENCH. — Buckbush — Stem — 2,640 ppm. TM

Vaccinium myrtillus L. — Bilberry, Dwarf Bilberry, Whortleberry — Leaf — 2,500 ppm. E

Vaccinium vitis-idaea var. minus LODD. — Cowberry, Lingen, Lingonberry — Leaf — 2,500 ppm. E

Liquidambar styraciflua L. — American Styrax, Sweetgum — Stem — 2,460 ppm. Em

Quercus velutina LAM. — Black Oak — Stem — 1,984 ppm. EM

Quercus stellata WANGENH. — Post Oak — Stem — 1,680 ppm. EM

Diospyros virginiana L. — American Persimmon — Leaf — 1,500 ppm. EM

Nyssa sylvatica MARSHALL — Black Gum, Black Tupelo — Stem — 1,320 ppm. EM

Pinus echinata MILLER — Shortleaf Pine — Shoot — 1,260 ppm. M

Camellia sinensis (L.) KUNTZE — Tea — Leaf — 1,200 ppm. E

Syzygium aromaticum (L.) MERR. & L. M. PERRY — Clove, Clovetree — Flower — 1,200 ppm. E

Diospyros virginiana L. — American Persimmon — Stem — 1,080 ppm. EM

Sassafras albidum (NUTT.) NEES — Sassafras — Leaf — 1,020 ppm. TEM

Vitis vinifera L. — European Grape, Grape, Grapevine, Parra (Sp.), Vid (Sp.), Vigne Vinifere (Fr.), Weinrebe (Ger.), Wine Grape — Stem — 986 ppm. EM

Rhus copallina L. — Dwarf Sumac, Winged Sumac — Stem — 915 ppm. EM

Jussiaea repens L. — Jussiaeae Herba, Pond Dragon — Plant — 799 ppm. M

Foeniculum vulgare MILLER — Fennel — Fruit — 721 ppm. M

Sassafras albidum (NUTT.) NEES — Sassafras — Stem — 680 ppm. TEM

Agathosma betulina (P. J. BERGIUS) PILLANS — Buchu, Honey Buchu, Mountain Buchu — Leaf — 675 ppm. M

Cinnamomum aromaticum NEES — Canela de la China (Sp.), Canelero chino (Sp.), Canelle de Cochinchine (Fr.), Cannelier Casse (Fr.), Cannelier de Chine (Fr.), Cassia, Cassia Bark, Cassia Lignea, China Junk Cassia, Chinazimt (Ger.), Chinese Cassia, Chinese Cinnamon, Chinesischer Zimtbaum (Ger.), Kashia-Keihi (Jap.), Saigon Cinnamon, Zimtcassie (Ger.) — Bark — 600 ppm. TEM

Amomum xanthioides WALL. — Bastard Cardamom, Chin Kousha, Malabar Cardamom, Tavoy Cardamom — Seed — 565 ppm. E

Morinda sp — Morinda — Root — 520 ppm. M

Spinacia oleracea L. — Spinach — Plant — 485 ppm. E

Rhus copallina L. — Dwarf Sumac, Winged Sumac — Leaf — 480 ppm. EM

Alisma plantago-aquatica L. — Mud Plantain, Tse-Hsieh, Water Plantain, Ze-Xie — Rhizome — 479 ppm. M

Trifolium pratense L. — Cowgrass, Peavine Clover, Purple Clover, Red Clover — Hay — 464 ppm. EM

Lophatherum gracile BROGN. — Dan Zhu Ye — Plant — 445 ppm. M

Anethum graveolens L. — Dill, Garden Dill — Plant — 435 ppm. E

Lantana camara L. — Lantana, Wild Sage — Shoot — 412 ppm. M

Coptis chinensis FRANCH. — Chinese Goldthread, Huang-Lian, Huang-Lien — Rhizome — 398 ppm. M

Coptis japonica (THUNB.) MAKINO — Huang-Lia, Huang-Lian, Huang-Lien, Japanese Goldthread — Rhizome — 398 ppm. M

Coptis spp.. — Generic Goldthread — Rhizome — 398 ppm. M

Petroselinum crispum (MILLER) NYMAN EX A. W. HILLL — Parsley — Plant — 375 ppm. E

Nepeta cataria L. — Catnip — Plant — 374 ppm. M

Vaccinium myrtillus L. — Bilberry, Dwarf Bilberry, Whortleberry — Fruit — 370 ppm. E

Cinnamomum sieboldii — Japanese Cinnamon — Bark — 360 ppm. TEM

Zingiber officinale ROSCOE — Ginger — Rhizome — 350 ppm. EM

Cynanchum atratum BUNGE — Bai-Wei, Pai-Wei — Root — 341 ppm. EM

Polygonum cuspidatum SIEBOLD & ZUCC. — Giant Knotweed, Hu-Zhang, Japanese Knotweed, Mexican Bamboo — Plant — 330 ppm. TEM

Akebia quinata (THUNB.) DECNE — Chocolate Vine — Stem — 310 ppm. M

Acorus calamus L. — Calamus, Flagroot, Myrtle Flag, Sweet Calamus, Sweetflag, Sweetroot — Rhizome — 309 ppm. M

Rhizophora mangle L. — Red Mangrove — Leaf — 300 ppm. M

Rubus chingii HU — Chinese Raspberry — Fruit — 287 ppm. EM

Crocus sativus L. — Saffron — Silk Stigma — Style — 284 ppm.

Elettaria cardamomum (L.) MATON — Cardamom — Fruit — 280 ppm. EM

Centella asiatica (L.) URBAN — Gotu Kola, Pennywort — Leaf — 277 ppm. EM

Annona squamosa L. — Sugar-Apple, Sweetsop — Leaf — 253 ppm. E

Quercus alba L. — White Oak — Bark — 253 ppm. EM

Vaccinium vitis-idaea var. minus LODD. — Cowberry, Lingen, Lingonberry — Fruit — 250 ppm. E

Asarum heterotropoides MAEK. — Asian Wild Ginger — Root — 248 ppm. M

Asarum sieboldii (MIQ.) MAEK. — Siebold's Wild Ginger — Root — 248 ppm. M

Lactuca sativa L. — Lettuce — Leaf — 240 ppm. E

Caulophyllum thalictroides (L.) MICHX. — Blue Cohosh — Root — 237 ppm. M

Siegesbeckia orientalis L. — Hsi Chien, Saint Paul's Wort — Plant — 231 ppm. M

Helianthus tuberosus L. — Jerusalem Artichoke — Tuber — 228 ppm. E

Eriobotrya japonica (THUNB.) LINDL. — Loquat — Leaf — 224 ppm. E

Cinnamomum sieboldii — Japanese Cinnamon Root — Bark — 220 ppm. TEM

Ananas comosus (L.) MERR. — Pineapple — Fruit — 209 ppm. E

Cypripedium pubescens WILLD. — Yellow Ladyslipper — Root — 209 ppm. M

Avena sativa L. — Oats — Seed — 204 ppm. EM

Vaccinium macrocarpon AITON — American Cranberry, Cranberry, Large Cranberry — Fruit — 200 ppm. E

Lygodium japonicum (THUNB.) SW. — Climbing Fern — Pollen or Spore — 191 ppm. M

Elytrigia repens (L.) DESV. EX NEVSKI — Couchgrass, Doggrass, Quackgrass, Twitchgrass, Wheatgrass — Plant — 188 ppm. EM

Hydrangea arborescens L. — Hydrangea, Smooth Hydrangea — Root — 187 ppm. EM

Isatis tinctoria L. — Dyer's Woad — Root — 181 ppm. M

Panax ginseng C. A. MEYER — Chinese Ginseng, Ginseng, Korean Ginseng, Oriental Ginseng — Root — 180 ppm. M

Perilla frutescens (L.) BRITTON — Perilla — Plant — 180 ppm. TEM

Taraxacum mongolicum HAND.-MAZZ. — Mongoloid Dandelion — Plant — 178 ppm. EM

Urtica dioica L. — European Nettle, Stinging Nettle — Leaf — 172 ppm. EM

Juncus effusus L. — Rush — Pith — 171 ppm. TEM

Artemisia vulgaris L. — Mugwort — Plant — 170 ppm. M

Cinnamomum burmannii (NEES) BLUME — Java Cinnamon, Padang Cassia — Bark — 170 ppm. TEM

Avena sativa L. — Oats — Plant — 168 ppm. EM

Oenothera biennis L. — Evening-Primrose — Seed — 168 ppm. EM

Hyoscyamus niger L. — Henbane — Seed — 166 ppm. T

Arctostaphylos uva-ursi (L.) SPRENGEL — Bearberry, Uva Ursi — Leaf — 165 ppm. M

Viscum album L. — European Mistletoe — Leaf — 159 ppm. TM

Panax quinquefolius L. — American Ginseng, Ginseng — Plant — 156 ppm. M

Stellaria media (L.) VILLARS — Chickweed, Common Chickweed — Plant — 153 ppm. E

Hibiscus sabdariffa L. — Acedera de Guinea (Sp.), Indian Sorrel, Jamaica Sorrel, Kharkadi, Malventee (Ger.), Red Sorrel, Rosa de Jamaica (Sp.), Rosella (Ger.), Roselle, Sereni (Sp.), Sorrel — Flower — 151 ppm. E

Phaseolus vulgaris var. vulgaris — Black Bean, Dwarf Bean, Field Bean, Flageolet Bean, French Bean, Garden Bean, Green Bean, Haricot, Haricot Bean, Haricot Vert, Kidney Bean, Navy Bean, Pop Bean, Popping Bean, Snap Bean, String Bean, Wax Bean — Fruit — 150 ppm. E

Manganese, cont.

Silybum marianum (L.) GAERTN. — Lady's Thistle, Milk Thistle — Plant — 147 ppm. M

Stevia rebaudiana (BERTONI) BERTONI — Ca-A-E, Stevia, Sweet Leaf of Paraguay — Leaf — 147 ppm. E

Rubus idaeus L. — Raspberry, Red Raspberry — Leaf — 146 ppm. EM

Rumex crispus L. — Curly Dock, Lengua De Vaca, Sour Dock, Yellow Dock — Root — 145 ppm. TEM

Nardostachys chinensis BATALIN — Chinese Spikenard — Rhizome — 141 ppm. M

Boehmeria nivea (L.) GAUDICH. — Ramie — Plant — 140 ppm. M

Cinnamomum verum J. PRESL — Ceylon Cinnamon, Cinnamon — Bark — 140 ppm. TEM

Atractylodes ovata DC. — Bai-Zhu, Pai-Chu — Rhizome — 139 ppm. M

Eucommia ulmoides OLIV. — Du Zhong, Gutta-Percha Tree, Tu Chung — Bark — 135 ppm. M

Rhus glabra L. — Smooth Sumac — Stem — 134 ppm. EM

Taraxacum officinale WEBER EX F. H. WIGG. — Dandelion — Plant — 130 ppm. EM

Euphrasia officinalis L. — Eyebright — Plant — 126 ppm. M

Fragaria spp.. — Strawberry — Fruit — 125 ppm. E

Nelumbo nucifera L. — Water Lotus — Seed — 125 ppm. EM

Rubus chamaemorus L. — Cloudberry — Fruit — 125 ppm. EM

Forsythia suspensa VAHL — Lian-Jiao, Lien-Chiao — Fruit — 120 ppm. M

Hordeum vulgare L. — Barley, Barleygrass — Seed — 120 ppm. EM

Houttuynia cordata THUNB. — Dokudami, Fishwort, Yu Xing Cao — Plant — 120 ppm. EM

Magnolia officinalis REHDER & E. H. WILSON — Chinese Magnolia, Hou Pu, Magnolia-Bark — Bark — 120 ppm. EM

Verbascum thapsus L. — Flannelleaf, Flannelplant, Great Mullein, Mullein, Velvetplant — Leaf — 120 ppm. M

Pulsatilla chinensis (BUNGE) REGEL — Chinese Anemone — Root — 119 ppm. M

Bupleurum chinense DC. — Chai-Hu — Root — 114 ppm. M

Asimina triloba (L.) DUNAL — Pawpaw — Fruit — 111 ppm. E

Angelica dahurica BENTH & HOOK. — Bai Zhi — Root — 110 ppm. M

Celosia cristata L. — Cockscomb — Flower — 109 ppm. M

Triticum aestivum L. — Wheat — Plant — 105 ppm. EM

Cymbopogon citratus (DC. ex NEES) STAPF — Lemongrass, West Indian Lemongrass — Plant — 104 ppm. EM

Cinnamomum verum J. PRESL — Ceylon Cinnamon, Cinnamon — Leaf — 101.6 ppm. TEM

Echinacea spp.. — Coneflower, Echinacea — Root — 101 ppm. M

Valerianella locusta (L.) LATERRADE — Corn Salad, Lamb's Lettuce — Plant — 179-201 ppm. E

Abelmoschus esculentus (L.) MOENCH — Okra — Fruit — 100 ppm. EM

Annona cherimola MILL. — Cherimoya — Seed — 100 ppm. E

Asparagus officinalis L. — Asparagus — Shoot — 100 ppm. E

Corylus avellana L. — Cobnut, English Filbert, European Filbert, European Hazel, Hazel — Seed — 100 ppm. E

Glechoma hederacea L. — Alehoof — Plant — 100 ppm. M

Lycopersicon esculentum MILLER — Tomato — Fruit — 100 ppm. TEM

Lycopodium clavatum L. — Antler Herb, Clubmoss — Plant — 100 ppm. TM

Petasites japonicus (SIEBOLD & ZUCC.) MAXIM. — Butterbur — Plant — 100 ppm. T

Phaseolus lunatus L. — Butter Bean, Lima Bean — Seed — 100 ppm. E

Cucumis sativus L. — Cucumber — Fruit — 98 ppm. E

Gentiana scabra BUNGE — Japanese Gentian — Root — 98 ppm. M

Eriocaulon sp — Oriental Pipewort — Leaf — 96 ppm. M

Prunella vulgaris L. — Heal-All, Self-Heal — Flower — 96 ppm.

Schisandra chinensis (TURCZ.) BAILL. — Chinese Magnolia Vine, Five-Flavor-Fruit, Magnolia Vine, Schizandra, Wu Wei Zi, Wu Wei Zu — Fruit — 96 ppm. M

Rubia cordifolia L. — Madder — Root — 94 ppm. M

Molybdenum

Carya glabra (MILLER) SWEET — Pignut Hickory — Shoot — 33 ppm. E

Phaseolus vulgaris var. vulgaris — Black Bean, Dwarf Bean, Field Bean, Flageolet Bean, French Bean, Garden Bean, Green Bean, Haricot, Haricot Bean, Haricot Vert, Kidney Bean, Navy Bean, Pop Bean, Popping Bean, Snap Bean, String Bean, Wax Bean — Fruit — 20 ppm. E

Carya ovata (MILL.) K. KOCH — Shagbark Hickory — Shoot — 18 ppm. E

Capsicum annuum L. — Bell Pepper, Cherry Pepper, Cone Pepper, Green Pepper, Paprika, Sweet Pepper — Fruit — 15 ppm. E

Phaseolus lunatus L. — Butter Bean, Lima Bean — Seed — 15 ppm. E

Panax quinquefolius L. — American Ginseng, Ginseng — Plant — 14 ppm. M

Petroselinum crispum (MILLER) NYMAN EX A. W. HILLL — Parsley — Plant — 14 ppm. E

Phaseolus vulgaris var. vulgaris — Black Bean, Dwarf Bean, Field Bean, Flageolet Bean, French Bean, Garden Bean, Green Bean, Haricot, Haricot Bean, Haricot Vert, Kidney Bean, Navy Bean, Pop Bean, Popping Bean, Snap Bean, String Bean, Wax Bean — Seed — 14 ppm. E

Quercus alba L. — White Oak — Stem — 9.12 ppm. EM

Brassica oleracea var. capitata L. — Cabbage, Red Cabbage, White Cabbage — Leaf — 8.7 ppm. E

Vigna unguiculata subsp. sesquipedalis (L.) VERDC. — Asparagus Bean, Pea Bean, Yardlong Bean — Seed — 8 ppm. E

Zea mays L. — Corn — Seed — 6.3 ppm. E

Quercus velutina LAM. — Black Oak — Stem — 6.2 ppm. EM

Lycopersicon esculentum MILLER — Tomato — Fruit — 6 ppm. TEM

Fagopyrum esculentum MOENCH. — Buckwheat — Seed — 5.5 ppm. E

Rhus glabra L. — Smooth Sumac — Stem — 4.69 ppm. EM

Quercus rubra L. — Northern Red Oak — Stem — 4.62 ppm. EM

Glycine max (L.) MERR. — Soybean — Seed — 4 ppm. E

Brassica oleracea var. botrytis L. — Cauliflower — Leaf — 3.76 ppm. E

Pisum sativum L. — Pea — Seed — 3 ppm. E

Cucumis sativus L. — Cucumber — Fruit — 2.8 ppm. E

Juniperus virginiana L. — Red Cedar — Shoot — 2.64 ppm. TEM

Allium cepa L. — Onion, Shallot — Bulb — 2.3 ppm. E

Solanum tuberosum L. — Potato — Tuber — 2.1 ppm. E

Lactuca sativa L. — Lettuce — Leaf — 2 ppm. E

Prunus serotina subsp. serotina — Black Cherry, Wild Cherry — Leaf — 1.9 ppm. TEM

Asparagus officinalis L. — Asparagus — Shoot — 1.8 ppm. E

Brassica oleracea var. botrytis L. — Cauliflower — Stem — 1.76 ppm. E

Prunus domestica L. — Plum — Fruit — 1.7 ppm. TEM

Cichorium endivia L. — Endive, Escarole — Leaf — 1.68 ppm. E

Brassica pekinensis (LOUR.) RUPR. — Chinese Cabbage — Leaf — 1.47 ppm. E

Nyssa sylvatica MARSHALL — Black Gum, Black Tupelo — Leaf — 1.4 ppm. EM

Tephrosia candida (ROXB.) DC. — White Tephrosia — Plant — 1.25 ppm. TM

Valerianella locusta (L.) LATERRADE — Corn Salad, Lamb's Lettuce — Plant — 2.35-2.41 ppm. E

Diospyros virginiana L. — American Persimmon — Stem — 1.08 ppm. EM

Prunus persica (L.) BATSCH — Peach — Fruit — 1.05 ppm. TEM

Brassica rapa var. rapa — Rapini, Seven-Top Turnip, Turnip — Root — 1 ppm. E

Nitrogen

Cucumis sativus L. — Cucumber — Fruit — 80,000 ppm. E

Tephrosia purpurea PERS. — Purple Tephrosia, Wild Indigo — Leaf — 72,500 ppm. TM

Brassica oleracea var. botrytis L. — Cauliflower — Leaf — 71,800 ppm. E

Acacia farnesiana (L.) WILLD. — Cassie, Huisache, Opopanax, Popinac, Sweet Acacia — Leaf — 68,800 ppm. M

Urtica dioica L. — European Nettle, Stinging Nettle — Leaf — 55,555 ppm. EM

Anethum graveolens L. — Dill, Garden Dill — Plant — 55,300 ppm. E

Lactuca sativa L. — Lettuce — Leaf — 54,000 ppm. E

Indigofera tinctoria L. — Common Indigo — Leaf — 51,100 ppm.

Pisum sativum L. — Pea — Seed — 50,000 ppm. E

Brassica oleracea var. botrytis L. — Cauliflower — Flower — 47,500 ppm. E

Spinacia oleracea L. — Spinach — Leaf — 45,700 ppm. E

Phaseolus vulgaris var. vulgaris — Black Bean, Dwarf Bean, Field Bean, Flageolet Bean, French Bean, Garden Bean, Green Bean, Haricot, Haricot Bean, Haricot Vert, Kidney Bean, Navy Bean, Pop Bean, Popping Bean, Snap Bean, String Bean, Wax Bean — Fruit — 41,000 ppm. E

Petroselinum crispum (MILLER) NYMAN EX A. W. HILLL — Parsley — Leaf — 40,700 ppm. E

Arachis hypogaea L. — Groundnut, Peanut — Seed — 40,000 ppm. EM

Nicotiana tabacum L. — Tobacco — Leaf — 40,000 ppm.

Raphanus sativus L. — Radish — Root — 38,570 ppm. E

Armoracia rusticana GAERTN. ET AL. — Horseradish — Root — 38,461 ppm. E

Brassica oleracea var. capitata L. — Cabbage, Red Cabbage, White Cabbage — Leaf — 37,500 ppm. E

Annona squamosa L. — Sugar-Apple, Sweetsop — Leaf — 36,000 ppm. E

Beta vulgaris subsp. vulgaris — Beet, Beetroot, Garden Beet, Sugar Beet — Root — 35,830 ppm. E

Bromelia pinguin L. — Wild Pineapple — Shoot — 35,800 ppm. TE

Momordica charantia L. — Bitter Melon, Sorosi — Fruit — 33,800 ppm. E

Melilotus indica LAM. — Small-Flowered Melilot — Plant — 33,600 ppm. TEM

Pastinaca sativa L. — Parsnip — Root — 33,160 ppm. E

Hibiscus sabdariffa L. — Acedera de Guinea (Sp.), Indian Sorrel, Jamaica Sorrel, Kharkadi, Malventee (Ger.), Red Sorrel, Rosa de Jamaica (Sp.), Rosella (Ger.), Roselle, Sereni (Sp.), Sorrel — Seed — 32,900 ppm. E

Senna obtusifolia (L.) H.IRWIN & BARNEBY — Sicklepod — Seed — 31,300 ppm. TE

Ilex paraguariensis ST. HIL. — Mate, Paraguay Tea, South American Holly — Leaf — 30,000 ppm. M

Corylus avellana L. — Cobnut, English Filbert, European Filbert, European Hazel, Hazel — Seed — 28,000 ppm. E

Eriobotrya japonica (THUNB.) LINDL. — Loquat — Seed — 26,000 ppm. E

Lycopersicon esculentum MILLER — Tomato — Leaf — 26,000 ppm. TEM

Bixa orellana L. — Achiote, Annato, Annatto, Annoto, Arnato, Bija, Lipstick Pod, Lipsticktree — Seed — 25,200 ppm. E

Brassica napus var. napobrassica var. napobrassica (L.) REICHB. — Rutabaga, Swede, Swedish Turnip — Root — 25,000 ppm. E

Pterocarpus marsupium ROXB. — Indian Kino, Malabar Kino, bijasal — Leaf — 25,000 ppm.

Zingiber officinale ROSCOE — Ginger — Rhizome — 24,440 ppm. EM

Crocus sativus L. — Saffron — Silk Stigma — Style — 24,300 ppm.

Tephrosia candida (ROXB.) DC. — White Tephrosia — Plant — 23,600 ppm. TM

Capsicum annuum L. — Bell Pepper, Cherry Pepper, Cone Pepper, Green Pepper, Paprika, Sweet Pepper — Fruit — 23,330 ppm. E

Lycopersicon esculentum MILLER — Tomato — Fruit — 23,330 ppm. TEM

Coffea arabica L. — Coffee — Seed — 23,000 ppm. EM

Theobroma cacao L. — Cacao, Chocolate — Seed — 22,800 ppm. E

Rheum rhabarbarum L. — Rhubarb — Plant — 22,000 ppm. E

Daucus carota L. — Carrot — Root — 20,000 ppm. E

Panax quinquefolius L. — American Ginseng, Ginseng — Plant — 20,000 ppm. M

Ribes rubrum L. — Red Currant, White Currant — Fruit — 20,000 ppm. E

Apium graveolens L. — Celery — Root — 19,090 ppm. E

Rubus chamaemorus L. — Cloudberry — Fruit — 18,125 ppm. EM

Brassica rapa var. rapa — Rapini, Seven-Top Turnip, Turnip — Root — 18,000 ppm. E

Spondias dulcis FORST. — Ambarella — Fruit — 17,900 ppm. E

Allium cepa L. — Onion, Shallot — Bulb — 17,690 ppm. E

Solanum tuberosum L. — Potato — Tuber — 17,000 ppm. E

Citrus paradisi MacFAD. — Grapefruit — Fruit — 16,360 ppm. E

Rauvolfia serpentina (L.) BENTH. ex KURZ — Indian Snakeroot, Serpentine Wood — Seed — 16,000 ppm.

Musa x paradisiaca L. — Banana, Plantain — Fruit — 15,000 ppm. E

Ribes uva-crispa L. — Gooseberry — Fruit — 15,000 ppm. E

Genipa americana L. — Genipap, Jagua — Fruit — 13,900 ppm. EM

Citrus sinensis (L.) OSBECK — Orange — Fruit — 13,845 ppm. E

Amphicarpaea bracteata (L.) FERNALD — Hog Peanut — Shoot — 0 26,500 ppm. EM

Citrus reticulata BLANCO — Mandarin, Tangerine — Fruit — 13,075 ppm. E

Prunus persica (L.) BATSCH — Peach — Fruit — 13,075 ppm. TEM

Ribes nigrum L. — Black Currant — Fruit — 12,775 ppm. E

Sorbus aucuparia L. — Rowan Berry, Mountain Ash — Fruit — 11,900 ppm. TEM

Genipa americana L. — Genipap, Jagua — Seed — 11,100 ppm. EM

Solanum melongena L. — Aubergine, Eggplant — Fruit — 10,250 ppm. E

Acrocomia totai MART. — Gru-Gru Nut, Mbocaya — Seed — 0-20,200 ppm. E

Fragaria spp.. — Strawberry — Fruit — 10,000 ppm. E

Prunus domestica L. — Plum — Fruit — 10,000 ppm. TEM

Malva parviflora L. — Cheeseweed — Plant — 9,400 ppm. EM

Rosa canina L. — Dog Rose, Dogbrier, Rose — Fruit — 9,000 ppm. EM

Lantana camara L. — Lantana, Wild Sage — Shoot — 8,800 ppm. M

Melilotus alba MEDIK. — White Melilot — Plant — 8,300 ppm. TEM

Vitis vinifera L. — European Grape, Grape, Grapevine, Parra (Sp.), Vid (Sp.), Vigne Vinifere (Fr.), Weinrebe (Ger.), Wine Grape — Fruit — 7,220 ppm. EM

Averrhoa carambola L. — Carambola, Star — Fruit — Fruit — 10,200-12,800 ppm. E

Spondias dulcis FORST. — Ambarella — Seed — 6,200 ppm. E

Phyllanthus emblica L. — Emblic, Myrobalan — Fruit — 5,445 ppm. E

Vaccinium macrocarpon AITON — American Cranberry, Cranberry, Large Cranberry — Fruit — 5,000 ppm. E

Cyphomandra betacea (CAV.) SENDT. — Tamarillo, Tree Tomato — Fruit — 4,450 ppm.

Persea schiedeana NEES. — Palta De Monte, Wild Avocado, Wild Pear — Fruit — 1,910-8,680 ppm. E

Prunus dulcis (MILLER) D. A. WEBB — Almond — Seed — 4,315 ppm. TEM

Malva neglecta WALLR. — Cheeses, Common Mallow — Plant — 4,200 ppm. EM

Malus domestica BORKH. — Apple — Fruit — 4,000 ppm. E

Acrocomia totai MART. — Gru-Gru Nut, Mbocaya — Fruit — 0-6,700 ppm. E

Malva sylvestris L. — High Mallow — Leaf — 3,300 ppm. EM

Hibiscus rosa-sinensis L. — Chinese hibiscus, Shoe-flower — Flower — 640-6,275 ppm. E

Pyrus communis L. — Pear — Fruit — 3,000 ppm. E

Annona muricata L. — Soursop — Fruit — 2,700 ppm. E

Annona cherimola MILL. — Cherimoya — Fruit — 2,270 ppm. E

Ananas comosus (L.) MERR. — Pineapple — Fruit — 1,150 ppm. E

Cocos nucifera L. — Coconut, Coconut Palm, Cocotero (Sp.), Copra, Kokospalme (Ger.), Nariyal — Hull Husk — 1,100 ppm. E

Spondias tuberosa ARRUDA — Imbu, Umbu — Fruit — 1,100 ppm. E

Passiflora edulis SIMS — Maracuya, Passionfruit — Plant — 960-1,920 ppm. E

Phosphorus

Beta vulgaris subsp. vulgaris — Beet, Beetroot, Garden Beet, Sugar Beet — Root — 45,580 ppm. E

Xanthosoma sagittifolium (L.) SCHOTT — Malanga, Tannia, Yautia — Leaf — 38,416 ppm. E

Chenopodium album L. — Lamb's Quarters — Leaf — 36,833 ppm. TEM

Momordica charantia L. — Bitter Melon, Sorosi — Leaf — 33,467 ppm. E

Physalis ixocarpa BROT. — Tomatillo — Fruit — 30,250 ppm. E

Linum usitatissimum L. — Flax, Linseed — Seed — 20,335 ppm. E

Luffa aegyptiaca MILLER — Luffa, Smooth Loofah, Vegetable Sponge — Seed — 18,300 ppm. E

Lepidium sativum L. — Garden Cress — Seed — 17,500 ppm. E

Equisetum arvense L. — Field Horsetail, Horsetail — Plant — 14,762 ppm. M

Citrullus lanatus (THUNB.) MATSUM. & NAKAI — Watermelon — Seed — 14,600 ppm. E

Luffa aegyptiaca MILLER — Luffa, Smooth Loofah, Vegetable Sponge — Leaf — 14,141 ppm. E

Sesamum indicum L. — Ajonjoli (Sp.), Beni, Benneseed, Sesame, Sesamo (Sp.) — Leaf — 14,000 ppm. EM

Lactuca sativa L. — Lettuce — Leaf — 13,920 ppm. E

Phaseolus vulgaris var. vulgaris — Black Bean, Dwarf Bean, Field Bean, Flageolet Bean, French Bean, Garden Bean, Green Bean, Haricot, Haricot Bean, Haricot Vert, Kidney Bean, Navy Bean, Pop Bean, Popping Bean, Snap Bean, String Bean, Wax Bean — Fruit — 13,500 ppm. E

Sclerocarya caffra SOND. — Marula — Seed — 12,985 ppm.

Cucurbita pepo L. — Pumpkin — Seed — 12,982 ppm. E

Cucumis sativus L. — Cucumber — Fruit — 12,600 ppm. E

Ipomoea aquatica FORSSKAL — Swamp Cabbage, Water Spinach — Leaf — 12,360 ppm. E

Nasturtium officinale R. BR. — Berro, Watercress — Herb — 12,000 ppm. E

Cannabis sativa L. — Hemp, Indian Hemp, Marihuana, Marijuana — Seed — 11,227 ppm. M

Phaseolus lunatus L. — Butter Bean, Lima Bean — Sprout Seedling — 10,611 ppm. E

Raphanus sativus L. — Radish — Fruit — 10,526 ppm. E

Asparagus officinalis L. — Asparagus — Shoot — 10,244 ppm. E

Avena sativa L. — Oats — Seed — 10,200 ppm. EM

Cucurbita pepo L. — Pumpkin — Flower — 10,100 ppm. E

Amaranthus sp. — Pigweed — Leaf — 10,082 ppm. EM

Crescentia alata L. — Jicaro — Seed — 10,020 ppm. M

Arachis hypogaea L. — Groundnut, Peanut — Plant — 10,000 ppm. EM

Terminalia catappa L. — Indian Almond, Malabar Almond, Tropical Almond — Seed — 9,835 ppm. M

Erythroxylum coca var. coca — Coca — Leaf — 9,740 ppm. EM

Elytrigia repens (L.) DESV. EX NEVSKI — Couchgrass, Doggrass, Quackgrass, Twitchgrass, Wheatgrass — Plant — 9,510 ppm. EM

Sinapis alba L. — White Mustard — Seed — 9,330 ppm. TEM

Papaver somniferum L. — Opium Poppy, Poppyseed Poppy — Seed — 9,277 ppm. E

Hordeum vulgare L. — Barley, Barleygrass — Seed — 9,200 ppm. EM

Brassica oleracea var. botrytis L. — Cauliflower — Leaf — 9,090 ppm. E

Phaseolus lunatus L. — Butter Bean, Lima Bean — Seed — 9,000 ppm. E

Sesamum indicum L. — Ajonjoli (Sp.), Beni, Benneseed, Sesame, Sesamo (Sp.) — Seed — 8,898 ppm. EM

Avena sativa L. — Oats — Plant — 8,800 ppm. EM

Phoenix dactylifera L. — Date Palm — Fruit — 8,795 ppm. E

Prunus dulcis (MILLER) D. A. WEBB — Almond — Seed — 8,735 ppm. TEM

Lycopersicon esculentum MILLER — Tomato — Fruit — 8,400 ppm. TEM

Momordica charantia L. — Bitter Melon, Sorosi — Fruit — 8,333 ppm. E

Amorphophallus campanulatus BLUME — Elephant-Foot Yam — Shoot — 8,100 ppm. TEM

Glycine max (L.) MERR. — Soybean — Seed — 8,040 ppm. E

Brassica chinensis L. — Bok-Choy, Celery Cabbage, Celery Mustard, Chinese Cabbage, Chinese Mustard, Chinese White Cabbage, Pak-Choi — Leaf — 7,907 ppm. E

Abelmoschus esculentus (L.) MOENCH — Okra — Seed — 7,900 ppm. EM

Apium graveolens L. — Celery — Root — 7,900 ppm. E

Portulaca oleracea L. — Purslane, Verdolaga — Plant — 7,740 ppm. E

Mentha x piperita subsp. nothosubsp. pipcrita — Peppermint — Leaf — 7,720 ppm. TEM

Anethum graveolens L. — Dill, Garden Dill — Plant — 7,625 ppm. E

Borago officinalis L. — Beebread, Beeplant, Borage, Talewort — Leaf — 7,579 ppm. TEM

Rumex crispus L. — Curly Dock, Lengua De Vaca, Sour Dock, Yellow Dock — Root — 7,570 ppm.
— Leaf — 7,568 ppm. TEM

Brassica pekinensis (LOUR.) RUPR. — Chinese Cabbage — Leaf — 7,560 ppm. E

Basella alba L. — Vinespinach — Leaf — 7,535 ppm. EM

Helianthus annuus L. — Girasol, Sunflower — Seed — 7,449 ppm. E

Limonia acidissima L. — Elephant Apple, Manzana De Elefante, Wood-Apple — Seed — 14,300-14,895 ppm. EM

Brassica oleracea var. botrytis L. — Cauliflower — Flower — 7,375 ppm. E

Pastinaca sativa L. — Parsnip — Root — 7,365 ppm. E

Glycine max (L.) MERR. — Soybean — Fruit — 7,305 ppm. E

Acacia tortilis (FORSSK.) HAYNE — Umbrella Thorn — Seed — 7,300 ppm. M

Capsella bursa-pastoris (L.) MEDICUS — Shepherd's Purse — Plant — 7,288 ppm. EM

Oenothera biennis L. — Evening-Primrose — Seed — 7,257 ppm. EM

Brassica napus var. napobrassica var. napobrassica (L.) REICHB. — Rutabaga, Swede, Swedish Turnip — Root — 7,250 ppm. E

Triticum aestivum L. — Wheat — Plant — 7,200 ppm. EM

Lepidium sativum L. — Garden Cress — Leaf — 7,170 ppm. E

Nelumbo nucifera L. — Water Lotus — Seed — 7,130 ppm. EM

Lupinus mutabilis SWEET — Andean Lupine, Chocho, Tarhui — Seed — 7,100 ppm. TE

Silybum marianum (L.) GAERTN. — Lady's Thistle, Milk Thistle — Plant — 7,060 ppm. M

Hordeum vulgare L. — Barley, Barleygrass — Plant — 6,900 ppm. EM

Apium graveolens L. — Celery — Plant — 6,849 ppm — Seed — 6,843 ppm. E

Triticum aestivum L. — Wheat — Seed — 6,800 ppm. EM

Urtica dioica L. — European Nettle, Stinging Nettle — Leaf — 6,800 ppm. EM

Agathosma betulina (P. J. BERGIUS) PILLANS — Buchu, Honey Buchu, Mountain Buchu — Leaf — 6,780 ppm. M

Corchorus olitorius L. — Jew's Mallow, Mulukiya, Nalta Jute — Leaf — 6,755 ppm. EM

Physalis angulata L. — Bolsa Mullaca, Winter Cherry — Fruit — 1,350-13,500 ppm. E

Vigna radata (L.) WILCZEK — Green Gram, Mungbean — Sprout Seedling — 6,560 ppm. E

Brassica oleracea var. capitata L. — Cabbage, Red Cabbage, White Cabbage — Leaf — 6,500 ppm. E

Bertholletia excelsa BONPL. — Brazilnut, Brazilnut-Tree, Creamnut, Paranut — Seed — 6,208 ppm. E

Hibiscus sabdariffa L. — Acedera de Guinea (Sp.), Indian Sorrel, Jamaica Sorrel, Kharkadi, Malventee (Ger.), Red Sorrel, Rosa de Jamaica (Sp.), Rosella (Ger.), Roselle, Sereni (Sp.), Sorrel — Leaf — 6,458 ppm. E

Coriandrum sativum L. — Chinese Parsley, Cilantro, Coriander — Leaf — 6,452 ppm. E

Allium schoenoprasum L. — Chives — Leaf — 6,437 ppm. E

Petroselinum crispum (MILLER) NYMAN EX A. W. HILLL — Parsley — Plant — 6,425 ppm. E

Luffa aegyptiaca MILLER — Luffa, Smooth Loofah, Vegetable Sponge — Fruit — 6,400 ppm. E

Pisum sativum L. — Pea — Plant — 6,400 ppm. E

Vigna unguiculata subsp. sesquipedalis (L.) VERDC. — Asparagus Bean, Pea Bean, Yardlong Bean — Seed — 6,375 ppm. E

Sechium edule (JACQ.) SW. — Chayote — Shoot — 6,350 ppm. EM

Ceiba pentandra (L.) GAERTN. — Kapok, Silk-Cotton Tree — Seed — 9,700-12,690 ppm. M

Carica papaya L. — Papaya — Leaf — 6,311 ppm. EM

Curcuma longa L. — Indian Saffron, Turmeric — Rhizome — 6,307 ppm. E

Carum carvi L. — Caraway, Carum, Comino (Sp.), Comino de prado (Sp.), Kummel (Ger.) — Fruit — 6,302 ppm. E

Abelmoschus esculentus (L.) MOENCH — Okra — Fruit — 6,300 ppm. EM

Anacardium occidentale L. — Cashew — Seed — 6,255 ppm. E

Pisum sativum L. — Pea — Seed — 6,250 ppm. E

Cynara cardunculus subsp. cardunculus — Artichoke — Flower — 6,240 ppm. E

Spinacia oleracea L. — Spinach — Plant — 6,232 ppm. E

Tropaeolum majus L. — Nasturtium — Shoot — 6,200 ppm. E

Lens culinaris MEDIK. — Lentil — Sprout Seedling — 6,165 ppm. E

Ipomoea batatas (L.) LAM — Sweet Potato — Leaf — 6,090 ppm. E

Vigna subterranea (L.) VERDC. — Bambarra Groundnut, Groundbean — Seed — 6,042 ppm. E

Acrocomia totai MART. — Gru-Gru Nut, Mbocaya — Fruit — 0-12,000 ppm. E

Hibiscus sabdariffa L. — Acedera de Guinea (Sp.), Indian Sorrel, Jamaica Sorrel, Kharkadi, Malventee (Ger.), Red Sorrel, Rosa de Jamaica (Sp.), Rosella (Ger.), Roselle, Sereni (Sp.), Sorrel — Seed — 6,000 ppm. E

Vetiveria zizanioides (L.) NASH — Cus-Cus, Cuscus Grass, Vetiver — Fruit — 6,000 ppm. E

Foeniculum vulgare MILLER — Fennel — Fruit — 5,960 ppm. M

Hordeum vulgare L. — Barley, Barleygrass — Stem — 5,950 ppm. EM

Beta vulgaris subsp. vulgaris — Beet, Beetroot, Garden Beet, Sugar Beet — Leaf — 5,946 ppm. E

Juglans nigra L. — Black Walnut — Seed — 5,882 ppm. E

Phaseolus vulgaris subsp. var. vulgaris — Black Bean, Dwarf Bean, Field Bean, Flageolet Bean, French Bean, Garden Bean, Green Bean, Haricot, Haricot Bean, Haricot Vert, Kidney Bean, Navy Bean, Pop Bean, Popping Bean, Snap Bean, String Bean, Wax Bean — Seed — 5,880 ppm. E

Lupinus mutabilis SWEET — Andean Lupine, Chocho, Tarhui — Fruit — 5,875 ppm. TE

Raphanus sativus L. — Radish — Root — 5,850 ppm. E

Solanum melongena L. — Aubergine, Eggplant — Fruit — 5,836 ppm. E

Colocasia esculenta (L.) SCHOTT — Taro — Leaf — 5,800 ppm. E

Cichorium endivia L. — Endive, Escarole — Leaf — 5,760 ppm. E

Cassia tora L. — Sickle Senna — Sprout Seedling — 5,700 ppm. M

Verbascum thapsus L. — Flannelleaf, Flannelplant, Great Mullein, Mullein, Velvetplant — Leaf — 5,700 ppm. M

Phaseolus vulgaris var. vulgaris — Black Bean, Dwarf Bean, Field Bean, Flageolet Bean, French Bean, Garden Bean, Green Bean, Haricot, Haricot Bean, Haricot Vert, Kidney Bean, Navy Bean, Pop Bean, Popping Bean, Snap Bean, String Bean, Wax Bean — Leaf — 5,682 ppm. E

Cuminum cyminum L. — Cumin — Fruit — 5,673 ppm. EM

Cyclanthera pedata (L.) SCHRADER — Achocha — Fruit — 5,615 ppm. EM

Oryza sativa L. — Rice — Seed — 5,588 ppm. E

Theobroma cacao L. — Cacao, Chocolate — Seed — 5,571 ppm. E

Cucurbita spp.. — Summer Squash — Fruit — 5,540 ppm. E

Allium cepa L. — Onion, Shallot — Leaf — 5,513 ppm. E

Lycopersicon esculentum MILLER — Tomato — Leaf — 5,500 ppm. TEM

Sonchus oleraceus L. — Cerraja, Sow Thistle — Leaf — 5,440 ppm. EM

Vigna aconitifolia (JACQ.) MARECHAL — Mat Bean, Moth Bean — Seed — 5,418 ppm. E

Glycine max (L.) MERR. — Soybean — Plant — 5,410 ppm. E

Vigna aconitifolia (JACQ.) MARECHAL — Mat Bean, Moth Bean — Plant — 5,400 ppm. E

Perilla frutescens (L.) BRITTON — Perilla — Seed — 5,339 ppm. TEM

Zingiber officinale ROSCOE — Ginger — Rhizome — 5,323 ppm. EM

Aralia cordata L. — Udo — Leaf — 5,320 ppm. EM

Pistacia vera L. — Pistachio — Seed — 5,280 ppm. E

Lens culinaris MEDIK. — Lentil — Seed — 5,275 ppm. E

Pisum sativum L. — Pea — Fruit — 5,240 ppm. E

Cucurbita pepo L. — Pumpkin — Fruit — 5,238 ppm. E

Phytolacca americana L. — Pokeweed — Shoot — 5,238 ppm. TEM

Chrysanthemum coronarium L. — Garland Chrysanthemum — Leaf — 5,230 ppm. M

Allium sativum var. sativum L. — Garlic — Bulb — 5,220 ppm. E

Perilla frutescens (L.) BRITTON — Perilla — Leaf — 5,214 ppm. TEM

Colocasia esculenta (L.) SCHOTT — Taro — Root — 5,204 ppm. E

Helianthus tuberosus L. — Jerusalem Artichoke — Tuber — 5,200 ppm. E

Mimulus glabratus HBK. — Huaca-Mullo — Shoot — 5,200 ppm. M

Panax quinquefolius L. — American Ginseng, Ginseng — Plant — 5,200 ppm. M

Tephrosia purpurea PERS. — Purple Tephrosia, Wild Indigo — Leaf — 5,200 ppm. TM

Rosa canina L. — Dog Rose, Dogbrier, Rose — Fruit — 5,180 ppm. EM

Ocimum basilicum L. — Basil, Cuban Basil, Sweet Basil — Leaf — 5,168 ppm. E

Spondias dulcis FORST. — Ambarella — Fruit — 5,115 ppm. E

Brassica oleracea var. gongylodes L. — Kohlrabi — Stem — 5,110 ppm. E

Foeniculum vulgare MILLER — Fennel — Plant — 5,100 ppm. M

Juglans regia L. — English Walnut — Seed — 5,100 ppm. E

Daucus carota L. — Carrot — Root — 5,090 ppm. E

Vicia faba L. — Broadbean, Faba Bean, Habas — Seed — 5,070 ppm. E

Erythrina berteroana URB. — Pito — Shoot — 5,060 ppm. E

Psophocarpus tetragonolobus (L.) DC. — Asparagus Pea, Goa Bean, Winged Bean — Seed — 5,058 ppm. E

Chrysanthemum parthenium (L.) BERNH. — Feverfew — Plant — 5,010 ppm. M

Armoracia rusticana GAERTN. ET AL. — Horseradish — Root — 5,000 ppm. E

Brassica rapa var. rapa — Rapini, Seven-Top Turnip, Turnip — Root — 5,000 ppm. E

Bromelia pinguin L. — Wild Pineapple — Shoot — 5,000 ppm. TE

Coix lacryma-jobi L. — Adlay, Adlay Millet, Job's Tears, Yi-Yi-Ren — Seed — 5,000 ppm. EM

Ephedra nevadensis S. WATS. — Brigham Tea, Mormon Tea — Plant — 5,000 ppm. M

Malva sylvestris L. — High Mallow — Leaf — 5,000 ppm. EM

Vicia faba L. — Broadbean, Faba Bean, Habas — Seed — 5,000 ppm. E

Brassica oleracea var. gemmifera DC — Brussel-Sprout, Brussels-Sprouts — Leaf — 4,927 ppm. E

Lupinus albus L. — White Lupine — Seed — 4,900 ppm. TE

Glycine max (L.) MERR. — Soybean — Sprout Seedling — 4,891 ppm. E

Malva parviflora L. — Cheeseweed — Plant — 4,891 ppm. EM

Cajanus cajan (L.) HUTH — Pigeonpea — Fruit — 4,888 ppm. E

Benincasa hispida (THUNB.) COGN. — Waxgourd — Fruit — 4,870 ppm.

Pimpinella anisum L. — Anise, Sweet Cumin — Fruit — 4,862 ppm. EM

Vigna unguiculata subsp. sesquipedalis (L.) VERDC. — Asparagus Bean, Pea Bean, Yardlong Bean — Fruit — 4,856 ppm. E

Anthriscus cerefolium (L.) HOFFM. — Chervil — Leaf — 4,850 ppm. E

Juglans cinerea L. — Butternut — Seed — 4,834 ppm. E

Lablab purpureus (L.) SWEET — Bonavist Bean, Hyacinth Bean, Lablab Bean — Seed — 4,800 ppm. TEM

Solanum torvum SW. — Susumba, Wild Eggplant — Fruit — 4,795 ppm. E

Nelumbo nucifera L. — Water Lotus — Rhizome — 4,785 ppm. EM

Trachyspermum ammi (L.) SPRAGUE ex TURRILL — Ajwan — Fruit — 4,784 ppm. EM

Humulus lupulus L. — Hops — Fruit — 4,760 ppm. TEM

Mentha spicata L. — Hortela da Folha Miuda, Spearmint — Plant — 4,706 ppm. TEM

Mucuna pruriens (L.) DC. — Cowage, Velvetbean — Seed — 4,700 ppm. EM

Xanthosoma sagittifolium (L.) SCHOTT — Malanga, Tannia, Yautia — Root — 4,700 ppm. E

Coriandrum sativum L. — Chinese Parsley, Cilantro, Coriander — Fruit — 4,687 ppm. E

Tetragonia tetragonioides (PALLAS) KUNTZE — New Zealand Spinach — Leaf — 4,665 ppm. E

Corylus avellana L. — Cobnut, English Filbert, European Filbert, European Hazel, Hazel — Seed — 4,622 ppm. E

Prunus serotina subsp. serotina — Black Cherry, Wild Cherry — Leaf — 4,608 ppm. TEM

Ricinus communis L. — Castor Bean — Leaf — 4,600 ppm. T

Taraxacum officinale WEBER EX F. H. WIGG. — Dandelion — Leaf — 4,583 ppm. EM

Brassica nigra (L.) W. D. J. KOCH — Black Mustard — Leaf — 4,563 ppm. E

Allium ampeloprasum L. — Elephant Garlic, Kurrat — Leaf — 4,528 ppm. E

Acacia farnesiana (L.) WILLD. — Cassie, Huisache, Opopanax, Popinac, Sweet Acacia — Leaf — 4,519 ppm. M

Cajanus cajan (L.) HUTH — Pigeonpea — Seed — 4,500 ppm. E

Morus alba L. — Sang-Pai-Pi, White Mulberry — Leaf — 4,500 ppm. EM

Trifolium pratense L. — Cowgrass, Peavine Clover, Purple Clover, Red Clover — Shoot — 4,500 ppm. EM

Vigna radata (L.) WILCZEK — Green Gram, Mungbean — Seed — 4,500 ppm. E

Stellaria media (L.) VILLARS — Chickweed, Common Chickweed — Plant — 4,480 ppm. E

Vigna angularis (WILLD.) OHWI & H. OHASHI — Adzuki Bean — Seed — 4,402 ppm. E

Sphenostylis stenocarpa (HOCHST. ex A. RICH) HARMS — African Yam Bean, Yam Pea — Seed — 4,393 ppm.

Arctium lappa L. — Burdock, Gobo, Great Burdock — Root — 4,370 ppm. EM

Hibiscus sabdariffa L. — Acedera de Guinea (Sp.), Indian Sorrel, Jamaica Sorrel, Kharkadi, Malventee (Ger.), Red Sorrel, Rosa de Jamaica (Sp.), Rosella (Ger.), Roselle, Sereni (Sp.), Sorrel — Flower — 4,348 ppm. E

Vigna mungo (L.) HEPPER — Black Gram — Seed — 4,321 ppm. E

Chrysanthemum coronarium L. — Garland Chrysanthemum — Bud — 4,300 ppm. M

Trigonella foenum-graecum L. — Alholva (Sp.), Bockshornklee (Ger.), Fenugreek, Greek Clover, Greek Hay — Seed — 4,285 ppm. EM

Cichorium intybus L. — Chicory, Succory, Witloof — Leaf — 4,284 ppm. E

Cicer arietinum L. — Chickpea, Garbanzo — Seed — 4,275 ppm. E

Schisandra chinensis (TURCZ.) BAILL. — Chinese Magnolia Vine, Five-Flavor-Fruit, Magnolia Vine, Schizandra, Wu Wei Zi, Wu Wei Zu — Fruit — 4,260 ppm. M

Arachis hypogaea L. — Groundnut, Peanut — Seed — 4,248 ppm. EM

Symphoricarpos orbiculatus MOENCH. — Buckbush — Stem — 4,224 ppm. TM

Physalis peruviana L. — Cape Gooseberry, Ground Cherry — Fruit — 4,215 ppm. E

Solanum tuberosum L. — Potato — Tuber — 4,200 ppm. E

Chenopodium album L. — Lamb's Quarters — Seed — 4,160 ppm. TEM

Camellia sinensis (L.) KUNTZE — Tea — Leaf — 4,150 ppm. E

Lycium chinense MILL. — Chinese Boxthorn, Chinese Matrimony Vine, Chinese Wolfberry, Chinesischer Bocks-dorn (Ger.), Daun Koki (Indones.), Gou Qi (Chin.), Kaukichai (Malays.), Kuko (Jap.), Lyciet de Chine (Fr.), Spina Santa Cinese (Ital.), Wolfberry — Leaf — 4,135 ppm. EM

Cnidoscolus chayamansa McVAUGH — Chaya — Leaf — 4,100 ppm. E

Salix alba L. — White Willow — Bark — 4,100 ppm. M

Prunus domestica L. — Plum — Fruit — 4,080 ppm. TEM

Zea mays L. — Corn — Seed — 4,066 ppm. E

Phaseolus coccineus L. — Scarlet Runner Bean — Seed — 4,046 ppm. E

Allium cepa L. — Onion, Shallot — Bulb — 4,038 ppm. E

Balanites aegyptiacus (L.) DELILE — Desert Date, Soapberry Tree, Zachunbaum (Ger.), betu (India), dattier du desert (Fr.), dattier sauvage (Fr.), heglik (Fr.), hingotia (India), lalo (India), mirobal-ano de Egipto (Sp.), zachun (India) — Fruit — 4,000 ppm.

Solanum nigrum L. — Black Nightshade — Leaf — 4,000 ppm. E

Phaseolus vulgaris var. vulgaris — Black Bean, Dwarf Bean, Field Bean, Flageolet Bean, French Bean, Garden Bean, Green Bean, Haricot, Haricot Bean, Haricot Vert, Kidney Bean, Navy Bean, Pop Bean, Popping Bean, Snap Bean, String Bean, Wax Bean — Sprout Seedling — 3,978 ppm. E

Allium sativum var. sativum L. — Garlic — Flower — 3,966 ppm. E

Canavalia ensiformis (L.) DC. — Jack Bean — Seed — 3,898 ppm. E

Capsicum annuum L. — Bell Pepper, Cherry Pepper, Cone Pepper, Green Pepper, Paprika, Sweet Pepper — Fruit — 3,885 ppm. E

Rhodymenia palmata — Dulse — Plant — 3,860 ppm. E

Arachis hypogaea L. — Groundnut, Peanut — Leaf — 3,814 ppm. EM

Balanites aegyptiacus (L.) DELILE — Desert Date, Soapberry Tree, Zachunbaum (Ger.), betu (India), dattier du desert (Fr.), dattier sauvage (Fr.), heglik (Fr.), hingotia (India), lalo (India), mirobal-ano de Egipto (Sp.), zachun (India) — Shoot — 3,800 ppm.

Mangifera indica L. — Mango — Leaf — 3,800 ppm. EM

Capsicum frutescens L. — Cayenne, Chili, Hot Pepper, Red Chili, Spur Pepper, Tabasco — Fruit — 3,794 ppm. E

Origanum majorana L. — Marjoram, Sweet Marjoram — Plant — 3,725 ppm. E

Anethum graveolens L. — Dill, Garden Dill — Fruit — 3,723 ppm. E

Sechium edule (JACQ.) SW. — Chayote — Fruit — 3,715 ppm. EM

Oenothera biennis L. — Evening-Primrose — Plant — 3,700 ppm. EM

Trichosanthes anguina L. — Snakegourd — Fruit — 3,700 ppm. E

Allium ampeloprasum L. — Elephant Garlic, Kurrat — Root — 3,650 ppm. E

Taraxacum officinale WEBER EX F. H. WIGG. — Dandelion — Root — 3,620 ppm. EM

Phosphorus, cont.

Brassica oleracea var. acephala DC — Curly Kale, Kale, Kitchen Kale, Scotch Kale — Leaf — 3,600 ppm. E

Chenopodium ambrosioides L. — Epazote, Wormseed — Leaf — 3,585 ppm. TEM

Carthamus tinctorius L. — Safflower — Seed — 3,526 ppm. M

Canavalia ensiformis (L.) DC. — Jack Bean — Fruit — 3,509 ppm. E

Citrus mitis BLANCO — Calamansi, Calamondin — Fruit — 700-7,000 ppm. E

Glechoma hederacea L. — Alehoof — Plant — 3,500 ppm. M

Melilotus indica LAM. — Small-Flowered Melilot — Plant — 3,500 ppm. TEM

Ribes nigrum L. — Black Currant — Fruit — 3,500 ppm. E

Bixa orellana L. — Achiote, Annato, Annatto, Annoto, Arnato, Bija, Lipstick Pod, Lipsticktree — Seed — 3,490 ppm. E

Oryza sativa L. — Rice — Plant — 3,478 ppm. E

Rheum rhabarbarum L. — Rhubarb — Leaf — 3,472 ppm.
— Plant — 3,462 ppm. E

Boehmeria nivea (L.) GAUDICH. — Ramie — Leaf — 3,460 ppm. M

Rhus copallina L. — Dwarf Sumac, Winged Sumac — Leaf — 3,456 ppm. EM

Lablab purpureus (L.) SWEET — Bonavist Bean, Hyacinth Bean, Lablab Bean — Fruit — 3,409 ppm. TEM

Acacia tortilis (FORSSK.) HAYNE — Umbrella Thorn — Fruit — 3,400 ppm. M

Annona muricata L. — Soursop — Fruit — 3,400 ppm. E

Anogeissus latifolia WALL. — Gum Ghatti — Leaf — 3,400 ppm. M

Carthamus tinctorius L. — Safflower — Plant — 3,400 ppm. M

Cyphomandra betacea (CAV.) SENDT. — Tamarillo, Tree Tomato — Fruit — 3,400 ppm.

Artemisia dracunculus L. — Tarragon — Plant — 3,391 ppm. M

Allium sativum var. sativum L. — Garlic — Leaf — 3,382 ppm. E

Angelica sinensis (OLIV.) DIELS — Chinese Angelica, Dang Gui, Dang Quai, Dang Qui, Dong Gui, Dong Quai — Root — 3,340 ppm. M

Carya illinoensis (WANGENH.) K. KOCH — Pecan — Seed — 3,340 ppm. E

Ribes rubrum L. — Red Currant, White Currant — Fruit — 3,310 ppm. E

Ginkgo biloba L. — Ginkgo, Maidenhair Tree — Seed — 3,268 ppm. TEM

Nelumbo nucifera L. — Water Lotus — Fruit — 3,267 ppm. EM

Sassafras albidum (NUTT.) NEES — Sassafras — Stem — 3,264 ppm. TEM

Tragopogon porrifolius L. — Salsify — Root — 3,262 ppm. E

Spondias mombin L. — Yellow Mombin, Yellow Plum — Fruit — 3,250 ppm. E

Chamaemelum nobile (L.) ALL. — Garden Camomile, Perennial Camomile, Roman Camomile — Flower — 3,220 ppm. M

Trifolium pratense L. — Cowgrass, Peavine Clover, Purple Clover, Red Clover — Flower — 3,220 ppm. EM

Eryngium floridanum L. — Florida Eryngium — Shoot — 3,215 ppm. M

Fagopyrum esculentum MOENCH. — Buckwheat — Seed — 3,200 ppm. E

Gleditsia triacanthos L. — Honey Locust — Seed — 3,200 ppm.

Morus alba L. — Sang-Pai-Pi, White Mulberry — Fruit — 3,200 ppm. EM

Passiflora edulis SIMS — Maracuya, Passionfruit — Seed — 0-6,400 ppm. E

Robinia pseudoacacia L. — Black Locust — Leaf — 3,200 ppm. T

Fragaria spp.. — Strawberry — Fruit — 3,191 ppm. E

Spirulina pratensis — Spirulina — Plant — 3,190 ppm. E

Calathea macrosepala SCHUM. — Chufle — Flower — 490-6,365 ppm.

Punica granatum L. — Granado (Sp.), Granatapfelbaum (Ger.), Granatapfelstrauch (Ger.), Grenadier (Fr.), Mangrano (Sp.), Pomegranate, Romanzeiro (Port.), Zakuro (Jap.) — Fruit — 3,182 ppm. E

Stevia rebaudiana (BERTONI) BERTONI — Ca-A-E, Stevia, Sweet Leaf of Paraguay — Leaf — 3,180 ppm. E

Psophocarpus tetragonolobus (L.) DC. — Asparagus Pea, Goa Bean, Winged Bean — Leaf — 3,175 ppm. E

Juniperus virginiana L. — Red Cedar — Shoot — 3,168 ppm. TEM

Artemisia vulgaris L. — Mugwort — Leaf — 3,150 ppm. M

Prunus persica (L.) BATSCH — Peach — Bark — 3,150 ppm. TEM

Alocasia macrorrhiza (L.) G. DON — Giant Taro — Root — 3,125 ppm. E

Anacardium occidentale L. — Cashew — Fruit — 3,125 ppm. E

Pinus cembroides ZUCC. — Mexican Pinyon — Seed — 5,150-6,235 ppm. M

Acacia senegal (L.) WILLD. — Gum Arabic, Gum Arabic Tree, Kher, Senegal Gum, Sudan Gum Arabic — Seed — 3,100 ppm. M

Medicago sativa subsp. sativa — Alfalfa, Lucerne — Plant — 3,100 ppm. E

Peucedanum decursivum (MIQ.) MAX. — Qian Hu — Plant — 3,100 ppm. M

Abrus precatorius L. — Coral Beadplant, Crab's Eye, Indian Licorice, Jequerity, Jequirity Bean, Licorice Vine, Love Bean, Lucky Bean, Minnie-Minnies, Prayer Beads, Precatory Bean, Red Beadvine, Rosary Pea, Weatherplant, Weathervine — Leaf — 3,095 ppm.

Actinidia chinensis PLANCHON — Kiwi — Fruit — 3,060 ppm.

Cichorium intybus L. — Chicory, Succory, Witloof — Root — 3,050 ppm. E

Passiflora ligularis JUSS. — Granadilla, Sweet Granadilla — Fruit — 300-6,095 ppm. E

Passiflora quadrangularis L. — Granadilla — Fruit — 3,035 ppm. E

Persea americana MILLER — Avocado — Fruit — 3,030 ppm. E

Pachira macrocarpa WALP. — Large-Fruited Provision Tree — Seed — 3,025 ppm. E

Amorphophallus campanulatus BLUME — Elephant-Foot Yam — Root — 3,020 ppm. TEM

Genipa americana L. — Genipap, Jagua — Fruit — 3,000 ppm. EM

Prunus armeniaca L. — Apricot — Seed — 3,000 ppm. TEM

Tropaeolum tuberosum R. & P. — Anu, Mashua — Root — 3,000 ppm. E

Cenchrus biflorus ROXB — Two-Flowered Sandspur — Seed — 2,990 ppm. E

Prunus armeniaca L. — Apricot — Fruit — 2,982 ppm. TEM

Liquidambar styraciflua L. — American Styrax, Sweetgum — Leaf — 2,952 ppm. EM

Achillea millefolium L. — Milfoil, Yarrow — Plant — 2,950 ppm. M

Sida rhombifolia L. — Broomweed, Teaplant — Leaf — 2,930 ppm. M

Piper auritum HBK. — Cordoncillo, Hierba Santa, Hoja Santa — Leaf — 2,920 ppm. EM

Lagenaria siceraria (MOLINA) STANDLEY. — Calabash Gourd, White-Flowered Gourd — Fruit — 2,915 ppm. E

Citrullus lanatus (THUNB.) MATSUM. & NAKAI — Watermelon — Fruit — 2,900 ppm. E

Liquidambar styraciflua L. — American Styrax, Sweetgum — Stem — 2,880 ppm. EM

Theobroma bicolor HBK. — Nicaraguan Cacao, Pataste — Seed — 5,490-5,695 ppm. E

Centella asiatica (L.) URBAN — Gotu Kola, Pennywort — Leaf — 2,804 ppm. EM

Manihot esculenta CRANTZ — Cassava, Tapioca, Yuca — Leaf — 2,800 ppm. E

Panicum maximum JACQ. — Guinea grass — Leaf — 0-5,600 ppm. M

Polygonum cuspidatum SIEBOLD & ZUCC. — Giant Knotweed, Hu-Zhang, Japanese Knotweed, Mexican Bamboo — Plant — 2,800 ppm. TEM

Solanum melongena L. — Aubergine, Eggplant — Leaf — 2,794 ppm. E

Valerianella radata — Plant — 4,647-5,552 ppm. E

Ullucus tuberosus LOZ. — Melloco, Ulluco — Root — 2,775 ppm. E

Phaseolus coccineus L. — Scarlet Runner Bean — Fruit — 2,770 ppm. E

Ficus carica L. — Echte Feige (Ger.), Feigenbaum (Ger.), Fico (Ital.), Fig, Figueira (Port.), Figuier Commun (Fr.), Higo (Sp.), Higuera Comun (Sp.) — Fruit — 2,764 ppm. E

Piper betel L. — Betel Pepper — Leaf — 2,740 ppm. EM

Sophora japonica L. — Japanese Pagoda Tree — Seed — 2,723 ppm. TM

Pinus pinea L. — Italian Stone Pine, Pignolia — Seed — 5,080-5,445 ppm. M

Acacia farnesiana (L.) WILLD. — Cassie, Huisache, Opopanax, Popinac, Sweet Acacia — Seed — 2,700 ppm. M

Cnicus benedictus L. — Blessed Thistle — Plant — 2,700 ppm. M

Gentiana lutea L. — Gentian, Yellow Gentian — Root — 2,700 ppm. M

Artocarpus altilis (PARKINS.) FOSBERG — Breadfruit — Seed — 1,750-5,385 ppm. E

Amorphophallus konjac K. KOCH — Devil's Tongue, Elephant Yam, Konjac, Leopard Palm, Snake Palm, Umbrella Arum — Leaf — 2,692 ppm. TEM

Artocarpus heterophyllus LAM. — Jackfruit — Seed — 2,685 ppm. E

Eriobotrya japonica (THUNB.) LINDL. — Loquat — Fruit — 2,667 ppm. E

Ribes uva-crispa L. — Gooseberry — Fruit — 2,665 ppm. E

Gliricidia sepium STEUD. — Mata Raton — Flower — 2,645 ppm. M

Carya glabra (MILLER) SWEET — Pignut Hickory — Shoot — 2,640 ppm. E

Cucumis melo subsp. ssp melo var.cantalupensis NAUDIN — Cantaloupe, Melon, Muskmelon, Netted Melon, Nutmeg Melon, Persian Melon — Fruit — 2,640 ppm. E

Brassica oleracea var. viridis l. L. — Collards, Cow Cabbage, Spring-Heading Cabbage, Tall Kale, Tree Kale — Leaf — 2,622 ppm. E

Raphanus sativus L. — Radish — Leaf — 2,609 ppm. E

Perideridia gairdneri (HOOK. & ARN.) MATHIAS — Squawroot — Root — 2,600 ppm. EM

Spartium junceum L. — Genet, Spanish Broom, Weaver's Broom — Stem — 2,600 ppm.

Diospyros virginiana L. — American Persimmon — Stem — 2,592 ppm. EM

Prunus serotina subsp. serotina — Black Cherry, Wild Cherry — Stem — 2,592 ppm. TEM

Althaea officinalis L. — Marshmallow, White Mallow — Root — 2,560 ppm. M

Citrus paradisi MacFAD. — Grapefruit — Fruit — 2,545 ppm. E

Mentha pulegium L. — European Pennyroyal — Plant — 2,520 ppm. TEM

Thymus vulgaris L. — Common Thyme, Garden Thyme, Thyme — Plant — 2,502 ppm. EM

Rubus chamaemorus L. — Cloudberry — Fruit — 2,500 ppm. EM

Vigna aconitifolia (JACQ.) MARECHAL — Mat Bean, Moth Bean — Fruit — 2,500 ppm. E

Platycodon grandiflorum (JACQ.) A.DC. — Balloon Flower, Chieh-Keng, Jie-Geng — Root — 2,493 ppm. TEM

Fucus vesiculosus L. — Bladderwrack, Kelp — Plant — 2,490 ppm. EM

Blighia sapida KOENIG — Akee, Seso Vegetal — Seed — 2,455 ppm. M

Phyllanthus acidus (L.) SKEELS — Indian Gooseberry, Otaheite Gooseberry — Fruit — 2,442 ppm. E

Pueraria montana var. lobata (WILLD.) MAESEN & S. M. ALMEIDA — Kudsu, Kudzu — Shoot — 2,440 ppm. EM

Quercus alba L. — White Oak — Stem — 2,432 ppm. EM

Rhus glabra L. — Smooth Sumac — Stem — 2,412 ppm. EM

Nepeta cataria L. — Catnip — Plant — 2,410 ppm. M

Origanum vulgare L. — Common Turkish Oregano, European Oregano, Oregano, Pot Marjoram, Wild Marjoram, Wild Oregano — Plant — 2,402 ppm. E

Azadirachta indica A. JUSS. — Neem — Fruit — 2,400 ppm. — Leaf — 2,400 ppm. M

Boehmeria nivea (L.) GAUDICH. — Ramie — Shoot — 2,400 ppm. M

Cajanus cajan (L.) HUTH — Pigeonpea — Plant — 2,400 ppm. E

Chrysanthemum cinerariifolium (TREVIR.) VIS. — Pyrethrum — Shoot — 2,400 ppm. M

Cocos nucifera L. — Coconut, Coconut Palm, Cocotero (Sp.), Copra, Kokospalme (Ger.), Nariyal — Seed — 2,400 ppm. E

Musa x paradisiaca L. — Banana, Plantain — Leaf — 2,400 ppm. E

Myristica fragrans HOUTT. — Mace, Muskatnussbaum (Ger.), Nutmeg, nogal moscado (Sp.), nuez moscada (Sp.) — Seed — 2,400 ppm. E

Rhynchosia minima DC. — Burn Mouth Vine — Shoot — 2,400 ppm. TM

Potassium

Lactuca sativa L. — Lettuce — Leaf — 121,800 ppm. E

Cichorium endivia L. — Endive, Escarole — Leaf — 96,000 ppm. E

Vigna mungo (L.) HEPPER — Black Gram — Seed — 89,790 ppm. E

Chenopodium album L. — Lamb's Quarters — Leaf — 87,100 ppm. TEM

Raphanus sativus L. — Radish — Root — 85,700 ppm. E

Brassica pekinensis (LOUR.) RUPR. — Chinese Cabbage — Leaf — 81,900 ppm. E

Portulaca oleracea L. — Purslane, Verdolaga — Plant — 81,200 ppm. E

Avena sativa L. — Oats — Plant — 78,900 ppm. EM

Chrysanthemum coronarium L. — Garland Chrysanthemum — Bud — 76,745 ppm. M

Anethum graveolens L. — Dill, Garden Dill — Plant — 76,450 ppm. E

Taraxacum officinale WEBER EX F. H. WIGG. — Dandelion — Root — 75,000 ppm. EM

Amaranthus sp. — Pigweed — Leaf — 73,503 ppm. EM

Cucumis sativus L. — Cucumber — Fruit — 72,500 ppm. E

Brassica chinensis L. — Bok-Choy, Celery Cabbage, Celery Mustard, Chinese Cabbage, Chinese Mustard, Chinese White Cabbage, Pak-Choi — Leaf — 69,143 ppm. E

Spinacia oleracea L. — Spinach — Plant — 69,077 ppm. E

Borago officinalis L. — Beebread, Beeplant, Borage, Talewort — Leaf — 67,210 ppm. TEM

Rheum rhabarbarum L. — Rhubarb — Plant — 66,400 ppm. E

Nasturtium officinale R. BR. — Berro, Watercress — Herb — 66,000 ppm. E

Aralia cordata L. — Udo — Leaf — 65,950 ppm. EM

Beta vulgaris subsp. vulgaris — Beet, Beetroot, Garden Beet, Sugar Beet — Leaf — 61,798 ppm. E

Lycopersicon esculentum MILLER — Tomato — Fruit — 58,800 ppm. TEM

Phaseolus vulgaris var. vulgaris — Black Bean, Dwarf Bean, Field Bean, Flageolet Bean, French Bean, Garden Bean, Green Bean, Haricot, Haricot Bean, Haricot Vert, Kidney Bean, Navy Bean, Pop Bean, Popping Bean, Snap Bean, String Bean, Wax Bean — Fruit — 58,500 ppm. E

Apium graveolens L. — Celery — Plant — 57,800 ppm. E

Lepidium sativum L. — Garden Cress — Leaf — 57,170 ppm. E

Apium graveolens L. — Celery — Root — 56,360 ppm. E

Asparagus officinalis L. — Asparagus — Shoot — 55,200 ppm. E

Houttuynia cordata THUNB. — Dokudami, Fishwort, Yu Xing Cao — Plant — 54,300 ppm. EM

Petroselinum crispum (MILLER) NYMAN EX A. W. HILLL — Parsley — Plant — 53,833 ppm. E

Colocasia esculenta (L.) SCHOTT — Taro — Leaf — 51,774 ppm. E

Anthriscus cerefolium (L.) HOFFM. — Chervil — Leaf — 51,200 ppm. E

Beta vulgaris subsp. vulgaris — Beet, Beetroot, Garden Beet, Sugar Beet — Root — 50,000 ppm. E

Lycium chinense MILL. — Chinese Boxthorn, Chinese Matrimony Vine, Chinese Wolfberry, Chinesischer Bocksdorn (Ger.), Daun Koki (Indones.), Gou Qi (Chin.), Kaukichai (Malays.), Kuko (Jap.), Lyciet de Chine (Fr.), Spina Santa Cinese (Ital.), Wolfberry — Leaf — 49,808 ppm. EM

Ipomoea aquatica FORSSKAL — Swamp Cabbage, Water Spinach — Leaf — 49,200 ppm. E

Brassica oleracea var. botrytis L. — Cauliflower — Flower — 49,080 ppm. E

Coriandrum sativum L. — Chinese Parsley, Cilantro, Coriander — Leaf — 48,177 ppm. E

Lycopersicon esculentum MILLER — Tomato — Leaf — 47,000 ppm. TEM

Perilla frutescens (L.) BRITTON — Perilla — Leaf — 46,429 ppm. TEM

Daucus carota L. — Carrot — Root — 46,360 ppm. E

Glechoma hederacea L. — Alehoof — Plant — 46,000 ppm. M

Corchorus olitorius L. — Jew's Mallow, Mulukiya, Nalta Jute — Leaf — 45,500 ppm. EM

Momordica charantia L. — Bitter Melon, Sorosi — Fruit — 45,000 ppm. E

Vigna unguiculata subsp. sesquipedalis (L.) VERDC. — Asparagus Bean, Pea Bean, Yardlong Bean — Shoot — 44,520 ppm. E

Prunus domestica L. — Plum — Fruit — 44,200 ppm. TEM

Cucumis melo subsp. melo var.cantalupensis NAUDIN — Cantaloupe, Melon, Muskmelon, Netted Melon, Nutmeg Melon, Persian Melon — Fruit — 44,000 ppm. E

Hordeum vulgare L. — Barley, Barleygrass — Plant — 44,000 ppm. EM

Brassica napus var. napobrassica var. napobrassica (L.) REICHB. — Rutabaga, Swede, Swedish Turnip — Root — 43,850 ppm. E

Triticum aestivum L. — Wheat — Plant — 43,500 ppm. EM

Raphanus sativus L. — Radish — Leaf — 43,478 ppm. E

Ocimum basilicum L. — Basil, Cuban Basil, Sweet Basil — Leaf — 42,900 ppm. E

Brassica oleracea var. capitata L. — Cabbage, Red Cabbage, White Cabbage — Leaf — 42,500 ppm. E

Ipomoea batatas (L.) LAM — Sweet Potato — Leaf — 42,256 ppm. E

Petasites japonicus (SIEBOLD & ZUCC.) MAXIM. — Butterbur — Plant — 42,000 ppm. T

Sechium edule (JACQ.) SW. — Chayote — Shoot — 41,890 ppm. EM

Curcuma longa L. — Indian Saffron, Turmeric — Rhizome — 41,271 ppm. E

Artemisia vulgaris L. — Mugwort — Plant — 41,000 ppm. M

Cucurbita pepo L. — Pumpkin — Fruit — 40,476 ppm. E

Pastinaca sativa L. — Parsnip — Root — 40,000 ppm. E

Rumex acetosa L. — Garden Sorrel — Leaf — 40,000 ppm. TEM

Foeniculum vulgare MILLER — Fennel — Plant — 39,700 ppm. M

Helianthus tuberosus L. — Jerusalem Artichoke — Tuber — 39,700 ppm. E

Chrysanthemum coronarium L. — Garland Chrysanthemum — Leaf — 39,385 ppm. M

Xanthosoma sagittifolium (L.) SCHOTT — Malanga, Tannia, Yautia — Root — 39,100 ppm. E

Phaseolus lunatus L. — Butter Bean, Lima Bean — Seed — 39,000 ppm. E

Brassica oleracea var. gongylodes L. — Kohlrabi — Stem — 38,890 ppm. E

Centella asiatica (L.) URBAN — Gotu Kola, Pennywort — Leaf — 38,693 ppm. EM

Annona cherimola MILL. — Cherimoya — Seed — 38,000 ppm. E

Brassica oleracea var. botrytis L. — Cauliflower — Leaf — 37,270 ppm. E

Urtica dioica L. — European Nettle, Stinging Nettle — Leaf — 37,220 ppm. EM

Cichorium intybus L. — Chicory, Succory, Witloof — Leaf — 37,128 ppm. E

Physalis ixocarpa BROT. — Tomatillo — Fruit — 36,250 ppm. E

Pueraria montana var. lobata (WILLD.) MAESEN & S. M. ALMEIDA — Kudsu, Kudzu — Shoot — 36,050 ppm. EM

Annona muricata L. — Soursop — Fruit — 36,000 ppm. E

Phaseolus coccineus L. — Scarlet Runner Bean — Seed — 35,807 ppm. E

Cucurbita pepo L. — Pumpkin — Flower — 35,670 ppm. E

Mentha arvensis var. piperascens MALINV. EX L. H. BAILEY — Cornmint, Field Mint, Japanese Mint — Plant — 35,100 ppm. TEM

Oenothera biennis L. — Evening-Primrose — Herb — 35,100 ppm. EM

Capsicum annuum L. — Bell Pepper, Cherry Pepper, Cone Pepper, Green Pepper,

Paprika, Sweet Pepper — Fruit — 35,000 ppm. E

Nelumbo nucifera L. — Water Lotus — Rhizome — 34,925 ppm. EM

Capsicum frutescens L. — Cayenne, Chili, Hot Pepper, Red Chili, Spur Pepper, Tabasco — Fruit — 34,272 ppm. E

Panax quinquefolius L. — American Ginseng, Ginseng — Plant — 33,800 ppm. M

Tephrosia purpurea PERS. — Purple Tephrosia, Wild Indigo — Leaf — 33,800 ppm. TM

Lagenaria siceraria (MOLINA) STANDLEY. — Calabash Gourd, White-Flowered Gourd — Fruit — 33,635 ppm. E

Liquidambar styraciflua L. — American Styrax, Sweetgum — Stem — 33,600 ppm. Em

Capsella bursa-pastoris (L.) MEDICUS — Shepherd's Purse — Plant — 33,390 ppm. EM

Momordica charantia L. — Bitter Melon, Sorosi — Leaf — 33,117 ppm. E

Artemisia dracunculus L. — Tarragon — Plant — 32,719 ppm. M

Abelmoschus esculentus (L.) MOENCH — Okra — Fruit — 32,500 ppm. EM

Solanum melongena L. — Aubergine, Eggplant — Fruit. E 32,000 ppm.

Allium schoenoprasum L. — Chives — Leaf — 31,250 ppm. E

Armoracia rusticana GAERTN. ET AL. — Horseradish — Root — 31,150 ppm. E

Cucurbita spp.. — Summer Squash — Fruit — 30,855 ppm. E

Brassica oleracea var. acephala DC — Curly Kale, Kale, Kitchen Kale, Scotch Kale — Leaf — 30,000 ppm. E

Brassica rapa var. rapa — Rapini, Seven-Top Turnip, Turnip — Root — 30,000 ppm. E

Solanum tuberosum L. — Potato — Tuber — 30,000 ppm. E

Allium ampeloprasum L. — Elephant Garlic, Kurrat — Leaf — 29,811 ppm. E

Cynara cardunculus subsp. cardunculus — Artichoke — Flower — 29,780 ppm. E

Rhus copallina L. — Dwarf Sumac, Winged Sumac — Leaf — 29,760 ppm. EM

Peucedanum decursivum (MIQ.) MAX. — Qian Hu — Plant — 29,600 ppm. M

Brassica oleracea var. gemmifera DC — Brussel-Sprout, Brussels-Sprouts — Leaf — 29,343 ppm. E

Carica papaya L. — Papaya — Leaf — 28,978 ppm. EM

Benincasa hispida (THUNB.) COGN. — Waxgourd — Fruit — 28,450 ppm.

Brassica nigra (L.) W. D. J. KOCH — Black Mustard — Leaf — 28,215 ppm. E

Amomum xanthioides WALL. — Bastard Cardamom, Chin Kousha, Malabar Cardamom, Tavoy Cardamom — Seed — 28,100 ppm.

Amorphophallus campanulatus BLUME — Elephant-Foot Yam — Root — 28,020 ppm. TEM

Luffa aegyptiaca MILLER — Luffa, Smooth Loofah, Vegetable Sponge — Fruit — 27,800 ppm. E

Eriobotrya japonica (THUNB.) LINDL. — Loquat — Fruit — 27,632 ppm. E

Glycine max (L.) MERR. — Soybean — Seed — 27,600 ppm. E

Taraxacum officinale WEBER EX F. H. WIGG. — Dandelion — Leaf — 27,569 ppm. EM

Persea americana MILLER — Avocado — Fruit — 27,470 ppm. E

Prunus serotina subsp. serotina — Black Cherry, Wild Cherry — Leaf — 26,880 ppm. TEM

Trifolium pratense L. — Cowgrass, Peavine Clover, Purple Clover, Red Clover — Shoot — 26,700 ppm. EM

Angelica dahurica BENTH & HOOK. — Bai Zhi — Root — 26,600 ppm. M

Perilla frutescens (L.) BRITTON — Perilla — Plant — 26,100 ppm. TEM

Cnicus benedictus L. — Blessed Thistle — Plant — 26,000 ppm. M

Arundo donax L. — Giant Reed — Plant — 25,500 ppm.

Nyssa sylvatica MARSHALL — Black Gum, Black Tupelo — Leaf — 25,480 ppm. EM

Carica papaya L. — Papaya — Fruit — 25,469 ppm. EM

Dioscorea pentaphylla L. — Mountain Yam — Root — 25,350 ppm. E

Potassium, cont.

Pisum sativum L. — Pea — Plant — 25,200 ppm. E

Zingiber officinale ROSCOE — Ginger — Rhizome — 25,079 ppm. EM

Hordeum vulgare L. — Barley, Barleygrass — Stem — 25,000 ppm. EM

Salvia officinalis L. — Sage — Leaf — 24,700 ppm. EM

Vitis vinifera L. — European Grape, Grape, Grapevine, Parra (Sp.), Vid (Sp.), Vigne Vinifere (Fr.), Weinrebe (Ger.), Wine Grape — Fruit — 24,640 ppm. EM

Valerianella locusta (L.) LATERRADE — Corn Salad, Lamb's Lettuce — Plant — 4,573-48,864 ppm. E

Malpighia glabra L. — Acerola — Fruit — 24,345 ppm. EM

Manihot esculenta CRANTZ — Cassava, Tapioca, Yuca — Root — 24,260 ppm. E

Brassica oleracea var. viridis l. L. — Collards, Cow Cabbage, Spring-Heading Cabbage, Tall Kale, Tree Kale — Leaf — 24,257 ppm. E

Allium sativum var. sativum L. — Garlic — Leaf — 23,971 ppm. E

Nepeta cataria L. — Catnip — Plant — 23,500 ppm. M

Cymbopogon citratus (DC. ex NEES) STAPF — Lemongrass, West Indian Lemongrass — Plant — 23,000 ppm. EM

Genipa americana L. — Genipap, Jagua — Fruit — 22,900 ppm. EM

Annona reticulata L. — Custard Apple — Fruit — 22,810 ppm. E

Taraxacum mongolicum HAND.-MAZZ. — Mongoloid Dandelion — Plant — 22,800 ppm. EM

Pisum sativum L. — Pea — Fruit — 22,737 ppm. E

Rhodymenia palmata — Dulse — Plant — 22,700 ppm. E

Mentha x piperita subsp. nothosubsp. piperita — Peppermint — Leaf — 22,600 ppm. TEM

Prunus armeniaca L. — Apricot — Fruit — 22,565 ppm. TEM

Chrysanthemum parthenium (L.) BERNH. — Feverfew — Plant — 22,500 ppm. M

Fragaria spp.. — Strawberry — Leaf — 22,500 ppm. E

Carthamus tinctorius L. — Safflower — Flower — 22,400 ppm. M

Lophatherum gracile BROGN. — Dan Zhu Ye — Plant — 22,400 ppm. M

Phytelephas aequatorialis SPRUCE — Equatorial Ivory Palm — Mesocarp — 2,510-44,590 ppm. EM

Vigna unguiculata subsp. sesquipedalis (L.) VERDC. — Asparagus Bean, Pea Bean, Yardlong Bean — Fruit — 22,212 ppm. E

Allium cepa L. — Onion, Shallot — Bulb — 22,164 ppm. E

Prunus persica (L.) BATSCH — Peach — Fruit — 22,072 ppm. TEM

Artemisia capillaris THUNB. — Capillary Wormwood — Plant — 22,000 ppm. M

Artemisia vulgaris L. — Mugwort — Shoot — 22,000 ppm. M

Polygonum cuspidatum SIEBOLD & ZUCC. — Giant Knotweed, Hu-Zhang, Japanese Knotweed, Mexican Bamboo — Plant — 22,000 ppm. TEM

Scutellaria lateriflora L. — Mad-Dog, Skullcap, Scullcap — Plant — 21,800 ppm. M

Colocasia esculenta (L.) SCHOTT — Taro — Root — 21,760 ppm. E

Sassafras albidum (NUTT.) NEES — Sassafras — Leaf — 21,760 ppm. TEM

Tetragonia tetragonioides (PALLAS) KUNTZE — New Zealand Spinach — Leaf — 21,665 ppm. E

Psidium guajava L. — Guava — Fruit — 21,658 ppm. E

Erythroxylum coca var. coca — Coca — Leaf — 21,600 ppm. EM

Rheum palmatum L. — Chinese Rhubarb — Rhizome — 21,600 ppm. E

Aristolochia debilis SIEB. & ZUCC. — Chinese Birthwort — Fruit — 21,500 ppm. TEM

Sechium edule (JACQ.) SW. — Chayote — Fruit — 21,430 ppm. EM

Ribes rubrum L. — Red Currant, White Currant — Fruit — 21,250 ppm. E

Ribes nigrum L. — Black Currant — Fruit — 21,110 ppm. E

Fucus vesiculosus L. — Bladderwrack, Kelp — Plant — 21,100 ppm. EM

Phaseolus vulgaris var. vulgaris — Black Bean, Dwarf Bean, Field Bean, Flageolet Bean, French Bean, Garden Bean, Green Bean, Haricot, Haricot Bean, Haricot Vert, Kidney Bean, Navy Bean, Pop Bean, Popping Bean, Snap Bean, String Bean, Wax Bean — Seed — 21,070 ppm. E

Rosa canina L. — Dog Rose, Dogbrier, Rose — Fruit — 21,000 ppm. EM

Cuminum cyminum L. — Cumin — Fruit — 20,916 ppm. EM

Ribes uva-crispa L. — Gooseberry — Fruit — 20,830 ppm. E

Lablab purpureus (L.) SWEET — Bonavist Bean, Hyacinth Bean, Lablab Bean — Seed — 20,775 ppm. TEM

Rhus copallina L. — Dwarf Sumac, Winged Sumac — Stem — 20,740 ppm. EM

Spondias dulcis FORST. — Ambarella — Fruit — 20,700 ppm. E

Celosia cristata L. — Cockscomb — Flower — 20,600 ppm. M

Raphanus sativus L. — Radish — Fruit — 20,495 ppm. E

Siegesbeckia orientalis L. — Hsi Chien, Saint Paul's wort — Plant — 20,400 ppm. M

Humulus lupulus L. — Hops — Fruit — 20,350 ppm. TEM

Angelica laxiflora DIELS — Tu Huo — Root — 20,300 ppm. M

Medicago sativa subsp. sativa — Alfalfa, Lucerne — Plant — 20,300 ppm. E

Phaseolus vulgaris var. vulgaris — Black Bean, Dwarf Bean, Field Bean, Flageolet Bean, French Bean, Garden Bean, Green Bean, Haricot, Haricot Bean, Haricot Vert, Kidney Bean, Navy Bean, Pop Bean, Popping Bean, Snap Bean, String Bean, Wax Bean — Sprout Seedling — 20,108 ppm. E

Lonicera japonica THUNB. — Japanese Honeysuckle — Flower — 20,100 ppm. M

Vitis vinifera L. — European Grape, Grape, Grapevine, Parra (Sp.), Vid (Sp.), Vigne Vinifere (Fr.), Weinrebe (Ger.), Wine Grape — Stem — 20,100 ppm. EM

Achyranthes bidentata BLUME — Chaff Flower — Root — 20,000 ppm. M

Polystichum polyblepharum (ROEM.) PRESL — Chinese Polystichum — Plant — 20,000 ppm. T

Trifolium pratense L. — Cowgrass, Peavine Clover, Purple Clover, Red Clover — Flower — 20,000 ppm. EM

Quisqualis indica L. — Rangoon Creeper — Fruit — 19,900 ppm. TE

Actinidia chinensis PLANCHON — Kiwi — Fruit — 19,600 ppm.

Plantago asiatica L. — Asian Plantain — Plant — 19,600 ppm. EM

Cornus officinalis SIEB. & ZUCC. — Chinese Dogwood — Fruit — 19,500 ppm. EM

Foeniculum vulgare MILLER — Fennel — Fruit — 19,400 ppm. M

Prunus persica (L.) BATSCH — Peach — Bark — 19,400 ppm. TEM

Symphoricarpos orbiculatus MOENCH. — Buckbush — Stem — 19,360 ppm. TM

Prunus cerasus L. — Sour Cherry — Fruit — 19,277 ppm. TEM

Bupleurum chinense DC. — Chai-Hu — Root — 19,200 ppm. M

Jussiaea repens L. — Jussiaeae Herba, Pond Dragon — Plant — 19,200 ppm. M

Punica granatum L. — Granado (Sp.), Granatapfelbaum (Ger.), Granatapfelstrauch (Ger.), Grenadier (Fr.), Mangrano (Sp.), Pomegranate, Romanzeiro (Port.), Zakuro (Jap.) — Fruit — 18,950 ppm. E

Psophocarpus tetragonolobus (L.) DC. — Asparagus Pea, Goa Bean, Winged Bean — Seed — 18,873 ppm. E

Liquidambar styraciflua L. — American Styrax, Sweetgum — Leaf — 18,860 ppm. Em

Physalis peruviana L. — Cape Gooseberry, Ground Cherry — Fruit — 18,710 ppm. E

Carya glabra (MILLER) SWEET — Pignut Hickory — Shoot — 18,700 ppm. E

Origanum vulgare L. — Common Turkish Oregano, European Oregano, Oregano, Pot Marjoram, Wild Marjoram, Wild Oregano — Plant — 18,647 ppm. E

Cimicifuga dahurica (TURCZ. EX FISCH. & C. A. MEY.) MAXIM. — Sheng Ma — Rhizome — 18,600 ppm. M

Potassium, cont.

Stellaria media (L.) VILLARS — Chickweed, Common Chickweed — Plant — 18,400 ppm. E

Peperomia pereskiifolia — Perejil — Leaf — 5,480-36,535 ppm.

Asarum heterotropoides MAEK. — Asian Wild Ginger — Root — 18,200 ppm. M

Asarum sieboldii (MIQ.) MAEK. — Siebold's Wild Ginger — Root — 18,200 ppm. M

Tussilago farfara L. — Coltsfoot — Flower — 18,200 ppm. TM

Cajanus cajan (L.) HUTH — Pigeonpea — Seed — 18,103 ppm. E

Vigna radata (L.) WILCZEK — Green Gram, Mungbean — Sprout Seedling — 18,092 ppm. E

Citrullus lanatus (THUNB.) MATSUM. & NAKAI — Watermelon — Fruit — 18,000 ppm. E

Equisetum arvense L. — Field Horsetail, Horsetail — Plant — 18,000 ppm. M

Lycopodium clavatum L. — Antler Herb, Clubmoss — Plant — 18,000 ppm. TM

Achillea millefolium L. — Milfoil, Yarrow — Plant — 17,800 ppm. M

Stevia rebaudiana (BERTONI) BERTONI — Ca-A-E, Stevia, Sweet Leaf of Paraguay — Leaf. — 17,800 ppm. E

Peperomia pelucida — Pepper elder, Yerba de la plata — Leaf — 2,770-35,510 ppm.

Amaranthus spinosus L. — Spiny pigweed — Leaf — 3,370-35,276 ppm. EM

Camellia sinensis (L.) KUNTZE — Tea — Plant — 17,600 ppm. E

Arachis hypogaea L. — Groundnut, Peanut — Plant — 17,500 ppm. EM

Cajanus cajan (L.) HUTH — Pigeonpea — Fruit — 17,472 ppm. E

Linum usitatissimum L. — Flax, Linseed — Hay — 17,400 ppm. E

Schisandra chinensis (TURCZ.) BAILL. — Chinese Magnolia Vine, Five-Flavor-Fruit, Magnolia Vine, Schizandra, Wu Wei Zi, Wu Wei Zu — Fruit — 17,400 ppm. M

Origanum majorana L. — Marjoram, Sweet Marjoram — Plant — 17,225 ppm. E

Moringa oleifera LAM. — Ben Nut, Benzo-live Tree, Drumstick Tree, Horseradish Tree, Jacinto (Sp.), Moringa, West Indian Ben — Fruit — 4,610-39,065 ppm. E

Cistanche salsa (C.A.MEYER) G. BECK — Broomrape, Cistanchis Herba, Jou Tsung Jung — Plant — 17,100 ppm. M

Mentha x rotundifolia (L.) HUDSON — Applemint — Leaf — 17,100 ppm. TEM

Tragopogon porrifolius L. — Salsify — Root — 16,964 ppm. E

Drynaria fortunei (KUNZE) J. SMITH — Fortune's Fern — Rhizome — 16,900 ppm. M

Angelica sinensis (OLIV.) DIELS — Chinese Angelica, Dang Gui, Dang Quai, Dang Qui, Dong Gui, Dong Quai — Root — 16,800 ppm. M

Arctium lappa L. — Burdock, Gobo, Great Burdock — Root — 16,800 ppm. EM

Ligustrum japonicum THUNB. — Japanese Privet, Ligustri Fructus — Fruit — 16,800 ppm. M

Ligustrum lucidum W. T. AITON — Chinese Privet, Glossy Privet, Ligustri Fructus, Privet, White Waxtree — Fruit — 16,800 ppm. M

Artocarpus altilis (PARKINS.) FOSBERG — Breadfruit — Fruit — 16,700 ppm. E

Lycium chinense MILL. — Chinese Boxthorn, Chinese Matrimony Vine, Chinese Wolfberry, Chinesischer Bocksdorn (Ger.), Daun Koki (Indones.), Gou Qi (Chin.), Kaukichai (Malays.), Kuko (Jap.), Lyciet de Chine (Fr.), Spina Santa Cinese (Ital.), Wolfberry — Fruit — 16,700 ppm. EM

Spondias tuberosa ARRUDA — Imbu, Umbu — Fruit — 16,700 ppm. E

Nelumbo nucifera L. — Water Lotus — Seed — 16,652 ppm. EM

Canavalia ensiformis (L.) DC. — Jack Bean — Seed — 16,600 ppm. E

Citrus paradisi MacFAD. — Grapefruit — Fruit — 16,360 ppm. E

Isatis tinctoria L. — Dyer's Woad — Root — 16,300 ppm. M

Diospyros virginiana L. — American Persimmon — Stem — 16,200 ppm. EM

Syzygium aromaticum (L.) MERR. & L. M. PERRY — Clove, Clovetree — Flower — 16,200 ppm. E

Musa x paradisiaca L. — Banana, Plantain — Fruit — 16,150 ppm. E

Pachyrhizus erosus RICH. ex DC. — Yambean, Jicamba — Tuber — 16,130 ppm. E

Acorus calamus L. — Calamus, Flagroot, Myrtle Flag, Sweet Calamus, Sweetflag, Sweetroot — Rhizome — 16,000 ppm. M

Diospyros virginiana L. — American Persimmon — Leaf — 16,000 ppm. EM

Pimpinella anisum L. — Anise, Sweet Cumin — Fruit — 15,923 ppm. EM

Symphytum officinale L. — Comfrey — Root — 15,900 ppm. TM

Phyllanthus acidus (L.) SKEELS — Indian Gooseberry, Otaheite Gooseberry — Fruit — 15,895 ppm. E

Psidium cattleianum SABINE — Strawberry Guava — Fruit — 15,880 ppm. E

Pisum sativum L. — Pea — Seed — 15,830 ppm. E

Ipomoea batatas (L.) LAM — Sweet Potato — Root — 15,740 ppm. E

Asimina triloba (L.) DUNAL — Pawpaw — Fruit — 15,726 ppm. E

Carum carvi L. — Caraway, Carum, Comino (Sp.), Comino de prado (Sp.), Kummel (Ger.) — Fruit — 15,665 ppm. E

Murraya sp. — Curry Leaf — Fruit — 15,612 ppm. EM

Cinnamomum aromaticum NEES — Canela de la China (Sp.), Canelero chino (Sp.), Canelle de Cochinchine (Fr.), Cannelier Casse (Fr.), Cannelier de Chine (Fr.), Cassia, Cassia Bark, Cassia Lignea, China Junk Cassia, Chinazimt (Ger.), Chinese Cassia, Chinese Cinnamon, Chinesischer Zimtbaum (Ger.), Kashia-Keihi (Jap.), Saigon Cinnamon, Zimtcassie (Ger.) — Bark — 15,500 ppm. TEM

Citrus medica L. — Citron — Fruit — 15,500 ppm. E

Eriobotrya japonica (THUNB.) LINDL. — Loquat — Leaf — 15,500 ppm. E

Tamarindus indica L. — Indian Tamarind, Kilytree, Tamarind — Fruit — 15,415 ppm. M

Apium graveolens L. — Celery — Seed — 15,330 ppm. E

Mentha pulegium L. — European Pennyroyal — Plant — 15,310 ppm. TEM

Acanthopanax gracilistylis W.W.SMITH — Wu Chia Pi Root — Bark — 15,300 ppm. M

Gardenia jasminoides J. ELLIS — Cape Jasmine, Gardenia, Jasmin, Shan-Chih-Tzu, Shan-Zhi-Zi, Zhi Zi — Fruit — 15,300 ppm. M

Artocarpus heterophyllus LAM. — Jackfruit — Fruit — 15,125 ppm. E

Prunus serotina subsp. serotina — Black Cherry, Wild Cherry — Stem — 15,120 ppm. TEM

Glycine max (L.) MERR. — Soybean — Sprout Seedling — 15,081 ppm. E

Piper nigrum L. — Black Pepper, Pepper, White Pepper — Fruit — 15,077 ppm. EM

Dioscorea alata L. — Greater Yam, Winged Yam — Root — 15,040 ppm. E

Trachyspermum ammi (L.) SPRAGUE ex TURRILL — Ajwan — Fruit — 15,011 ppm. EM

Linum usitatissimum L. — Flax, Linseed — Seed — 15,009 ppm. E

Equisetum hyemale L. — Horsetail, Scouring Rush — Plant — 14,900 ppm. M

Geranium thunbergii SIEB. & ZUCC — Gennoshiouko, Oriental Geranium — Plant — 14,900 ppm. EM

Juglans nigra L. — Black Walnut — Hull Husk — 14,900 ppm. E

Coriandrum sativum L. — Chinese Parsley, Cilantro, Coriander — Fruit — 14,781 ppm. E

Rhus glabra L. — Smooth Sumac — Stem — 14,740 ppm. EM

Citrus limon (L.) BURMAN f. — Lemon — Fruit — 14,700 ppm. E

Euodia rutaecarpa BENTH. — Wou Chou Yu — Fruit — 14,600 ppm.

Panicum maximum JACQ. — Guinea grass — Leaf — 5,900-29,200 ppm. M

Cichorium intybus L. — Chicory, Succory, Witloof — Root — 14,500 ppm. E

Firmiana simplex (L.) W. F. WIGHT — Chinese Parasol — Seed — 14,500 ppm. EM

Scrophularia buergeriana MIQ. — Hsuan-Shen, Yuan-Shen — Root — 14,500 ppm. M

Vigna angularis (WILLD.) OHWI & H. OHASHI — Adzuki Bean — Seed — 14,487 ppm. E

Carya ovata (MILL.) K. KOCH — Shagbark Hickory — Shoot — 14,400 ppm. E

Sambucus canadensis L. — American Elder, American Elderberry, Elderberry, Sweet Elder — Fruit — 14,356 ppm.

Vigna aconitifolia (JACQ.) MARECHAL — Mat Bean, Moth Bean — Seed — 14,230 ppm. E

Pulsatilla chinensis (BUNGE) REGEL — Chinese Anemone — Root — 14,200 ppm. M

Tribulus terrestris L. — Puncture-vine — Leaf — 0-28,400 ppm.

Vigna radata (L.) WILCZEK — Green Gram, Mungbean — Seed — 14,170 ppm. E

Anethum graveolens L. — Dill, Garden Dill — Fruit — 14,122 ppm. E

Juniperus virginiana L. — Red Cedar — Shoot — 14,080 ppm. TEM

Phyllanthus emblica L. — Emblic, Myrobalan — Fruit — 13,960 ppm. E

Glehnia littoralis F. SCHMIDT & MIQUEL — Bei Sha Shen — Root — 13,900 ppm. EM

Citrus aurantium L. — Bitter Orange, Petitgrain — Fruit — 13,800 ppm. E

Citrus sinensis (L.) OSBECK — Orange — Fruit — 13,772 ppm. E

Larrea tridentata (SESSE & MOC. ex DC.) COV. — Chaparral, Creosote Bush — Plant — 13,700 ppm. M

Allium sativum var. sativum L. — Garlic — Bulb — 13,669 ppm. E

Rubus idaeus L. — Raspberry, Red Raspberry — Leaf — 13,400 ppm. EM

Chondrus crispus (L.) STACKH. — Irish Moss — Plant — 13,310 ppm. E

Ephedra spp.. — Ma-Huang — Plant — 13,300 ppm. M

Annona squamosa L. — Sugar-Apple, Sweetsop — Fruit — 13,290 ppm. E

Chaenomeles lagenaria KOIDZ. — Chinese Quince, Mu-Kua — Fruit — 13,200 ppm. E

Chamaemelum nobile (L.) ALL. — Garden Camomile, Perennial Camomile, Roman Camomile — Flower — 13,200 ppm. M

Cynanchum atratum BUNGE — Bai-Wei, Pai-Wei — Root — 13,200 ppm. EM

Ephedra sinica STAPF — Chinese Ephedra, Ma Huang — Plant — 13,200 ppm. M

Verbascum thapsus L. — Flannelleaf, Flannelplant, Great Mullein, Mullein, Velvetplant — Leaf — 13,200 ppm. M

Vicia faba L. — Broadbean, Faba Bean, Habas — Seed — 13,160 ppm. E

Citrus reticulata BLANCO — Mandarin, Tangerine — Fruit — 13,127 ppm. E

Sorbus aucuparia L. — Rowan Berry, Mountain Ash — Fruit — 13,075 ppm. TEM

Catalpa ovata G. DON — Hsin-Pa-Pi, Kisasage — Fruit — 13,000 ppm. EM

Euphrasia officinalis L. — Eyebright — Plant — 13,000 ppm. M

Rosa laevigata MICHX. — Cherokee Rose — Fruit — 13,000 ppm. EM

Gastrodia elata BLUME — Tian Ma — Rhizome — 12,900 ppm.

Perideridia gairdneri (HOOK. & ARN.) MATHIAS — Squawroot — Root — 12,900 ppm. EM

Elettaria cardamomum (L.) MATON — Cardamom — Seed — 12,857 ppm. EM

Eleocharis dulcis (BURM. F) TRIN. — Water chestnut — Tuber — 4,810-25,450 ppm.

Cassia tora L. — Sickle Senna — Seed — 12,700 ppm. M

Tamarindus indica L. — Indian Tamarind, Kilytree, Tamarind — Flower — 12,700 ppm. M

Cucurbita foetidissima HBK. — Buffalo Gourd — Leaf — 0-25,300 ppm. E

Vigna unguiculata subsp. sesquipedalis (L.) VERDC. — Asparagus Bean, Pea Bean, Yardlong Bean — Seed — 12,635 ppm. E

Lobelia inflata L. — Indian Tobacco, Lobelia — Leaf — 12,600 ppm. TM

Oryza sativa L. — Rice — Plant — 12,600 ppm. E

Rubia cordifolia L. — Madder — Root — 12,600 ppm. M

Sassafras albidum (NUTT.) NEES — Sassafras — Stem — 12,580 ppm. TEM

Rubus chingii HU — Chinese Raspberry — Fruit — 12,500 ppm. EM

Artemisia herba-alba ASSO. — Desert Wormwood — Plant — 12,400 ppm. M

Allium sativum var. sativum L. — Garlic — Shoot — 12,242 ppm. E

Rumex crispus L. — Curly Dock, Lengua De Vaca, Sour Dock, Yellow Dock — Root — 12,200 ppm. TEM

Viscum album L. — European Mistletoe — Leaf — 12,200 ppm. TM

Zea mays L. — Corn — Silk Stigma — Style — 12,200 ppm. E

Cydonia oblonga MILLER — Quince — Fruit — 12,160 ppm. E

Malus domestica BORKH. — Apple — Fruit — 12,140 ppm. E

Althaea officinalis L. — Marshmallow, White Mallow — Root — 12,100 ppm. M

Zizyphus jujuba MILL. — Da-Zao, Jujube, Ta-Tsao — Fruit — 12,035 ppm. EM

Tamarindus indica L. — Indian Tamarind, Kilytree, Tamarind — Leaf — 11,974 ppm. M

Crataegus cuneata SIEB. & ZUCC. — Hawthorn — Fruit — 11,900 ppm. M

Petasites japonicus (SIEBOLD & ZUCC.) MAXIM. — Butterbur — Plant — 11,900 ppm. T

Prunella vulgaris L. — Heal-All, Self-Heal — Flower — 11,900 ppm.

Raphanus sativus L. — Radish — Seed — 11,900 ppm. E

Rubus chamaemorus L. — Cloudberry — Fruit — 11,875 ppm. EM

Averrhoa carambola L. — Carambola, Star — Fruit — Fruit — 1,400-23,500 ppm. E

Agathosma betulina (P. J. BERGIUS) PILLANS — Buchu, Honey Buchu, Mountain Buchu — Leaf — 11,700 ppm. M

Atractylodes ovata DC. — Bai-Zhu, Pai-Chu — Rhizome — 11,700 ppm. M

Salvia miltiorrhiza BUNGE — Dan-Shen, Red Sage, Tan-Shen — Root — 11,700 ppm. EM

Ficus carica L. — Echte Feige (Ger.), Feigenbaum (Ger.), Fico (Ital.), Fig, Figueira (Port.), Figuier Commun (Fr.), Higo (Sp.), Higuera Comun (Sp.) — Fruit — 11,662 ppm. E

Salvia officinalis L. — Sage — Plant — 11,630 ppm. EM

Satureja hortensis L. — Summer Savory — Plant — 11,549 ppm. E

Lens culinaris MEDIK. — Lentil — Sprout Seedling — 11,495 ppm. E

Pistacia vera L. — Pistachio — Seed — 11,493 ppm. E

Cocos nucifera L. — Coconut, Coconut Palm, Cocotero (Sp.), Copra, Kokospalme (Ger.), Nariyal — Seed — 11,491 ppm. E

Zea mays L. — Corn — Seed — 11,450 ppm. E

Glycyrrhiza glabra L. — Commom Licorice, Licorice, Licorice-Root, Smooth Licorice — Plant — 11,400 ppm. M

Mimosa pudica L. — Sensitive — Plant — Leaf — 11,400 ppm. M

Ginkgo biloba L. — Ginkgo, Maidenhair Tree — Seed — 11,394 ppm. TEM

Lupinus albus L. — White Lupine — Seed — 11,300 ppm. TE

Rosmarinus officinalis L. — Rosemary — Plant — 11,284 ppm. EM

Pyrus communis L. — Pear — Fruit — 11,250 ppm. E

Alisma plantago-aquatica L. — Mud Plantain, Tse-Hsieh, Water Plantain, Ze-Xie — Rhizome — 11,200 ppm. M

Pueraria pseudohirsuta TANG & WANG — Chinese Kudzu — Root — 11,200 ppm. EM

Spondias purpurea L. — Purple Jobo, Purple Plum — Fruit — 11,155 ppm. E

Crataegus laevigata (POIR.) DC — English Hawthorn, Hawthorn, Whitethorn, Woodland Hawthorn — Fruit — 11,000 ppm. M

Panax japonicus C.A.MEYER — Japanese Ginseng — Rhizome — 11,000 ppm. M

Acrocomia totai MART. — Gru-Gru Nut, Mbocaya — Fruit — 0-21,800 ppm. E

Nardostachys chinensis BATALIN — Chinese Spikenard — Rhizome — 10,800 ppm. M

Polygonum multiflorum THUNB. — Chinese Cornbind, Chinese Knotweed, Fleeceflower, Fo Ti, He Shou Wu — Root — 10,800 ppm. TEM

Panax ginseng C. A. MEYER — Chinese Ginseng, Ginseng, Korean Ginseng, Oriental Ginseng — Root — 10,700 ppm. M

Potassium, cont.

Sophora japonica L. — Japanese Pagoda Tree — Seed — 10,660 ppm. TM

Glycine max (L.) MERR. — Soybean — Plant — 10,600 ppm. E

Ophiopogon japonicus KER-GAWL. — Mai-Men-Dong, Mai-Men-Tung — Tuber — 10,600 ppm. M

Schizonepeta tenuifolia BRIQ. — Ching-Chieh, Jing-Jie — Plant — 10,600 ppm. M

Lens culinaris MEDIK. — Lentil — Seed — 10,440 ppm. E

Corylus avellana L. — Cobnut, English Filbert, European Filbert, European Hazel, Hazel — Seed — 10,433 ppm. E

Cimicifuga racemosa (L.) NUTT. — Black Cohosh, Black Snakeroot — Root — 10,300 ppm. M

Valeriana officinalis L. — Common Valerian, Garden-Heliotrope, Valerian — Root — 10,300 ppm. M

Cicer arietinum L. — Chickpea, Garbanzo — Seed — 10,220 ppm.E

Notopterygium incisum TING. — Qiang Huo — Rhizome — 10,200 ppm. M

Trigonella foenum-graecum L. — Alholva (Sp.), Bockshornklee (Ger.), Fenugreek, Greek Clover, Greek Hay — Seed — 10,200 ppm. EM

Morus alba L. — Sang-Pai-Pi, White Mulberry — Fruit — 10,133 ppm. EM

Anemarrhena asphodeloides BUNGE — Chih-Mu, Zhi-Mu — Rhizome — 10,100 ppm. M

Cyperus rotundus L. — Nutsedge — Rhizome — 10,100 ppm. EM

Astragalus membranaceus (FISCH. EX LINK) BUNGE — Huang Qi, Huang-Chi — Root — 10,000 ppm. M

Ananas comosus (L.) MERR. — Pineapple — Fruit — 9,932 ppm. E

Harpagophytum procumbens (BURCH.) DC. EX MEISN. — Devil's Claw, Grapple — Plant — Root — 9,910 ppm. M

Annona cherimola MILL. — Cherimoya — Fruit — 9,900 ppm. E

Hordeum vulgare L. — Barley, Barleygrass — Seed — 9,900 ppm. EM

Salix alba L. — White Willow — Bark — 9,830 ppm. M

Elytrigia repens (L.) DESV. EX NEVSKI — Couchgrass, Doggrass, Quackgrass, Twitchgrass, Wheatgrass — Plant — 9,780 ppm. EM

Magnolia denudata DESR. — Hsin-I, Xin-Yi — Flower — 9,780 ppm. EM

Magnolia fargesii CHENG — Hsin-I, Xin-Yi — Flower — 9,780 ppm. EM

Magnolia kobus DC. — Hsin-I, Xin-Yi — Flower — 9,780 ppm. EM

Rehmannia glutinosa (GAERTN.) LIBO-SCH. — Chinese Foxglove — Root — 9,730 ppm. M

Thymus vulgaris L. — Common Thyme, Garden Thyme, Thyme — Leaf — 9,680 ppm. EM

Juniperus communis L. — Common Juniper, Juniper — Fruit — 9,570 ppm. TEM

Forsythia suspensa VAHL — Lian-Jiao, Lien-Chiao — Fruit — 9,560 ppm. M

Senna occidentalis (L.) H. IRWIN & BARNEBY — Coffee Senna — Seed — 9,560 ppm. TE

Citrus aurantiifolia (CHRISTM.) SWINGLE — Lime — Fruit — 9,533 ppm. E

Smilax spp.. — Sarsaparilla — Root — 9,530 ppm. EM

Mangifera indica L. — Mango — Fruit — 9,475 ppm. EM

Passiflora foetida L. — Granadilla Cimarrona, Stinking Granadilla — Fruit — 3,410-18,945 ppm. E

Genipa americana L. — Genipap, Jagua — Seed — 9,400 ppm. EM

Hibiscus sabdariffa L. — Acedera de Guinea (Sp.), Indian Sorrel, Jamaica Sorrel, Kharkadi, Malventee (Ger.), Red Sorrel, Rosa de Jamaica (Sp.), Rosella (Ger.), Roselle, Sereni (Sp.), Sorrel — Flower — 9,400 ppm. E

Cypripedium pubescens WILLD. — Yellow Ladyslipper — Root — 9,340 ppm. M

Ruscus aculeatus L. — Box-Holly, Butcher's Broom — Root — 9,340 ppm. EM

Thymus vulgaris L. — Common Thyme, Garden Thyme, Thyme — Plant — 9,302 ppm. EM

Nyssa sylvatica MARSHALL — Black Gum, Black Tupelo — Stem — 9,240 ppm. EM

Quercus rubra L. — Northern Red Oak — Stem — 9,240 ppm. EM

Quercus stellata WANGENH. — Post Oak — Stem — 9,240 ppm. EM

Senna obtusifolia (L.) H.IRWIN & BARNE-BY — Sicklepod — Seed — 9,200 ppm. TE

Sinapis alba L. — White Mustard — Seed — 9,130 ppm. TEM

Polygonum multiflorum THUNB. — Chinese Cornbind, Chinese Knotweed, Fleeceflower, Fo Ti, He Shou Wu — Rhizome — 9,120 ppm. TEM

Scutellaria baicalensis GEORGI — Baikal Skullcap, Chinese Skullcap, Huang Qin — Root — 9,120 ppm. M

Alocasia macrorrhiza (L.) G. DON — Giant Taro — Root — 9,000 ppm. E

Lantana camara L. — Lantana, Wild Sage — Shoot — 9,000 ppm. M

Gentiana scabra BUNGE — Japanese Gentian — Root — 8,980 ppm. M

Belamcanda chinensis (L.) DC. — Blackberry Lily, Iris Tigre (Fr.), Leopard Lily, Leopardenblume (Ger.), Maravilla (Sp.), Mariposa (Sp.), Shenan — Rhizome — 8,940 ppm. M

Avena sativa L. — Oats — Seed — 8,900 ppm. EM

Phoenix dactylifera L. — Date Palm — Fruit — 8,780 ppm. E

Gentiana lutea L. — Gentian, Yellow Gentian — Root — 8,770 ppm. M

Cnidium officinale MAKINO — Jih-Chiung — Rhizome — 8,750 ppm. EM

Valerianella radata — Plant — 16,406-17,496 ppm. E

Diospyros virginiana L. — American Persimmon — Fruit — 8,710 ppm. EM

Phytelephas aequatorialis SPRUCE — Equatorial Ivory Palm — Flower — 5,070-17,365 ppm. EM

Rubidium

Carya ovata (MILL.) K. KOCH — Shagbark Hickory — Shoot — 192 ppm. E

Spinacia oleracea L. — Spinach — Leaf — 90 ppm. E

Petroselinum crispum (MILLER) NYMAN EX A. W. HILLL — Parsley — Leaf — 65 ppm. E

Vaccinium myrtillus L. — Bilberry, Dwarf Bilberry, Whortleberry — Fruit — 60 ppm. E

Rheum rhabarbarum L. — Rhubarb — Plant — 58 ppm. E

Taraxacum officinale WEBER EX F. H. WIGG. — Dandelion — Plant — 50 ppm. EM

Quercus alba L. — White Oak — Stem — 40 ppm. EM

Vigna unguiculata subsp. sesquipedalis (L.) VERDC. — Asparagus Bean, Pea Bean, Yardlong Bean — Seed — 39 ppm. E

Rubus chamaemorus L. — Cloudberry — Fruit — 38 ppm. EM

Anacardium occidentale L. — Cashew — Seed — 35 ppm. E

Polygonum cuspidatum SIEBOLD & ZUCC. — Giant Knotweed, Hu-Zhang, Japanese Knotweed, Mexican Bamboo — Plant — 33 ppm. TEM

Sorbus aucuparia L. — Rowan Berry, Mountain Ash — Fruit — 33 ppm. TEM

Beta vulgaris subsp. vulgaris — Beet, Beetroot, Garden Beet, Sugar Beet — Root — 32 ppm. E

Cinnamomum aromaticum NEES — Canela de la China (Sp.), Canelero chino (Sp.), Canelle de Cochinchine (Fr.), Cannelier Casse (Fr.), Cannelier de Chine (Fr.), Cassia, Cassia Bark, Cassia Lignea, China Junk Cassia, Chinazimt (Ger.), Chinese Cassia, Chinese Cinnamon, Chinesischer Zimtbaum (Ger.), Kashia-Keihi (Jap.), Saigon Cinnamon, Zimtcassie (Ger.) — Bark — 30 ppm. TEM

Anethum graveolens L. — Dill, Garden Dill — Plant — 28 ppm. E

Ribes nigrum L. — Black Currant — Fruit — 28 ppm. E

Brassica oleracea var. capitata L. — Cabbage, Red Cabbage, White Cabbage — Leaf — 27.5 ppm. E

Petasites japonicus (SIEBOLD & ZUCC.) MAXIM. — Butterbur — Plant — 26 ppm. T

Quercus rubra L. — Northern Red Oak — Stem — 26 ppm. EM

Rosa canina L. — Dog Rose, Dogbrier, Rose — Fruit — 25 ppm. EM

Brassica oleracea var. botrytis L. — Cauliflower — Leaf — 23 ppm. E

Ribes rubrum L. — Red Currant, White Currant — Fruit — 23 ppm. E

Solanum tuberosum L. — Potato — Tuber — 23 ppm. E

Carya illinoensis (WANGENH.) K. KOCH — Pecan — Seed — 22 ppm. E

Citrus paradisi MacFAD. — Grapefruit — Fruit — 22 ppm. E

Lycopersicon esculentum MILLER — Tomato — Fruit — 22 ppm. TEM

Vaccinium vitis-idaea var. minus LODD. — Cowberry, Lingen, Lingonberry — Fruit — 22 ppm. E

Quercus velutina LAM. — Black Oak — Stem — 21 ppm. EM

Cinnamomum burmannii (NEES) BLUME — Java Cinnamon, Padang Cassia — Bark — 20 ppm. TEM

Cinnamomum verum J. PRESL — Ceylon Cinnamon, Cinnamon — Bark — 20 ppm. TEM

Musa x paradisiaca L. — Banana, Plantain — Fruit — 20 ppm. E

Pyrus communis L. — Pear — Fruit — 20 ppm. E

Artemisia vulgaris L. — Mugwort — Plant — 19 ppm. M

Cucumis sativus L. — Cucumber — Fruit — 19 ppm. E

Peucedanum decursivum (MIQ.) MAX. — Qian Hu — Plant — 18 ppm. M

Urtica dioica L. — European Nettle, Stinging Nettle — Leaf — 17.8 ppm. EM

Carya glabra (MILLER) SWEET — Pignut Hickory — Shoot — 17 ppm. E

Cocos nucifera L. — Coconut, Coconut Palm, Cocotero (Sp.), Copra, Kokospalme (Ger.), Nariyal — Seed — 16 ppm. E

Raphanus sativus L. — Radish — Root — 15.7 ppm. E

Prunus domestica L. — Plum — Fruit — 15 ppm. TEM

Boehmeria nivea (L.) GAUDICH. — Ramie — Plant — 14 ppm. M

Arachis hypogaea L. — Groundnut, Peanut — Seed — 13 ppm. EM

Polystichum polyblepharum (ROEM.) PRESL — Chinese Polystichum — Plant — 13 ppm. T

Prunus dulcis (MILLER) D. A. WEBB — Almond — Seed — 13 ppm. TEM

Daucus carota L. — Carrot — Root — 12.7 ppm. E

Brassica oleracea var. botrytis L. — Cauliflower — Flower — 11 ppm. E

Corylus avellana L. — Cobnut, English Filbert, European Filbert, European Hazel, Hazel — Seed — 11 ppm. E

Glechoma hederacea L. — Alehoof — Plant — 11 ppm. M

Brassica napus var. napobrassica var. napobrassica (L.) REICHB. — Rutabaga, Swede, Swedish Turnip — Root — 10 ppm. E

Brassica rapa var. rapa — Rapini, Seven-Top Turnip, Turnip — Root — 10 ppm. E

Capsicum annuum L. — Bell Pepper, Cherry Pepper, Cone Pepper, Green Pepper, Paprika, Sweet Pepper — Fruit — 10 ppm. E

Malus domestica BORKH. — Apple — Fruit — 10 ppm. E

Pastinaca sativa L. — Parsnip — Root — 10 ppm. E

Pistacia vera L. — Pistachio — Seed — 10 ppm. E

Pisum sativum L. — Pea — Seed — 10 ppm. E

Juglans nigra L. — Black Walnut — Seed — 9.3 ppm. E

Apium graveolens L. — Celery — Root — 9 ppm. E

Cinnamomum sieboldii — Japanese Cinnamon — Root — Bark — 9 ppm. TEM

Citrus sinensis (L.) OSBECK — Orange — Fruit — 7.7 ppm. E

Phaseolus vulgaris var. vulgaris — Black Bean, Dwarf Bean, Field Bean, Flageolet Bean, French Bean, Garden Bean, Green Bean, Haricot, Haricot Bean, Haricot Vert, Kidney Bean, Navy Bean, Pop Bean, Popping Bean, Snap Bean, String Bean, Wax Bean — Fruit — 7 ppm. E

Allium cepa L. — Onion, Shallot — Bulb — 6.6 ppm. E

Fragaria spp. — Strawberry — Fruit — 6.5 ppm. E

Vitis vinifera L. — European Grape, Grape, Grapevine, Parra (Sp.), Vid (Sp.), Vigne Vinifere (Fr.), Weinrebe (Ger.), Wine Grape — Fruit — 5.5 ppm. EM

Quercus rubra L. — Northern Red Oak — Seed — 5 ppm. EM

Armoracia rusticana GAERTN. ET AL. — Horseradish — Root — 4.6 ppm. E

Carya ovata (MILL.) K. KOCH — Shagbark Hickory — Seed — 4 ppm. E

Vaccinium macrocarpon AITON — American Cranberry, Cranberry, Large Cranberry — Fruit — 3.5 ppm. E

Cinnamomum sieboldii — Japanese Cinnamon — Bark — 3 ppm. TEM

Juglans cinerea L. — Butternut — Seed — 2.5 ppm. E

Citrus reticulata BLANCO — Mandarin, Tangerine — Fruit — 2.4 ppm. E

Scandium

Rhus copallina L. — Dwarf Sumac, Winged Sumac — Plant. EM

Nyssa sylvatica MARSHALL — Black Gum, Black Tupelo — Leaf. EM

Sassafras albidum (NUTT.) NEES — Sassafras — Leaf — Stem. TEM

Bertholletia excelsa BONPL. — Brazilnut, Brazilnut-Tree, Creamnut, Paranut — Seed. E

Vigna unguiculata subsp. sesquipedalis (L.) VERDC. — Asparagus Bean, Pea Bean, Yardlong Bean — Seed. E

Carya illinoensis (WANGENH.) K. KOCH — Pecan — Seed. E

Carya ovata (MILL.) K. KOCH — Shagbark Hickory — Seed. E

Corylus avellana L. — Cobnut, English Filbert, European Filbert, European Hazel, Hazel — Seed. E

Juglans nigra L. — Black Walnut — Seed. E

Pistacia vera L. — Pistachio — Seed. E

Juglans cinerea L. — Butternut — Seed. E

Prunus dulcis (MILLER) D. A. WEBB — Almond — Seed. TEM

Quercus rubra L. — Northern Red Oak — Seed. EM

Anacardium occidentale L. — Cashew — Seed. E

Cocos nucifera L. — Coconut, Coconut Palm, Cocotero (Sp.), Copra, Kokospalme (Ger.), Nariyal — Seed. E

Selenium

Bertholletia excelsa BONPL. — Brazilnut, Brazilnut-Tree, Creamnut, Paranut — Seed — 497 ppm. E

Nepeta cataria L. — Catnip — Plant — 123 ppm. M

Silybum marianum (L.) GAERTN. — Lady's Thistle, Milk Thistle — Plant — 171 ppm. M

Hibiscus sabdariffa L. — Acedera de Guinea (Sp.), Indian Sorrel, Jamaica Sorrel, Kharkadi, Malventee (Ger.), Red Sorrel, Rosa de Jamaica (Sp.), Rosella (Ger.), Roselle, Sereni (Sp.), Sorrel — Flower — 143 ppm. E

Elytrigia repens (L.) DESV. EX NEVSKI — Couchgrass, Doggrass, Quackgrass, Twitchgrass, Wheatgrass — Plant — 102 ppm. EM

Polygonum multiflorum THUNB. — Chinese Cornbind, Chinese Knotweed, Fleeceflower, Fo Ti, He Shou Wu — Root — 74 ppm. TEM

Agathosma betulina (P. J. BERGIUS) PILLANS — Buchu, Honey Buchu, Mountain Buchu — Leaf — 70 ppm. M

Cymbopogon citratus (DC. ex NEES) STAPF — Lemongrass, West Indian Lemongrass — Plant — 62 ppm. EM

Mentha pulegium L. — European Pennyroyal — Plant — 25 ppm. TEM

Cypripedium pubescens WILLD. — Yellow Ladyslipper — Root — 49 ppm. M

Valeriana officinalis L. — Common Valerian, Garden-Heliotrope, Valerian — Root — 44 ppm. M

Caulophyllum thalictroides (L.) MICHX. — Blue Cohosh — Root — 35 ppm. M

Berberis vulgaris L. — Barberry — Root — 34 ppm. M

Cnicus benedictus L. — Blessed Thistle — Plant — 34 ppm. M

Myrica cerifera L. — Bayberry, Candle-Berry, Southern Bayberry, Wax Myrtle — Bark — 34 ppm. EM

Althaea officinalis L. — Marshma-llow, White Mallow — Root — 33 ppm. M

Rhodymenia palmata — Dulse — Plant — 33 ppm. E

Cimicifuga racemosa (L.) NUTT. — Black Cohosh, Black Snakeroot — Root — 32 ppm. M

Cucurbita pepo L. — Pumpkin — Seed — 32 ppm. E

Thymus vulgaris L. — Common Thyme, Garden Thyme, Thyme — Leaf — 16 ppm. EM

Trigonella foenum-graecum L. — Alholva (Sp.), Bockshornklee (Ger.), Fenugreek, Greek Clover, Greek Hay — Seed — 16 ppm. EM

Smilax spp. — Sarsaparilla — Root — 31 ppm. EM

Juglans nigra L. — Black Walnut — Fruit — 30 ppm. E

Panax ginseng C. A. MEYER — Chinese Ginseng, Ginseng, Korean Ginseng, Oriental Ginseng — Root — 25 ppm. M

Rubus idaeus L. — Raspberry, Red Raspberry — Leaf — 25 ppm. EM

Rumex crispus L. — Curly Dock, Lengua De Vaca, Sour Dock, Yellow Dock — Root — 25 ppm. TEM

Stevia rebaudiana (BERTONI) BERTONI — Ca-A-E, Stevia, Sweet Leaf of Paraguay — Leaf — 25 ppm. E

Hordeum vulgare L. — Barley, Barleygrass — Stem — 24 ppm. EM

Phyllanthus emblica L. — Emblic, Myrobalan — Fruit — 12 ppm. E

Ruscus aculeatus L. — Box-Holly, Butcher's Broom — Root — 24 ppm. EM

Aloe vera (L.) BURM. f. — Aloe, Bitter Aloes — Leaf — 23 ppm. EM

Viburnum opulus — Crampbark, European Cranberry Bush, Guelder Rose, Snowball Bush — Bark — 23 ppm. TEM

Mentha x piperita— Peppermint — Leaf — 11 ppm. TEM

Urtica dioica L. — European Nettle, Stinging Nettle — Leaf — 22 ppm. EM

Echinacea spp. — Coneflower, Echinacea — Root — 21 ppm. M

Carthamus tinctorius L. — Safflower — Flower — 20 ppm. M

Crataegus laevigata (POIR.) DC — English Hawthorn, Hawthorn, Whitethorn, Woodland Hawthorn — Fruit — 20 ppm. M

Larrea tridentata (SESSE & MOC. ex DC.) COV. — Chaparral, Creosote Bush — Plant — 19 ppm. M

Chondrus crispus (L.) STACKH. — Irish Moss — Plant — 18 ppm. E

Gentiana lutea L. — Gentian, Yellow Gentian — Root — 18 ppm. M

Vitis vinifera L. — European Grape, Grape, Grapevine, Parra (Sp.), Vid (Sp.), Vigne Vinifere (Fr.), Weinrebe (Ger.), Wine Grape — Stem — 18 ppm. EM

Chrysanthemum parthenium (L.) BERNH. — Feverfew — Plant — 17 ppm. M

Fucus vesiculosus L. — Bladderwrack, Kelp — Plant — 17 ppm. EM

Humulus lupulus L. — Hops — Fruit — 17 ppm. TEM

Scutellaria lateriflora L. — Mad-Dog, Skullcap, Scullcap — Plant — 8.3 ppm. M

Achillea millefolium L. — Milfoil, Yarrow — Plant — 16 ppm. M

Allium sativum var. sativum L. — Garlic — Bulb — 16 ppm. E

Arctostaphylos uva-ursi (L.) SPRENGEL — Bearberry, Uva Ursi — Leaf — 16 ppm. M

Foeniculum vulgare MILLER — Fennel — Fruit — 16 ppm. M

Hydrangea arborescens L. — Hydrangea, Smooth Hydrangea — Root — 16 ppm. EM

Trifolium pratense L. — Cowgrass, Peavine Clover, Purple Clover, Red Clover — Flower — 7.7 ppm. EM

Harpagophytum procumbens (BURCH.) DC. EX MEISN. — Devil's Claw, Grapple — Plant — Root — 15 ppm. M

Quercus alba L. — White Oak — Bark — 15 ppm. EM

Ulmus rubra MUHLENB. — Red Elm, Slippery Elm — Bark — 15 ppm. M

Arctium lappa L. — Burdock, Gobo, Great Burdock — Root — 14 ppm. EM

Plantago psyllium L. — Psyllium — Seed — 14 ppm. EM

Viscum album L. — European Mistletoe — Leaf — 14 ppm. TM

Avena sativa L. — Oats — Plant — 13 ppm. EM

Equisetum arvense L. — Field Horsetail, Horsetail — Plant — 13 ppm. M

Prunus persica (L.) BATSCH — Peach — Bark — 13 ppm. TEM

Centella asiatica (L.) URBAN — Gotu Kola, Pennywort — Leaf — 12 ppm. EM

Ephedra sinica STAPF — Chinese Ephedra, Ma Huang — Plant — 12 ppm. M

Prunus dulcis (MILLER) D. A. WEBB — Almond — Seed — 6 ppm. TEM

Frangula purshiana (DC.) J. G. COOPER — Cascara Buckthorn, Cascara Sagrada — Bark — 11 ppm. M

Salix alba L. — White Willow — Bark — 11 ppm. M

Hydrastis canadensis L. — Goldenseal — Root — 10 ppm. M

Zingiber officinale ROSCOE — Ginger — Rhizome — 10 ppm. EM

Dioscorea sp. — Wild Yam — Root — 9.4 ppm. E

Yucca baccata TORR. — Banana Yucca, Blue Yucca, Spanish Bayonet, Yucca — Root — 9 ppm. TEM

Taraxacum officinale WEBER EX F. H. WIGG. — Dandelion — Root — 8.6 ppm. EM

Chamaemelum nobile (L.) ALL. — Garden Camomile, Perennial Camomile, Roman Camomile — Flower — 7.8 ppm. M

Schisandra chinensis (TURCZ.) BAILL. — Chinese Magnolia Vine, Five-Flavor-Fruit, Magnolia Vine, Schizandra, Wu Wei Zi, Wu Wei Zu — Fruit — 7.4 ppm. M

Turnera diffusa WILLD. EX SCHULT. — Damiana — Leaf — 6.7 ppm. M

Symphytum officinale L. — Comfrey — Root — 5.7 ppm. TM

Zea mays L. — Corn — Silk Stigma — Style — 5.7 ppm. E

Cucumis sativus L. — Cucumber — Fruit — 2.8 ppm. E

Lobelia inflata L. — Indian Tobacco, Lobelia — Leaf — 5 ppm. TM

Verbascum thapsus L. — Flannelleaf, Flannel-plant, Great Mullein, Mullein, Velvetplant — Leaf — 5 ppm. M

Euphrasia officinalis L. — Eyebright — Plant — 4.7 ppm. M

Stellaria media (L.) VILLARS — Chickweed, Common Chickweed — Plant — 4.3 ppm. M

Angelica sinensis (OLIV.) DIELS — Chinese Angelica, Dang Gui, Dang Quai, Dang Qui, Dong Gui, Dong Quai — Root — 3.5 ppm. M

Juniperus communis L. — Common Juniper, Juniper — Fruit — 2.4 ppm. TEM

Tabebuia heptaphylla (VELL.) TOLEDO — Pau D'Arco — Bark — 2 ppm. M

Amorphophallus konjac K. KOCH — Devil's Tongue, Elephant Yam, Konjac, Leopard Palm, Snake Palm, Umbrella Arum — Root — 1.7 ppm. TEM

Glycine max (L.) MERR. — Soybean — Seed — 1.25 ppm. E

Glycyrrhiza glabra L. — Commom Licorice, Licorice, Licorice-Root, Smooth Licorice — Root — 1 ppm. M

Silicon

Urtica dioica L. — European Nettle, Stinging Nettle — Leaf — 6,500 ppm. EM

Carya glabra (MILLER) SWEET — Pignut Hickory — Shoot — 4,180 ppm. E

Quercus rubra L. — Northern Red Oak — Stem — 2,442 ppm. EM

Carya ovata (MILL.) K. KOCH — Shagbark Hickory — Shoot — 2,250 ppm. E

Bertholletia excelsa BONPL. — Brazilnut, Brazilnut-Tree, Creamnut, Paranut — Seed — 1,770 ppm. E

Juglans cinerea L. — Butternut — Seed — 1,450 ppm. E

Pistacia vera L. — Pistachio — Seed — 1,450 ppm. E

Petroselinum crispum (MILLER) NYMAN EX A. W. HILLL — Parsley — Leaf — 1,425 ppm. E

Juglans nigra L. — Black Walnut — Seed — 1,387 ppm. E

Anacardium occidentale L. — Cashew — Seed — 1,280 ppm. E

Brassica rapa var. rapa — Rapini, Seven-Top Turnip, Turnip — Root — 1,200 ppm. E

Phaseolus vulgaris var. vulgaris — Black Bean, Dwarf Bean, Field Bean, Flageolet Bean, French Bean, Garden Bean, Green Bean, Haricot, Haricot Bean, Haricot Vert, Kidney Bean, Navy Bean, Pop Bean, Popping Bean, Snap Bean, String Bean, Wax Bean — Fruit — 1,200 ppm. E

Carya ovata (MILL.) K. KOCH — Shagbark Hickory — Seed — 1,180 ppm. E

Cucumis sativus L. — Cucumber — Fruit — 1,000 ppm. E

Prunus dulcis (MILLER) D. A. WEBB — Almond — Seed — 960 ppm. TEM

Corylus avellana L. — Cobnut, English Filbert, European Filbert, European Hazel, Hazel — Seed — 900 ppm. E

Spinacia oleracea L. — Spinach — Leaf — 855 ppm. E

Lactuca sativa L. — Lettuce — Leaf — 800 ppm. E

Anethum graveolens L. — Dill, Garden Dill — Plant — 700 ppm. E

Ananas comosus (L.) MERR. — Pineapple — Fruit — 690 ppm. E

Phoenix dactylifera L. — Date Palm — Fruit — 660 ppm. E

Raphanus sativus L. — Radish — Root — 425 ppm. E

Equisetum arvense L. — Field Horsetail, Horsetail — Plant — 386 ppm. M

Cocos nucifera L. — Coconut, Coconut Palm, Cocotero (Sp.), Copra, Koko-spalme (Ger.), Nariyal — Seed — 370 ppm. E

Rhodymenia palmata — Dulse — Plant — 368 ppm. E

Vitis vinifera L. — European Grape, Grape, Grapevine, Parra (Sp.), Vid (Sp.), Vigne Vinifere (Fr.), Weinrebe (Ger.), Wine Grape — Stem — 365 ppm. EM

Musa x paradisiaca L. — Banana, Plantain — Fruit — 350 ppm. E

Ribes rubrum L. — Red Currant, White Currant — Fruit — 312 ppm. E

Euphrasia officinalis L. — Eyebright — Plant — 303 ppm. M

Echinacea spp. — Coneflower, Echinacea — Root — 301 ppm. M

Hydrastis canadensis L. — Goldenseal — Root — 287 ppm. M

Zingiber officinale ROSCOE — Ginger — Rhizome — 285 ppm. EM

Ruscus aculeatus L. — Box-Holly, Butcher's Broom — Root — 280 ppm. EM

Fragaria spp. — Strawberry — Fruit — 270 ppm. E

Elytrigia repens (L.) DESV. EX NEVSKI — Couchgrass, Doggrass, Quackgrass, Twitchgrass, Wheatgrass — Plant — 253 ppm. EM

Zea mays L. — Corn Silk — Stigma /Style — 237 ppm. E

Arctium lappa L. — Burdock, Gobo, Great Burdock — Root — 225 ppm. EM

Hydrangea arborescens L. — Hydrangea, Smooth Hydrangea — Root — 223 ppm. EM

Cypripedium pubescens WILLD. — Yellow Ladyslipper — Root — 222 ppm. M

Ribes nigrum L. — Black Currant — Fruit — 220 ppm. E

Thymus vulgaris L. — Common Thyme, Garden Thyme, Thyme — Leaf — 202 ppm. EM

Carya illinoensis (WANGENH.) K. KOCH — Pecan — Seed — 200 ppm. E

Rheum rhabarbarum L. — Rhubarb — Plant — 200 ppm. E

Sorbus aucuparia L. — Rowan Berry, Mountain Ash — Fruit — 190 ppm. TEM

Avena sativa L. — Oats — Plant — 183 ppm. EM

Mentha pulegium L. — European Penny-royal — Plant — 182 ppm. TEM

Glycyrrhiza glabra L. — Commom Licorice, Licorice, Licorice-Root, Smooth Licorice — Root — 158 ppm. M

Stellaria media (L.) VILLARS — Chickweed, Common Chickweed — Plant — 157 ppm. E

Centella asiatica (L.) URBAN — Gotu Kola, Pennywort — Leaf — 140 ppm. EM

Vaccinium vitis-idaea var. minus LODD. — Cowberry, Lingen, Lingonberry — Fruit — 133 ppm. E

Cymbopogon citratus (DC. ex NEES) STAPF — Lemongrass, West Indian Lemongrass — Plant — 132 ppm. EM

Stevia rebaudiana (BERTONI) BERTONI —
Ca-A-E, Stevia, Sweet Leaf of Paraguay
— Leaf — 132 ppm. E

Brassica oleracea — Cauliflower — Flower
— 125 ppm. E

Viburnum opulus — Crampbark, European
Cranberry Bush, Guelder Rose, Snowball Bush — Bark — 99 ppm. TEM

Daucus carota L. — Carrot — Root —
91 ppm. E

Hibiscus sabdariffa L. — Acedera de Guinea
(Sp.), Indian Sorrel, Jamaica Sorrel,
Kharkadi, Malventee (Ger.), Red Sorrel,
Rosa de Jamaica (Sp.), Rosella (Ger.),
Roselle, Sereni (Sp.), Sorrel — Flower
— 91 ppm. E

Brassica oleracea var. botrytis L. — Cauliflower — Leaf — 90 ppm. E

Smilax spp. — Sarsaparilla — Root — 88
ppm. EM

Tabebuia heptaphylla (VELL.) TOLEDO —
Pau D'Arco — Bark — 84 ppm. M

Beta vulgaris subsp. vulgaris — Beet, Beetroot, Garden Beet, Sugar Beet — Root
— 83 ppm. E

Fucus vesiculosus L. — Bladderwrack, Kelp
— Plant — 76 ppm. EM

Allium cepa L. — Onion, Shallot — Bulb —
75 ppm. E

Verbascum thapsus L. — Flannelleaf, Flannelplant, Great Mullein, Mullein, Velvetplant — Leaf — 74 ppm. M

Arctostaphylos uva-ursi (L.) SPRENGEL
— Bearberry, Uva Ursi — Leaf — 70
ppm. M

Malus domestica BORKH. — Apple — Fruit
— 70 ppm. E

Chondrus crispus (L.) STACKH. — Irish
Moss — Plant — 67 ppm. E

Caulophyllum thalictroides (L.) MICHX. —
Blue Cohosh — Root — 63 ppm. M

Prunus domestica L. — Plum — Fruit —
62 ppm. TEM

Rubus chamaemorus L. — Cloudberry —
Fruit — 62 ppm. EM

Pisum sativum L. — Pea — Seed —
59 ppm. E

Pastinaca sativa L. — Parsnip — Root —
50 ppm. E

Scutellaria lateriflora L. — Mad-Dog, Skullcap, Scullcap — Plant — 48 ppm. M

Carthamus tinctorius L. — Safflower —
Flower — 47 ppm. M

Taraxacum officinale WEBER EX F. H.
WIGG. — Dandelion — Root —
47 ppm. EM

Trigonella foenum-graecum L. — Alholva
(Sp.), Bockshornklee (Ger.), Fenugreek,
Greek Clover, Greek Hay — Seed — 47
ppm. EM

Chrysanthemum parthenium (L.) BERNH.
— Feverfew — Plant — 46 ppm. M

Achillea millefolium L. — Milfoil, Yarrow —
Plant — 45 ppm. M

Humulus lupulus L. — Hops — Fruit — 45
ppm. TEM

Juniperus communis L. — Common Juniper, Juniper — Fruit — 45 ppm. TEM

Agathosma betulina (P. J. BERGIUS) PIL-
LANS — Buchu, Honey Buchu, Mountain Buchu — Leaf — 43 ppm. M

Silver

Lycopersicon esculentum MILLER — Tomato — Fruit — 1.4 ppm. TEM

Quercus rubra L. — Northern Red Oak —
Stem — 1.32 ppm. EM

Carya glabra (MILLER) SWEET — Pignut
Hickory — Shoot. E

Brassica oleracea var. capitata L. — Cabbage,
Red Cabbage, White Cabbage — Leaf. E

Lactuca sativa L. — Lettuce — Leaf. E

Prunus domestica L. — Plum — Fruit. TEM

Prunus serotina subsp. serotina — Black
Cherry, Wild Cherry — Leaf. TEM

Phaseolus vulgaris var. vulgaris — Black
Bean, Dwarf Bean, Field Bean, Flageolet
Bean, French Bean, Garden Bean, Green
Bean, Haricot, Haricot Bean, Haricot
Vert, Kidney Bean, Navy Bean, Pop
Bean, Popping Bean, Snap Bean, String
Bean, Wax Bean — Fruit. E

Prunus persica (L.) BATSCH — Peach —
Fruit. TEM

Cichorium endivia L. — Endive, Escarole
— Leaf. E

Liquidambar styraciflua L. — American
Styrax, Sweetgum — Stem. EM

Quercus alba L. — White Oak — Stem. EM

Nyssa sylvatica MARSHALL — Black Gum,
Black Tupelo — Stem. EM

Brassica pekinensis (LOUR.) RUPR. — Chinese Cabbage — Leaf. E

Sassafras albidum (NUTT.) NEES — Sassafras — Leaf. TEM

Petroselinum crispum (MILLER) NYMAN EX A. W. HILLL — Parsley — Plant. E

Nyssa sylvatica MARSHALL — Black Gum, Black Tupelo — Leaf. EM

Solanum melongena L. — Aubergine, Eggplant — Fruit. E

Phaseolus vulgaris var. vulgaris — Black Bean, Dwarf Bean, Field Bean, Flageolet Bean, French Bean, Garden Bean, Green Bean, Haricot, Haricot Bean, Haricot Vert, Kidney Bean, Navy Bean, Pop Bean, Popping Bean, Snap Bean, String Bean, Wax Bean — Seed. E

Cucumis sativus L. — Cucumber — Fruit. E

Pinus echinata MILLER — Shortleaf Pine — Shoot. M

Asparagus officinalis L. — Asparagus — Shoot. E

Citrus paradisi MacFAD. — Grapefruit — Fruit. E

Cucumis melo var. cantalupensis NAUDIN — Cantaloupe, Melon, Muskmelon, Netted Melon, Nutmeg Melon, Persian Melon — Fruit. E

Capsicum annuum L. — Bell Pepper, Cherry Pepper, Cone Pepper, Green Pepper, Paprika, Sweet Pepper — Fruit. E

Prunus serotina subsp. serotina — Black Cherry, Wild Cherry — Stem. TEM

Malus domestica BORKH. — Apple — Fruit. E

Vitis vinifera L. — European Grape, Grape, Grapevine, Parra (Sp.), Vid (Sp.), Vigne Vinifere (Fr.), Weinrebe (Ger.), Wine Grape — Fruit. EM

Solanum tuberosum L. — Potato — Tuber. E

Citrus sinensis (L.) OSBECK — Orange — Fruit. E

Zea mays L. — Corn — Seed. E

Allium cepa L. — Onion, Shallot — Bulb. E

Pyrus communis L. — Pear — Fruit. E

Vigna unguiculata subsp. sesquipedalis (L.) VERDC. — Asparagus Bean, Pea Bean, Yardlong Bean — Seed. E

Sodium

Urtica dioica L. — European Nettle, Stinging Nettle — Leaf — 491,400 ppm. EM

Olea europaea subsp. europaea — Olive — Fruit — 110,092 ppm. E

Rhodymenia palmata — Dulse — Plant — 99,170 ppm. E

Chondrus crispus (L.) STACKH. — Irish Moss — Plant — 81,200 ppm. E

Fucus vesiculosus L. — Bladderwrack, Kelp — Plant — 56,100 ppm. EM

Tetragonia tetragonioides (PALLAS) KUNTZE — New Zealand Spinach — Leaf — 21,665 ppm. E

Brassica chinensis L. — Bok-Choy, Celery Cabbage, Celery Mustard, Chinese Cabbage, Chinese Mustard, Chinese White Cabbage, Pak-Choi — Leaf — 21,477 ppm. E

Lactuca sativa L. — Lettuce — Leaf — 18,560 ppm. E

Lycium chinense MILL. — Chinese Boxthorn, Chinese Matrimony Vine, Chinese Wolfberry, Chinesischer Bocksdorn (Ger.), Daun Koki (Indones.), Gou Qi (Chin.), Kaukichai (Malays.), Kuko (Jap.), Lyciet de Chine (Fr.), Spina Santa Cinese (Ital.), Wolfberry — Leaf — 18,365 ppm. EM

Apium graveolens L. — Celery — Plant — 17,135 ppm. E

Beta vulgaris subsp. vulgaris — Beet, Beetroot, Garden Beet, Sugar Beet — Leaf — 16,571 ppm. E

Chrysanthemum coronarium L. — Garland Chrysanthemum — Leaf — 16,300 ppm. M

Ipomoea aquatica FORSSKAL — Swamp Cabbage, Water Spinach — Leaf — 15,000 ppm. E

Brassica rapa var. rapa — Rapini, Seven-Top Turnip, Turnip — Root — 11,600 ppm. E

Borago officinalis L. — Beebread, Beeplant, Borage, Talewort — Plant — 11,440 ppm. TEM

Spinacia oleracea L. — Spinach — Plant — 10,669 ppm. E

Raphanus sativus L. — Radish — Leaf — 9,565 ppm. E

Daucus carota L. — Carrot — Root — 9,504 ppm. E

Avena sativa L. — Oats — Plant — 9,400 ppm. EM

Rhizophora mangle L. — Red Mangrove — Leaf — 9,200 ppm. M

Tephrosia purpurea PERS. — Purple Tephrosia, Wild Indigo — Leaf — 8,700 ppm. TM

Lantana camara L. — Lantana, Wild Sage — Leaf — 8,200 ppm. M

Nasturtium officinale R. BR. — Berro, Watercress — Herb — 8,200 ppm. E

Glycyrrhiza glabra L. — Commom Licorice, Licorice, Licorice-Root, Smooth Licorice — Root — 8,180 ppm. M

Coriandrum sativum L. — Chinese Parsley, Cilantro, Coriander — Leaf — 7,581 ppm. E

Portulaca oleracea L. — Purslane, Verdolaga — Plant — 7,400 ppm. E

Chrysanthemum coronarium L. — Garland Chrysanthemum — Bud — 6,990 ppm. M

Cynara cardunculus subsp. cardunculus — Artichoke — Flower — 6,840 ppm. E

Beta vulgaris subsp. vulgaris — Beet, Beet-root, Garden Beet, Sugar Beet — Root — 6,705 ppm. E

Lycopersicon esculentum MILLER — Tomato — Fruit — 6,600 ppm. TEM

Petroselinum crispum (MILLER) NYMAN EX A. W. HILLL — Parsley — Plant — 5,569 ppm. E

Mentha pulegium L. — European Pennyroyal — Plant — 5,410 ppm. TEM

Taraxacum officinale WEBER EX F. H. WIGG. — Dandelion — Leaf — 5,278 ppm. EM

Raphanus sativus L. — Radish — Root — 5,020 ppm. E

Cyrtosperma chamissonis (SCHOTT) MERR. — Swamp Taro — Root — 4,855 ppm. E

Panax quinquefolius L. — American Ginseng, Ginseng — Plant — 4,800 ppm. M

Trichosanthes anguina L. — Snakegourd — Fruit — 4,630 ppm. E

Rosa canina L. — Dog Rose, Dogbrier, Rose — Fruit — 4,600 ppm. EM

Brassica oleracea var. viridis l. L. — Collards, Cow Cabbage, Spring-Heading Cabbage, Tall Kale, Tree Kale — Leaf — 4,589 ppm. E

Cichorium endivia L. — Endive, Escarole — Leaf — 4,560 ppm. E

Brassica oleracea var. capitata L. — Cabbage, Red Cabbage, White Cabbage — Leaf — 4,510 ppm. E

Brassica nigra (L.) W. D. J. KOCH — Black Mustard — Leaf — 4,506 ppm. E

Curcuma longa L. — Indian Saffron, Turmeric — Rhizome — 4,290 ppm. E

Glycine max (L.) MERR. — Soybean — Seed — 3,800 ppm. E

Brassica oleracea var. acephala DC — Curly Kale, Kale, Kitchen Kale, Scotch Kale — Leaf — 3,650 ppm. E

Symphytum officinale L. — Comfrey — Root — 3,510 ppm. TM

Oryza sativa L. — Rice — Plant — 3,500 ppm. E

Anethum graveolens L. — Dill, Garden Dill — Plant — 3,308 ppm. E

Syzygium aromaticum (L.) MERR. & L. M. PERRY — Clove, Clovetree — Flower — 3,250 ppm. E

Brassica oleracea — Cauliflower — Leaf — 3,091 ppm. E

Triticum aestivum L. — Wheat — Plant — 3,000 ppm. EM

Vicia faba L. — Broadbean, Faba Bean, Habas — Seed — 2,980 ppm. E

Eucommia ulmoides OLIV. — Du Zhong, Gutta-Percha Tree, Tu Chung — Bark — 2,820 ppm. M

Agathosma betulina (P. J. BERGIUS) PILLANS — Buchu, Honey Buchu, Mountain Buchu — Leaf — 2,760 ppm. M

Manihot esculenta CRANTZ — Cassava, Tapioca, Yuca — Root — 2,655 ppm. E

Schisandra chinensis (TURCZ.) BAILL. — Chincsc Magnolia Vine, Five Flavor Fruit, Magnolia Vine, Schizandra, Wu Wei Zi, Wu Wei Zu — Fruit — 2,630 ppm. M

Vicia faba L. — Broadbean, Faba Bean, Habas — Seed — 2,630 ppm. E

Chamaemelum nobile (L.) ALL. — Garden Camomile, Perennial Camomile, Roman Camomile — Flower — 2,580 ppm. M

Mentha x rotundifolia (L.) HUDSON — Applemint — Leaf — 2,520 ppm. TEM

Sodium, cont.

Cichorium intybus L. — Chicory, Succory, Witloof — Root — 2,500 ppm. E

Morus alba L. — Sang-Pai-Pi, White Mulberry — Fruit — 2,467 ppm. EM

Amaranthus sp. — Pigweed — Leaf — 2,406 ppm. EM

Helianthus tuberosus L. — Jerusalem Artichoke — Tuber — 2,400 ppm. E

Carthamus tinctorius L. — Safflower — Flower — 2,320 ppm. M

Brassica oleracea var. botrytis L. — Cauliflower — Flower — 2,300 ppm. E

Hordeum vulgare L. — Barley, Barleygrass — Stem — 2,240 ppm. EM

Brassica oleracea var. gongylodes L. — Kohlrabi — Stem — 2,222 ppm. E

Pinellia ternata BREITENBACH — Ban-Xia, Pan-Hsia — Tuber — 2,200 ppm. TEM

Triticum aestivum L. — Wheat — Seed — 2,200 ppm. EM

Solanum melongena L. — Aubergine, Eggplant — Fruit — 2,150 ppm. E

Lycium chinense MILL. — Chinese Boxthorn, Chinese Matrimony Vine, Chinese Wolfberry, Chinesischer Bocksdorn (Ger.), Daun Koki (Indones.), Gou Qi (Chin.), Kaukichai (Malays.), Kuko (Jap.), Lyciet de Chine (Fr.), Spina Santa Cinese (Ital.), Wolfberry — Fruit — 2,140 ppm. EM

Allium cepa L. — Onion, Shallot — Bulb — 2,052 ppm. E

Panicum maximum JACQ. — Guinea grass — Leaf — 0-4,100 ppm. M

Cuminum cyminum L. — Cumin — Fruit — 2,028 ppm. EM

Brassica oleracea var. gemmifera DC — Brussel-Sprout, Brussels-Sprouts — Leaf — 1,990 ppm. E

Foeniculum vulgare MILLER — Fennel — Fruit — 1,980 ppm. M

Cistanche salsa (C.A.MEYER) G. BECK — Broomrape, Cistanchis Herba, Jou Tsung Jung — Plant — 1,970 ppm. M

Mentha x piperita — Peppermint — Leaf — 1,950 ppm. TEM

Nelumbo nucifera L. — Water Lotus — Rhizome — 1,935 ppm. EM

Brassica pekinensis (LOUR.) RUPR. — Chinese Cabbage — Leaf — 1,932 ppm. E

Blechnum orientale L. — Kuan Chung, Shield Fern — Rhizome — 1,930 ppm. TEM

Brassica napus var. napobrassica var. napobrassica (L.) REICHB. — Rutabaga, Swede, Swedish Turnip — Root — 1,930 ppm. E

Psidium cattleianum SABINE — Strawberry Guava — Fruit — 1,915 ppm. E

Apium graveolens L. — Celery — Seed — 1,900 ppm. E

Moringa oleifera LAM. — Ben Nut, Benzolive Tree, Drumstick Tree, Horseradish Tree, Jacinto (Sp.), Moringa, West Indian Ben — Fruit — 420-3,560 ppm. E

Glycine max (L.) MERR. — Soybean Sprout — Seedling — 1,622 ppm. E

Avena sativa L. — Oats — Seed — 1,600 ppm. EM

Arctium lappa L. — Burdock, Gobo, Great Burdock — Root — 1,520 ppm. EM

Benincasa hispida (THUNB.) COGN. — Waxgourd — Fruit — 1,500 ppm.

Thymus vulgaris L. — Common Thyme, Garden Thyme, Thyme — Leaf — 1,490 ppm. EM

Stellaria media (L.) VILLARS — Chickweed, Common Chickweed — Plant — 1,470 ppm. E

Perilla frutescens (L.) BRITTON — Perilla — Leaf — 1,429 ppm. TEM

Cichorium intybus L. — Chicory, Succory, Witloof — Leaf — 1,428 ppm. E

Phyllanthus emblica L. — Emblic, Myrobalan — Fruit — 1,384 ppm. E

Althaea officinalis L. — Marshmallow, White Mallow — Root — 1,370 ppm. M

Thymus vulgaris L. — Common Thyme, Garden Thyme, Thyme — Plant — 1,341 ppm. EM

Glycyrrhiza uralensis FISCH. EX DC. — Chinese Licorice, Gan-Cao, Kan-Tsao — Root — 1,340 ppm. M

Lepidium sativum L. — Garden Cress — Leaf — 1,320 ppm. E

Petasites japonicus (SIEBOLD & ZUCC.) MAXIM. — Butterbur Plant 1,270 ppm. T

Momordica charantia L. — Bitter Melon, Sorosi — Leaf — 1,234 ppm. E

Ipomoea batatas (L.) LAM — Sweet Potato — Root — 1,229 ppm. E

Cnicus benedictus L. — Blessed Thistle — Plant — 1,220 ppm. M

Malpighia glabra L. — Acerola — Fruit — 1,219 ppm. EM

Taraxacum officinale WEBER EX F. H. WIGG. — Dandelion — Root — 1,130 ppm. EM

Cucumis melo var. cantalupensis NAUDIN — Cantaloupe, Melon, Muskmelon, Netted Melon, Nutmeg Melon, Persian Melon — Fruit — 1,115 ppm. E

Syzygium jambos ALSTON — Pomarrosa, Rose Apple — Fruit — 340-2,200 ppm. E

Salvia officinalis L. — Sage — Leaf — 1,080 ppm. EM

Centella asiatica (L.) URBAN — Gotu Kola, Pennywort — Leaf — 1,040 ppm. EM

Annona muricata L. — Soursop — Fruit — 1,035 ppm. E

Cucurbita pepo L. — Pumpkin — Flower — 1,030 ppm. E

Linum usitatissimum L. — Flax, Linseed — Seed — 1,014 ppm. E

Alocasia macrorrhiza (L.) G. DON — Giant Taro — Root — 1,010 ppm. E

Artemisia capillaris THUNB. — Capillary Wormwood — Plant — 1,010 ppm. M

Abelmoschus esculentus (L.) MOENCH — Okra — Fruit — 1,000 ppm. EM

Scutellaria baicalensis GEORGI — Baikal Skullcap, Chinese Skullcap, Huang Qin — Root — 991 ppm. M

Gardenia jasminoides J. ELLIS — Cape Jasmine, Gardenia, Jasmin, Shan-Chih-Tzu, Shan-Zhi-Zi, Zhi Zi — Fruit — 985 ppm. M

Nigella sativa L. — Black Caraway, Black Cumin, Fennel-Flower, Nutmeg-Flower, Roman Coriander — Seed — 980 ppm. EM

Plantago asiatica L. — Asian Plantain — Plant — 950 ppm. EM

Cynanchum atratum BUNGE — Bai-Wei, Pai-Wei — Root — 940 ppm. EM

Eriocaulon sp — Oriental Pipewort — Leaf — 940 ppm. M

Oryza sativa L. — Rice — Seed — 939 ppm. E

Origanum majorana L. — Marjoram, Sweet Marjoram — Plant — 935 ppm. E

Senna obtusifolia (L.) H.IRWIN & BARNEBY — Sicklepod — Seed — 930 ppm. TE

Trigonella foenum-graecum L. — Alholva (Sp.), Bockshornklee (Ger.), Fenugreek, Greek Clover, Greek Hay — Seed — 915 ppm. EM

Anthriscus cerefolium (L.) HOFFM. — Chervil — Leaf — 895 ppm. E

Stevia rebaudiana (BERTONI) BERTONI — Ca-A-E, Stevia, Sweet Leaf of Paraguay — Leaf — 892 ppm. E

Tragopogon porrifolius L. — Salsify — Root — 870 ppm. E

Areca catechu L. — Betel Nut, Pin-Lang — Seed — 867 ppm. EM

Mentha arvensis var. piperascens MALINV. EX L. H. BAILEY — Cornmint, Field Mint, Japanese Mint — Plant — 860 ppm. TEM

Rheum rhabarbarum L. — Rhubarb — Plant — 855 ppm. E

Pimenta dioica (L.) MERR. — Allspice, Clover-Pepper, Jamaica-Pepper, Pimenta, Pimento — Fruit — 842 ppm. E

Phoenix dactylifera L. — Date Palm — Seed — 820 ppm. E

Syzygium cumini SKEELS — Aceituna Dulce, Jambolan, Java Plum — Fruit — 90-1,605 ppm. E

Myristica fragrans HOUTT. — Mace, Muskatnussbaum (Ger.), Nutmeg, nogal moscado (Sp.), nuez moscada (Sp.) — Aril — 800 ppm. E

Lycium chinense MILL. — Chinese Boxthorn, Chinese Matrimony Vine, Chinese Wolfberry, Chinesischer Bocksdorn (Ger.), Daun Koki (Indones.), Gou Qi (Chin.), Kaukichai (Malays.), Kuko (Jap.), Lyciet de Chine (Fr.), Spina Santa Cinese (Ital.), Wolfberry Root — Bark — 793 ppm. EM

Vigna radata (L.) WILCZEK — Green Gram, Mungbean Sprout — Seedling — 782 ppm. E

Taraxacum mongolicum HAND.-MAZZ. — Mongoloid Dandelion — Plant — 763 ppm. EM

Trigonella foenum-graecum L. — Alholva (Sp.), Bockshornklee (Ger.), Fenugreek, Greek Clover, Greek Hay — Leaf — 761 ppm. EM

Sodium, cont.

Myrica cerifera L. — Bayberry, Candle-Berry, Southern Bayberry, Wax Myrtle — Bark — 760 ppm. EM

Pachira macrocarpa WALP. — Large-Fruited Provision Tree — Seed — 760 ppm. E

Verbascum thapsus L. — Flannelleaf, Flannelplant, Great Mullein, Mullein, Velvetplant — Leaf — 760 ppm. M

Zea mays L. — Corn — Seed — 757 ppm. E

Corchorus olitorius L. — Jew's Mallow, Mulukiya, Nalta Jute — Leaf — 755 ppm. EM

Allium schoenoprasum L. — Chives — Leaf — 750 ppm. E

Dioscorea pentaphylla L. — Mountain Yam — Root — 750 ppm. E

Tamarindus indica L. — Indian Tamarind, Kilytree, Tamarind — Fruit — 743 ppm. M

Capsicum frutescens L. — Cayenne, Chili, Hot Pepper, Red Chili, Spur Pepper, Tabasco — Fruit — 734 ppm. E

Terminalia catappa L. — Indian Almond, Malabar Almond, Tropical Almond — Seed — 730 ppm. M

Harpagophytum procumbens (BURCH.) DC. EX MEISN. — Devil's Claw, Grapple Plant — Root — 718 ppm. M

Cucumis sativus L. — Cucumber — Fruit — 714 ppm. E

Opuntia ficus-indica (L.) MILL. — Indian Fig, Nopal, Nopalito, Prickly Pear — Seed — 714 ppm. EM

Carica papaya L. — Papaya — Leaf — 711 ppm. EM

Zingiber officinale ROSCOE — Ginger — Rhizome — 709 ppm. EM

Phaseolus vulgaris var. vulgaris — Black Bean, Dwarf Bean, Field Bean, Flageolet Bean, French Bean, Garden Bean, Green Bean, Haricot, Haricot Bean, Haricot Vert, Kidney Bean, Navy Bean, Pop Bean, Popping Bean, Snap Bean, String Bean, Wax Bean — Fruit — 707 ppm. E

Asparagus officinalis L. — Asparagus — Shoot — 685 ppm. E

Vigna unguiculata subsp. sesquipedalis (L.) VERDC. — Asparagus Bean, Pea Bean, Yardlong Bean — Shoot — 685 ppm. E

Cymbopogon citratus (DC. ex NEES) STAPF — Lemongrass, West Indian Lemongrass — Plant — 640 ppm. EM

Sesamum indicum L. — Ajonjoli (Sp.), Beni, Benneseed, Sesame, Sesamo (Sp.) — Seed — 634 ppm. EM

Phyllanthus acidus (L.) SKEELS — Indian Gooseberry, Otaheite Gooseberry — Fruit — 632 ppm. E

Piper nigrum L. — Black Pepper, Pepper, White Pepper — Fruit — 627 ppm. EM

Cocos nucifera L. — Coconut, Coconut Palm, Cocotero (Sp.), Copra, Kokospalme (Ger.), Nariyal — Seed — 626 ppm. E

Rehmannia glutinosa (GAERTN.) LIBOSCH. — Chinese Foxglove — Root — 626 ppm. M

Capsicum annuum L. — Bell Pepper, Cherry Pepper, Cone Pepper, Green Pepper, Paprika, Sweet Pepper — Fruit — 625 ppm. E

Artemisia dracunculus L. — Tarragon — Plant — 620 ppm. M

Trachyspermum ammi (L.) SPRAGUE ex TURRILL — Ajwan — Fruit — 605 ppm. EM

Luffa aegyptiaca MILLER — Luffa, Smooth Loofah, Vegetable Sponge — Fruit — 600 ppm. E

Nardostachys chinensis BATALIN — Chinese Spikenard — Rhizome — 596 ppm. M

Rosmarinus officinalis L. — Rosemary — Plant — 592 ppm. EM

Phytelephas aequatorialis — Spruce — Equatorial Ivory Palm — Mesocarp — 180-1,165 ppm. EM

Pisum sativum L. — Pea — Fruit — 578 ppm. E

Pastinaca sativa L. — Parsnip — Root — 575 ppm. E

Sechium edule (JACQ.) SW. — Chayote — Fruit — 570 ppm. EM

Passiflora edulis SIMS — Maracuya, Passionfruit — Fruit — 280-1,124 ppm. E

Equisetum arvense L. — Field Horsetail, Horsetail — Plant — 560 ppm. M

Allium sativum var. sativum L. — Garlic — Bulb — 559 ppm. E

Pachyrhizus erosus RICH. ex DC. — Yambean, Jicama — Tuber — 555 ppm. E

Carica papaya L. — Papaya — Fruit — 554 ppm. EM

Lens culinaris MEDIK. — Lentil Sprout — Seedling — 545 ppm. E

Mammea americana L. — Mamey — Fruit — 150-1,085 ppm.

Plantago psyllium L. — Psyllium — Seed — 540 ppm. EM

Xanthosoma sagittifolium (L.) SCHOTT — Malanga, Tannia, Yautia — Leaf — 540 ppm. E

Angelica sinensis (OLIV.) DIELS — Chinese Angelica, Dang Gui, Dang Quai, Dang Qui, Dong Gui, Dong Quai — Root — 539 ppm. M

Quercus velutina LAM. — Black Oak — Stem — 539 ppm. EM

Pistacia vera L. — Pistachio — Seed — 538 ppm. E

Belamcanda chinensis (L.) DC. — Blackberry Lily, Iris Tigre (Fr.), Leopard Lily, Leopardenblume (Ger.), Maravilla (Sp.), Mariposa (Sp.), Shenan — Rhizome — 527 ppm. M

Morus alba L. — Sang-Pai-Pi, White Mulberry Root — Bark — 520 ppm. EM

Persea americana MILLER — Avocado — Fruit — 520 ppm. E

Peperomia pelucida — Pepper elder, Yerba de la plata — Leaf — 80-1,025 ppm.

Aloe vera (L.) BURM. f. — Aloe, Bitter Aloes — Leaf — 510 ppm. EM

Camellia sinensis (L.) KUNTZE — Tea — Leaf — 500 ppm. E

Rumex acetosa L. — Garden Sorrel — Leaf — 500 ppm. TEM

Panax japonicus C.A.MEYER — Japanese Ginseng — Rhizome — 499 ppm. M

Raphanus sativus L. — Radish — Fruit — 495 ppm. E

Nelumbo nucifera L. — Water Lotus — Seed — 490 ppm. EM

Colocasia esculenta (L.) SCHOTT — Taro — Leaf — 484 ppm.   — Root — 480 ppm. E

Allium ampeloprasum L. — Elephant Garlic, Kurrat — Leaf — 472 ppm. E

Platycodon grandiflorum (JACQ.) A.DC. — Balloon Flower, Chieh-Keng, Jie-Geng — Root — 472 ppm. TEM

Citrus limon (L.) BURMAN f. — Lemon — Fruit — 470 ppm. E

Acanthopanax gracilistylis W.W.SMITH — Wu Chia Pi Root — Bark — 463 ppm. M

Eleocharis dulcis (BURM. F) TRIN. — Water chestnut — Tuber — 100-920 ppm.

Acorus calamus L. — Calamus, Flagroot, Myrtle Flag, Sweet Calamus, Sweetflag, Sweetroot — Rhizome — 459 ppm. M

Annona squamosa L. — Sugar-Apple, Sweetsop — Fruit — 457 ppm. E

Physalis ixocarpa BROT. — Tomatillo — Fruit — 454 ppm. E

Vitis vinifera L. — European Grape, Grape, Grapevine, Parra (Sp.), Vid (Sp.), Vigne Vinifere (Fr.), Weinrebe (Ger.), Wine Grape — Fruit — 454 ppm. EM

Lagenaria siceraria (MOLINA) STANDLEY. — Calabash Gourd, White-Flowered Gourd — Fruit — 450 ppm. E

Vigna mungo (L.) HEPPER — Black Gram — Seed — 449 ppm. E

Jussiaea repens L. — Jussiaeae Herba, Pond Dragon — Plant — 438 ppm. M

Erythroxylum coca var. coca — Coca — Leaf — 435 ppm. EM

Coriandrum sativum L. — Chinese Parsley, Cilantro, Coriander — Fruit — 430 ppm. E

Ephedra sinica STAPF — Chinese Ephedra, Ma Huang — Plant — 430 ppm. M

Pinus edulis ENGELM — Pinyon Pine — Seed — 675-860 ppm. EM

Psophocarpus tetragonolobus (L.) DC. — Asparagus Pea, Goa Bean, Winged Bean — Seed — 429 ppm. E

Bupleurum chinense DC. — Chai-Hu — Root — 428 ppm. M

Aralia cordata L. — Udo — Leaf — 425 ppm. EM

Glehnia littoralis F. SCHMIDT & MIQUEL — Bei Sha Shen - Root — 425 ppm. EM

Juniperus virginiana L. — Red Cedar — Shoot — 422 ppm. TEM

Vaccinium corymbosum L. — Blueberry — Fruit — 414 ppm. E

Larrea tridentata (SESSE & MOC. ex DC.) COV. — Chaparral, Creosote Bush — Plant — 410 ppm. M

Pyrus communis L. — Pear — Fruit — 407 ppm. E

Ipomoea batatas (L.) LAM — Sweet Potato — Leaf — 400 ppm. E

Xanthosoma sagittifolium (L.) SCHOTT — Malanga, Tannia, Yautia — Root — 400 ppm. E

Fritillaria thunbergii MIQ. — Bei-Mu, Fritillary — Bulb — 396 ppm. EM

Quercus rubra L. — Northern Red Oak — Stem — 396 ppm. EM

Canavalia ensiformis (L.) DC. — Jack Bean — Seed — 394 ppm. E

Ocimum basilicum L. — Basil, Cuban Basil, Sweet Basil — Plant — 386 ppm. E

Hibiscus sabdariffa L. — Acedera de Guinea (Sp.), Indian Sorrel, Jamaica Sorrel, Kharkadi, Malventee (Ger.), Red Sorrel, Rosa de Jamaica (Sp.), Rosella (Ger.), Roselle, Sereni (Sp.), Sorrel — Flower — 382 ppm. E

Phoenix dactylifera L. — Date Palm — Fruit — 380 ppm. E

Quercus alba L. — White Oak — Stem — 380 ppm. EM

Dioscorea bulbifera L. — Air Potato, Potato Yam — Rhizome — 378 ppm. E

Ficus carica L. — Echte Feige (Ger.), Feigenbaum (Ger.), Fico (Ital.), Fig, Figueira (Port.), Figuier Commun (Fr.), Higo (Sp.), Higuera Comun (Sp.) — Fruit — 366 ppm. E

Prunus persica (L.) BATSCH — Peach — Fruit — 366 ppm. TEM

Lens culinaris MEDIK. — Lentil — Seed — 360 ppm. E

Eriobotrya japonica (THUNB.) LINDL. — Loquat — Fruit — 351 ppm. E

Tamarindus indica L. — Indian Tamarind, Kilytree, Tamarind — Leaf — 351 ppm. M

Berberis vulgaris L. — Barberry — Root — 350 ppm. M

Punica granatum L. — Granado (Sp.), Granatapfelbaum (Ger.), Granatapfelstrauch (Ger.), Grenadier (Fr.), Mangrano (Sp.), Pomegranate, Romanzeiro (Port.), Zakuro (Jap.) — Fruit — 350 ppm. E

Dioscorea alata L. — Greater Yam, Winged Yam — Root — 335 ppm. E

Momordica charantia L. — Bitter Melon, Sorosi — Fruit — 333 ppm. E

Vigna unguiculata subsp. sesquipedalis (L.) VERDC. — Asparagus Bean, Pea Bean, Yardlong Bean — Fruit — 333 ppm. E

Vigna aconitifolia (JACQ.) MARECHAL — Mat Bean, Moth Bean — Seed — 332 ppm. E

Hyoscyamus niger L. — Henbane — Seed — 327 ppm. T

Solanum tuberosum L. — Potato — Tuber — 323 ppm. E

Alisma plantago-aquatica L. — Mud Plantain, Tse-Hsieh, Water Plantain, Ze-Xie — Rhizome — 322 ppm. M

Armoracia rusticana GAERTN. ET AL. — Horseradish — Root — 315 ppm. E

Strontium

Carya glabra (MILLER) SWEET — Pignut Hickory — Shoot — 1,100 ppm. E

Diospyros virginiana L. — American Persimmon — Leaf — 1,000 ppm. EM

Nyssa sylvatica MARSHALL — Black Gum, Black Tupelo — Leaf — 910 ppm. EM

Carya ovata (MILL.) K. KOCH — Shagbark Hickory — Shoot — 900 ppm. E

Nyssa sylvatica MARSHALL — Black Gum, Black Tupelo — Stem — 880 ppm. EM

Brassica oleracea var. capitata L. — Cabbage, Red Cabbage, White Cabbage — Leaf — 870 ppm. E

Liquidambar styraciflua L. — American Styrax, Sweetgum — Stem — 840 ppm. Em

Sassafras albidum (NUTT.) NEES — Sassafras — Leaf — 680 ppm. TEM

Rhus glabra L. — Smooth Sumac — Stem — 670 ppm. EM

Lactuca sativa L. — Lettuce — Shoot — 580 ppm. E

Quercus alba L. — White Oak — Plant — 532 ppm. EM

Prunus serotina subsp. serotina — Black Cherry, Wild Cherry — Stem — 480 ppm. TEM

Juniperus virginiana L. — Red Cedar — Shoot — 440 ppm. TEM

Symphoricarpos orbiculatus MOENCH. — Buckbush — Stem — 440 ppm. TM

Rhus copallina L. — Dwarf Sumac, Winged Sumac — Stem — 427 ppm. EM

Brassica pekinensis (LOUR.) RUPR. — Chinese Cabbage — Leaf — 420 ppm. E

Petroselinum crispum (MILLER) NYMAN EX A. W. HILLL — Parsley — Plant — 396 ppm. E

Diospyros virginiana L. — American Persimmon — Stem — 378 ppm. EM

Sassafras albidum (NUTT.) NEES — Sassafras — Stem — 370 ppm. TEM

Quercus rubra L. — Northern Red Oak — Stem — 330 ppm. EM

Rhus copallina L. — Dwarf Sumac, Winged Sumac — Leaf — 288 ppm. EM

Liquidambar styraciflua L. — American Styrax, Sweetgum — Leaf — 246 ppm. Em

Cichorium endivia L. — Endive, Escarole — Shoot — 240 ppm. E

Citrus paradisi MacFAD. — Grapefruit — Fruit — 220 ppm. E

Asparagus officinalis L. — Asparagus — Shoot — 200 ppm. E

Quercus velutina LAM. — Black Oak — Stem — 186 ppm. EM

Allium cepa L. — Onion, Shallot — Bulb — 162 ppm. E

Petasites japonicus (SIEBOLD & ZUCC.) MAXIM. — Butterbur — Plant — 160 ppm. T

Daucus carota L. — Carrot — Root — 148 ppm. E

Lycopersicon esculentum MILLER — Tomato — Fruit — 140 ppm. TEM

Peucedanum decursivum (MIQ.) MAX. — Qian Hu — Plant — 130 ppm. M

Quercus phellos L. — Willow Oak — Stem — 126 ppm. EM

Quercus stellata WANGENH. — Post Oak — Stem — 126 ppm. EM

Polygonum cuspidatum SIEBOLD & ZUCC. — Giant Knotweed, Hu-Zhang, Japanese Knotweed, Mexican Bamboo — Plant — 120 ppm. TEM

Taraxacum officinale WEBER EX F. H. WIGG. — Dandelion — Plant — 120 ppm. EM

Boehmeria nivea (L.) GAUDICH. — Ramie — Plant — 118 ppm. M

Citrus sinensis (L.) OSBECK — Orange — Fruit — 110 ppm. E

Glechoma hederacea L. — Alehoof — Plant — 110 ppm. M

Phaseolus vulgaris var. vulgaris — Black Bean, Dwarf Bean, Field Bean, Flageolet Bean, French Bean, Garden Bean, Green Bean, Haricot, Haricot Bean, Haricot Vert, Kidney Bean, Navy Bean, Pop Bean, Popping Bean, Snap Bean, String Bean, Wax Bean — Fruit — 105 ppm. E

Erythroxylum coca var. coca — Coca — Leaf — 104 ppm. EM

Phaseolus lunatus L. — Butter Bean, Lima Bean — Seed — 100 ppm. E

Cucumis sativus L. — Cucumber — Fruit — 98 ppm. E

Pinus echinata MILLER — Shortleaf Pine — Shoot — 84 ppm. M

Cinnamomum sieboldii — Japanese Cinnamon — Bark — 80 ppm. TEM

Cinnamomum verum J. PRESL — Ceylon Cinnamon, Cinnamon — Bark — 80 ppm. TEM

Bertholletia excelsa BONPL. — Brazilnut, Brazilnut-Tree, Creamnut, Paranut — Seed — 77 ppm. E

Beta vulgaris subsp. vulgaris — Beet, Beetroot, Garden Beet, Sugar Beet — Root — 70 ppm. E

Cinnamomum sieboldii — Japanese Cinnamon Root — Bark — 70 ppm. TEM

Cinnamomum burmannii (NEES) BLUME — Java Cinnamon, Padang Cassia — Bark — 60 ppm. TEM

Polystichum polyblepharum (ROEM.) PRESL — Chinese Polystichum — Plant — 60 ppm. T

Solanum tuberosum L. — Potato — Tuber — 60 ppm. E

Syzygium aromaticum (L.) MERR. & L. M. PERRY — Clove, Clovetree — Flower — 60 ppm. E

Vigna unguiculata subsp. sesquipedalis (L.) VERDC. — Asparagus Bean, Pea Bean, Yardlong Bean — Seed — 60 ppm. E

Prunus domestica L. — Plum — Fruit — 51 ppm. TEM

Artemisia vulgaris L. — Mugwort — Plant — 50 ppm. M

Cinnamomum aromaticum NEES — Canela de la China (Sp.), Canelero chino (Sp.), Canelle de Cochinchine (Fr.), Cannelier Casse (Fr.), Cannelier de Chine (Fr.), Cassia, Cassia Bark, Cassia Lignea, China Junk Cassia, Chinazimt (Ger.), Chinese Cassia, Chinese Cinnamon, Chinesischer Zimtbaum (Ger.), Kashia-Keihi (Jap.), Saigon Cinnamon, Zimtcassie (Ger.) — Bark — 50 ppm. TEM

Prunus persica (L.) BATSCH — Peach — Fruit — 45 ppm. TEM

Glycine max (L.) MERR. — Soybean — Seed — 42 ppm. E

Vitis vinifera L. — European Grape, Grape, Grapevine, Parra (Sp.), Vid (Sp.), Vigne Vinifere (Fr.), Weinrebe (Ger.), Wine Grape — Fruit — 38.5 ppm. EM

Phaseolus vulgaris var. vulgaris — Black Bean, Dwarf Bean, Field Bean, Flageolet Bean, French Bean, Garden Bean, Green Bean, Haricot, Haricot Bean, Haricot Vert, Kidney Bean, Navy Bean, Pop Bean, Popping Bean, Snap Bean, String Bean, Wax Bean — Seed — 34 ppm. E

Pimenta dioica (L.) MERR. — Allspice, Clover-Pepper, Jamaica-Pepper, Pimenta, Pimento — Plant — 20 ppm. E

Pyrus communis L. — Pear — Fruit — 18.5 ppm. E

Cucumis melo var. cantalupensis NAUDIN — Cantaloupe, Melon, Muskmelon, Netted Melon, Nutmeg Melon, Persian Melon — Fruit — 16.5 ppm. E

Prunus dulcis (MILLER) D. A. WEBB — Almond — Seed — 16 ppm. TEM

Zea mays L. — Corn — Seed — 14 ppm. E

Capsicum annuum L. — Bell Pepper, Cherry Pepper, Cone Pepper, Green Pepper, Paprika, Sweet Pepper — Fruit — 12 ppm. E

Pistacia vera L. — Pistachio — Seed — 10 ppm. E

Malus domestica BORKH. — Apple — Fruit — 8.6 ppm. E

Juglans nigra L. — Black Walnut — Seed — 7.1 ppm. E

Solanum melongena L. — Aubergine, Eggplant — Fruit — 5.6 ppm. E

Anacardium occidentale L. — Cashew — Seed — 4.2 ppm. E

Cocos nucifera L. — Coconut, Coconut Palm, Cocotero (Sp.), Copra, Kokospalme (Ger.), Nariyal — Seed — 2.8 ppm. E

Carya illinoensis (WANGENH.) K. KOCH — Pecan — Seed — 2.5 ppm. E

Carya ovata (MILL.) K. KOCH — Shagbark Hickory — Seed — 2.5 ppm. E

Quercus rubra L. — Northern Red Oak — Seed — 1.3 ppm. EM

Corylus avellana L. — Cobnut, English Filbert, European Filbert, European Hazel, Hazel — Seed. E

Spinacia oleracea L. — Spinach — Plant. E

Juglans cinerea L. — Butternut — Seed. E

Sulfur

Brassica oleracea var. botrytis L. — Cauliflower — Leaf — 11,800 ppm. E

Anethum graveolens L. — Dill, Garden Dill — Plant — 11,175 ppm. E

Pastinaca sativa L. — Parsnip — Root — 11,050 ppm. E

Armoracia rusticana GAERTN. ET AL. — Horseradish — Root — 10,000 ppm. E

Lepidium sativum L. — Garden Cress — Seed — 9,545 ppm. E

Brassica oleracea var. capitata L. — Cabbage, Red Cabbage, White Cabbage — Leaf — 8,750 ppm. E

Rhizophora mangle L. — Red Mangrove — Leaf — 7,900 ppm. M

Petasites japonicus (SIEBOLD & ZUCC.) MAXIM. — Butterbur — Plant — 7,300 ppm. T

Urtica dioica L. — European Nettle, Stinging Nettle — Leaf — 6,665 ppm. EM

Trichosanthes anguina L. — Snakegourd — Fruit — 6,480 ppm. E

Portulaca oleracea L. — Purslane, Verdolaga — Plant — 6,300 ppm. E

Raphanus sativus L. — Radish — Root — 6,140 ppm. E

Piper nigrum L. — Black Pepper, Pepper, White Pepper — Fruit — 5,760 ppm. EM

Spinacia oleracea L. — Spinach — Plant — 5,700 ppm. E

Morus alba L. — Sang-Pai-Pi, White Mulberry — Leaf — 5,600 ppm. EM

Cucumis sativus L. — Cucumber — Fruit — 5,250 ppm. E

Peucedanum decursivum (MIQ.) MAX. — Qian Hu — Plant — 5,200 ppm. M

Brassica rapa var. rapa — Rapini, Seven-Top Turnip, Turnip — Root — 5,100 ppm. E

Brassica napus var. napobrassica var. napobrassica (L.) REICHB. — Rutabaga, Swede, Swedish Turnip — Root — 5,000 ppm. E

Helianthus annuus L. — Girasol, Sunflower — Seed — 4,880 ppm. E

Anacardium occidentale L. — Cashew — Seed — 4,800 ppm. E

Petroselinum crispum (MILLER) NYMAN EX A. W. HILLL — Parsley — Plant — 4,700 ppm. E

Avena sativa L. — Oats — Plant — 4,100 ppm. EM

Allium cepa L. — Onion, Shallot — Bulb — 4,075 ppm. E

Glycine max (L.) MERR. — Soybean — Seed — 4,066 ppm. E

Hibiscus sabdariffa L. — Acedera de Guinea (Sp.), Indian Sorrel, Jamaica Sorrel, Kharkadi, Malventee (Ger.), Red Sorrel, Rosa de Jamaica (Sp.), Rosella (Ger.), Roselle, Sereni (Sp.), Sorrel — Seed — 4,000 ppm. E

Stellaria media (L.) VILLARS — Chickweed, Common Chickweed — Plant — 3,828 ppm. E

Lactuca sativa L. — Lettuce — Shoot — 3,800 ppm. E

Boehmeria nivea (L.) GAUDICH. — Ramie — Plant — 3,700 ppm. M

Vicia faba L. — Broadbean, Faba Bean, Habas — Seed — 3,630 ppm. E

Prunus dulcis (MILLER) D. A. WEBB — Almond — Seed — 3,420 ppm. TEM

Glechoma hederacea L. — Alehoof — Plant — 3,400 ppm. M

Asimina triloba (L.) DUNAL — Pawpaw — Fruit — 3,333 ppm. E

Taraxacum officinale WEBER EX F. H. WIGG. — Dandelion — Plant — 3,300 ppm. EM

Physalis ixocarpa BROT. — Tomatillo — Fruit — 3,250 ppm. E

Triticum aestivum L. — Wheat — Seed — 3,200 ppm. EM

Avena sativa L. — Oats — Seed — 3,100 ppm. EM

Triticum aestivum L. — Wheat — Plant — 2,900 ppm. EM

Juglans cinerea L. — Butternut — Seed — 2,870 ppm. E

Pistacia vera L. — Pistachio — Seed — 2,870 ppm. E

Artemisia vulgaris L. — Mugwort — Plant — 2,800 ppm. M

Annona muricata L. — Soursop — Fruit — 2,700 ppm. E

Juglans nigra L. — Black Walnut — Seed — 2,652 ppm. E

Polygonum cuspidatum SIEBOLD & ZUCC. — Giant Knotweed, Hu-Zhang, Japanese Knotweed, Mexican Bamboo — Plant — 2,600 ppm. TEM

Physalis peruviana L. — Cape Gooseberry, Ground Cherry — Fruit — 2,515 ppm. E

Capsicum annuum L. — Bell Pepper, Cherry Pepper, Cone Pepper, Green Pepper, Paprika, Sweet Pepper — Fruit — 2,440 ppm. E

Vigna radata (L.) WILCZEK — Green Gram, Mungbean — Seed — 2,378 ppm. E

Lycopersicon esculentum MILLER — Tomato — Fruit — 2,330 ppm. TEM

Mangifera indica L. — Mango — Seed — 2,300 ppm. EM

Pisum sativum L. — Pea — Plant — 2,300 ppm. — Seed — 2,290 ppm. E

Carya ovata (MILL.) K. KOCH — Shagbark Hickory — Seed — 2,180 ppm. E

Arachis hypogaea L. — Groundnut, Peanut — Seed — 2,100 ppm. EM

Polystichum polyblepharum (ROEM.) PRESL — Chinese Polystichum — Plant — 2,100 ppm. T

Citrus paradisi MacFAD. — Grapefruit — Fruit — 2,090 ppm. E

Corylus avellana L. — Cobnut, English Filbert, European Filbert, European Hazel, Hazel — Seed — 2,070 ppm. E

Vigna aconitifolia (JACQ.) MARECHAL — Mat Bean, Moth Bean — Seed — 2,018 ppm. E

Beta vulgaris subsp. vulgaris — Beet, Beet-root, Garden Beet, Sugar Beet — Root — 2,000 ppm. E

Genipa americana L. — Genipap, Jagua — Fruit — 2,000 ppm. EM

Vigna mungo (L.) HEPPER — Black Gram — Seed — 1,953 ppm. E

Azadirachta indica A. JUSS. — Neem — Seed — 1,921 ppm. M

Cinnamomum verum J. PRESL — Ceylon Cinnamon, Cinnamon — Bark — 1,900 ppm. TEM

Solanum tuberosum L. — Potato — Tuber — 1,900 ppm. E

Ribes rubrum L. — Red Currant, White Currant — Fruit — 1,782 ppm. E

Trigonella foenum-graecum L. — Alholva (Sp.), Bockshornklee (Ger.), Fenugreek, Greek Clover, Greek Hay — Plant — 1,670 ppm. EM

Daucus carota L. — Carrot — Root — 1,635 ppm. E

Larrea tridentata (SESSE & MOC. ex DC.) COV. — Chaparral, Creosote Bush — Plant — 1,600 ppm. M

Panax quinquefolius L. — American Ginseng, Ginseng — Plant — 1,500 ppm. M

Abelmoschus esculentus (L.) MOENCH — Okra — Fruit — 1,400 ppm. EM

Ribes nigrum L. — Black Currant — Fruit — 1,385 ppm. E

Cocos nucifera L. — Coconut, Coconut Palm, Cocotero (Sp.), Copra, Koko-spalme (Ger.), Nariyal — Seed — 1,370 ppm. E

Brassica pekinensis (LOUR.) RUPR. — Chinese Cabbage — Shoot — 1,365 ppm. E

Genipa americana L. — Genipap, Jagua — Seed — 1,300 ppm. EM

Fragaria spp. — Strawberry — Fruit — 1,270 ppm. E

Averrhoa carambola L. — Carambola, Star Fruit — Fruit — 1,000-1,300 ppm. E

Rheum rhabarbarum L. — Rhubarb — Plant — 1,240 ppm. E

Lens culinaris MEDIK. — Lentil — Seed — 1,220 ppm. E

Cinnamomum aromaticum NEES — Canela de la China (Sp.), Canelero chino (Sp.), Canelle de Cochinchine (Fr.), Cannelier Casse (Fr.), Cannelier de Chine (Fr.), Cassia, Cassia Bark, Cassia Lignea, China Junk Cassia, Chinazimt (Ger.), Chinese Cassia, Chinese Cinnamon, Chinesischer Zimtbaum (Ger.), Kashia-Keihi (Jap.), Saigon Cinnamon, Zimtcassie (Ger.) — Bark — 1,200 ppm. TEM

Rubus chamaemorus L. — Cloudberry — Fruit — 1,185 ppm. EM

Quercus rubra L. — Northern Red Oak — Seed — 1,160 ppm. EM

Linum usitatissimum L. — Flax, Linseed — Seed — 1,147 ppm. E

Zea mays L. — Corn — Fruit — 1,140 ppm. E

Ribes uva-crispa L. — Gooseberry — Fruit — 1,113 ppm. E

Vaccinium myrtillus L. — Bilberry, Dwarf Bilberry, Whortleberry — Fruit — 1,075 ppm. E

Vaccinium vitis-idaea var. minus LODD. — Cowberry, Lingen, Lingonberry — Fruit — 1,075 ppm. E

Juglans regia L. — English Walnut — Seed — 1,040 ppm. E

Apium graveolens L. — Celery — Root — 1,000 ppm. E

Cinnamomum burmannii (NEES) BLUME — Java Cinnamon, Padang Cassia — Bark — 1,000 ppm. TEM

Citrus reticulata BLANCO — Mandarin, Tangerine — Fruit — 1,000 ppm. E

Citrus sinensis (L.) OSBECK — Orange — Fruit — 1,000 ppm. E

Oryza sativa L. — Rice — Plant — 1,000 ppm. E

Rosa canina L. — Dog Rose, Dogbrier, Rose — Fruit — 1,000 ppm. EM

Dioscorea alata L. — Greater Yam, Winged Yam — Root — 990 ppm. E

Cichorium endivia L. — Endive, Escarole — Shoot — 912 ppm. E

Carica papaya L. — Papaya — Fruit — 900 ppm. EM

Cinnamomum sieboldii — Japanese Cinnamon — Bark — 900 ppm. TEM

Panicum maximum JACQ. — Guinea grass — Leaf — 0-1,800 ppm. M

Spondias dulcis FORST. — Ambarella — Seed — 900 ppm. E

Vitis vinifera L. — European Grape, Grape, Grapevine, Parra (Sp.), Vid (Sp.), Vigne Vinifere (Fr.), Weinrebe (Ger.), Wine Grape — Fruit — 888 ppm. EM

Camellia sinensis (L.) KUNTZE — Tea — Leaf — 880 ppm. E

Phaseolus vulgaris var. vulgaris — Black Bean, Dwarf Bean, Field Bean, Flageolet Bean, French Bean, Garden Bean, Green Bean, Haricot, Haricot Bean, Haricot Vert, Kidney Bean, Navy Bean, Pop Bean, Popping Bean, Snap Bean, String Bean, Wax Bean — Fruit — 875 ppm. E

Asparagus officinalis L. — Asparagus — Shoot — 864 ppm. E

Phyllanthus emblica L. — Emblic, Myrobalan — Fruit — 820 ppm. E

Secale cereale L. — Rye — Seed — 1,460-1,640 ppm. E

Carya illinoensis (WANGENH.) K. KOCH — Pecan — Seed — 800 ppm. E

Cinnamomum sieboldii — Japanese Cinnamon Root — Bark — 800 ppm. TEM

Allium ampeloprasum L. — Elephant Garlic, Kurrat — Leaf — 700 ppm. E

Prunus persica (L.) BATSCH — Peach — Fruit — 700 ppm. TEM

Moringa oleifera LAM. — Ben Nut, Benzolive Tree, Drumstick Tree, Horseradish Tree, Jacinto (Sp.), Moringa, West Indian Ben — Fruit — 0-1,370 ppm. — Leaf — 0-1,370 ppm. E

Tamarindus indica L. — Indian Tamarind, Kilytree, Tamarind — Leaf — 630 ppm. M

Mangifera indica L. — Mango — Fruit — 615 ppm. EM

Ipomoea batatas (L.) LAM — Sweet Potato — Root — 610 ppm. E

Phoenix dactylifera L. — Date Palm — Fruit — 590 ppm. E

Xanthosoma sagittifolium (L.) SCHOTT — Malanga, Tannia, Yautia — Root — 580 ppm. E

Colocasia esculenta (L.) SCHOTT — Taro — Root — 565 ppm. E

Amorphophallus campanulatus BLUME — Elephant-Foot Yam — Root — 530 ppm. TEM

Artocarpus altilis (PARKINS.) FOSBERG — Breadfruit — Fruit — 530 ppm. E

Musa x paradisiaca L. — Banana, Plantain — Fruit — 500 ppm. E

Vaccinium macrocarpon AITON — American Cranberry, Cranberry, Large Cranberry — Fruit — 500 ppm. E

Murraya sp. — Curry Leaf — Fruit — 450 ppm. EM

Syzygium jambos ALSTON — Pomarrosa, Rose Apple — Fruit — 130-840 ppm. E

Alocasia macrorrhiza (L.) G. DON — Giant Taro — Root — 400 ppm. E

Prunus domestica L. — Plum — Fruit — 400 ppm. TEM

Syzygium cumini SKEELS — Aceituna Dulce, Jambolan, Java Plum — Fruit — 130-800 ppm. E

Pyrus communis L. — Pear — Fruit — 300 ppm. E

Manihot esculenta CRANTZ — Cassava, Tapioca, Yuca — Root — 250 ppm. E

Tragopogon porrifolius L. — Salsify — Root — 250 ppm. E

Colocasia esculenta (L.) SCHOTT — Taro — Leaf — 240 ppm. E

Hordeum vulgare L. — Barley, Barleygrass — Seed — 200 ppm. EM

Cucumis melo var. cantalupensis NAUDIN — Cantaloupe, Melon, Muskmelon, Netted Melon, Nutmeg Melon, Persian Melon — Fruit — 198 ppm. E

Cyrtosperma chamissonis (SCHOTT) MERR. — Swamp Taro — Root — 195 ppm. E

Spondias dulcis FORST. — Ambarella — Fruit — 180 ppm. E

Solanum melongena L. — Aubergine, Eggplant — Fruit — 152 ppm. E

Psidium guajava L. — Guava — Fruit — 140 ppm. E

Phaseolus vulgaris var. vulgaris — Black Bean, Dwarf Bean, Field Bean, Flageolet Bean, French Bean, Garden Bean, Green Bean, Haricot, Haricot Bean, Haricot Vert, Kidney Bean, Navy Bean, Pop Bean, Popping Bean, Snap Bean, String Bean, Wax Bean — Seed — 137 ppm. E

Punica granatum L. — Granado (Sp.), Granatapfelbaum (Ger.), Granatapfelstrauch (Ger.), Grenadier (Fr.), Mangrano (Sp.), Pomegranate, Romanzeiro (Port.), Zakuro (Jap.) — Fruit — 120 ppm. E

Spondias tuberosa ARRUDA — Imbu, Umbu — Fruit — 120 ppm. E

Ananas comosus (L.) MERR. — Pineapple — Fruit — 70 ppm. E

Malus domestica BORKH. — Apple — Fruit — 23 ppm. E

Tantalum

Bertholletia excelsa BONPL. — Brazilnut, Brazilnut-Tree, Creamnut, Paranut — Seed. E

Carya illinoensis (WANGENH.) K. KOCH — Pecan — Seed. E

Carya ovata (MILL.) K. KOCH — Shagbark Hickory — Seed. E

Juglans nigra L. — Black Walnut — Seed. E

Juglans cinerea L. — Butternut — Seed. E

Prunus dulcis (MILLER) D. A. WEBB — Almond — Seed. TEM

Anacardium occidentale L. — Cashew — Seed. E

Corylus avellana L. — Cobnut, English Filbert, European Filbert, European Hazel, Hazel — Seed. E

Quercus rubra L. — Northern Red Oak — Seed. EM

Tellurium

Allium sativum var. sativum — Garlic — Bulb. E

Tin

Schisandra chinensis (TURCZ.) BAILL. — Chinese Magnolia Vine, Five-Flavor-Fruit, Magnolia Vine, Schizandra, Wu Wei Zi, Wu Wei Zu — Fruit — 940 ppm. M

Elytrigia repens (L.) DESV. EX NEVSKI — Couchgrass, Doggrass, Quackgrass,

Twitchgrass, Wheatgrass — Plant — 67 ppm. EM

Juniperus communis L. — Common Juniper, Juniper — Fruit — 63 ppm. TEM

Silybum marianum (L.) GAERTN. — Lady's Thistle, Milk Thistle — Plant — 42 ppm. M

Gentiana lutea L. — Gentian, Yellow Gentian — Root — 40 ppm. M

Cypripedium pubescens WILLD. — Yellow Ladyslipper — Root — 33 ppm. M

Rhodymenia palmata — Dulse — Plant — 33 ppm. E

Althaea officinalis L. — Marshmallow, White Mallow — Root — 29 ppm. M

Valeriana officinalis L. — Common Valerian, Garden-Heliotrope, Valerian — Root — 28 ppm. M

Chondrus crispus (L.) STACKH. — Irish Moss — Plant — 27 ppm. E

Urtica dioica L. — European Nettle, Stinging Nettle — Leaf — 27 ppm. EM

Achillea millefolium L. — Milfoil, Yarrow — Plant — 26 ppm. M

Berberis vulgaris L. — Barberry — Root — 26 ppm. M

Cnicus benedictus L. — Blessed Thistle — Plant — 25 ppm. M

Trifolium pratense L. — Cowgrass, Peavine Clover, Purple Clover, Red Clover — Flower — 25 ppm. EM

Fucus vesiculosus L. — Bladderwrack, Kelp — Plant — 24 ppm. EM

Glycyrrhiza glabra L. — Commom Licorice, Licorice, Licorice-Root, Smooth Licorice — Root — 24 ppm. M

Harpagophytum procumbens (BURCH.) DC. EX MEISN. — Devil's Claw, Grapple Plant — Root — 24 ppm. M

Mentha pulegium L. — European Pennyroyal — Plant — 24 ppm. TEM

Rumex crispus L. — Curly Dock, Lengua De Vaca, Sour Dock, Yellow Dock — Root — 24 ppm. TEM

Cucurbita pepo L. — Pumpkin — Seed — 23 ppm. E

Humulus lupulus L. — Hops — Fruit — 22 ppm. TEM

Myrica cerifera L. — Bayberry, Candle-Berry, Southern Bayberry, Wax Myrtle — Bark — 22 ppm. EM

Rosa canina L. — Dog Rose, Dogbrier, Rose — Fruit — 22 ppm. EM

Arctium lappa L. — Burdock, Gobo, Great Burdock — Root — 21 ppm. EM

Caulophyllum thalictroides (L.) MICHX. — Blue Cohosh — Root — 21 ppm. M

Chrysanthemum parthenium (L.) BERNH. — Feverfew — Plant — 21 ppm. M

Plantago psyllium L. — Psyllium — Seed — 21 ppm. EM

Ruscus aculeatus L. — Box-Holly, Butcher's Broom — Root — 21 ppm. EM

Dioscorea sp. — Wild Yam — Root — 19 ppm. E

Smilax spp. — Sarsaparilla — Root — 18 ppm. EM

Viburnum opulus — Crampbark, European Cranberry Bush, Guelder Rose, Snowball Bush — Bark — 18 ppm. TEM

Viscum album L. — European Mistletoe — Leaf — 18 ppm. TM

Echinacea spp. — Coneflower, Echinacea — Root — 17 ppm. M

Thymus vulgaris L. — Common Thyme, Garden Thyme, Thyme — Leaf — 17 ppm. EM

Panax ginseng C. A. MEYER — Chinese Ginseng, Ginseng, Korean Ginseng, Oriental Ginseng — Root — 16 ppm. M

Ulmus rubra MUHLENB. — Red Elm, Slippery Elm — Bark — 16 ppm. M

Stevia rebaudiana (BERTONI) BERTONI — Ca-A-E, Stevia, Sweet Leaf of Paraguay — Leaf — 15 ppm. E

Equisetum arvense L. — Field Horsetail, Horsetail — Plant — 14 ppm. M

Larrea tridentata (SESSE & MOC. ex DC.) COV. — Chaparral, Creosote Bush — Plant — 14 ppm. M

Crataegus laevigata (POIR.) DC — English Hawthorn, Hawthorn, Whitethorn, Woodland Hawthorn — Fruit — 13 ppm. M

Polygonum multiflorum THUNB. — Chinese Cornbind, Chinese Knotweed, Fleeceflower, Fo Ti, He Shou Wu — Root — 13 ppm. TEM

Taraxacum officinale WEBER EX F. H. WIGG. — Dandelion — Root — 13 ppm. EM

Zingiber officinale ROSCOE — Ginger — Rhizome — 13 ppm. EM

Centella asiatica (L.) URBAN — Gotu Kola, Pennywort — Leaf — 12 ppm. EM

Hordeum vulgare L. — Barley, Barleygrass — Stem — 12 ppm. EM

Juglans nigra L. — Black Walnut — Fruit — 12 ppm. E

Salix alba L. — White Willow — Bark — 12 ppm. M

Verbascum thapsus L. — Flannelleaf, Flannelplant, Great Mullein, Mullein, Velvetplant — Leaf — 12 ppm. M

Vitis vinifera L. — European Grape, Grape, Grapevine, Parra (Sp.), Vid (Sp.), Vigne Vinifere (Fr.), Weinrebe (Ger.), Wine Grape — Stem — 12 ppm. EM

Agathosma betulina (P. J. BERGIUS) PILLANS — Buchu, Honey Buchu, Mountain Buchu — Leaf — 11 ppm. M

Aloe vera (L.) BURM. f. — Aloe, Bitter Aloes — Leaf — 11 ppm. EM

Ephedra sinica STAPF — Chinese Ephedra, Ma Huang — Plant — 11 ppm. M

Foeniculum vulgare MILLER — Fennel — Fruit — 11 ppm. M

Hydrangea arborescens L. — Hydrangea, Smooth Hydrangea — Root — 11 ppm. EM

Mentha x piperita — Peppermint — Leaf — 11 ppm. TEM

Nepeta cataria L. — Catnip — Plant — 11 ppm. M

Turnera diffusa WILLD. EX SCHULT. — Damiana — Leaf — 11 ppm. M

Carthamus tinctorius L. — Safflower — Flower — 10 ppm. M

Chamaemelum nobile (L.) ALL. — Garden Camomile, Perennial Camomile, Roman Camomile — Flower — 10 ppm. M

Hibiscus sabdariffa L. — Acedera de Guinea (Sp.), Indian Sorrel, Jamaica Sorrel, Kharkadi, Malventee (Ger.), Red Sorrel, Rosa de Jamaica (Sp.), Rosella (Ger.), Roselle, Sereni (Sp.), Sorrel — Flower — 10 ppm. E

Prunus persica (L.) BATSCH — Peach — Bark — 9.4 ppm. TEM

Hydrastis canadensis L. — Goldenseal — Root — 9.3 ppm. M

Euphrasia officinalis L. — Eyebright — Plant — 8 ppm. M

Salvia officinalis L. — Sage — Leaf — 8 ppm. EM

Yucca baccata TORR. — Banana Yucca, Blue Yucca, Spanish Bayonet, Yucca — Root — 8 ppm. TEM

Cymbopogon citratus (DC. ex NEES) STAPF — Lemongrass, West Indian Lemongrass — Plant — 7.1 ppm. EM

Lobelia inflata L. — Indian Tobacco, Lobelia — Leaf — 7 ppm. TM

Symphytum officinale L. — Comfrey — Root — 6.7 ppm. TM

Allium sativum var. sativum L. — Garlic — Bulb — 6 ppm. E

Avena sativa L. — Oats — Plant — 6 ppm. EM

Frangula purshiana (DC.) J. G. COOPER — Cascara Buckthorn, Cascara Sagrada — Bark — 5.1 ppm. M

Capsicum annuum L. — Bell Pepper, Cherry Pepper, Cone Pepper, Green Pepper, Paprika, Sweet Pepper — Fruit — 5 ppm. E

Angelica sinensis (OLIV.) DIELS — Chinese Angelica, Dang Gui, Dang Quai, Dang Qui, Dong Gui, Dong Quai — Root — 4 ppm. M

Trigonella foenum-graecum L. — Alholva (Sp.), Bockshornklee (Ger.), Fenugreek, Greek Clover, Greek Hay — Seed — 4 ppm. EM

Tabebuia heptaphylla (VELL.) TOLEDO — Pau D'Arco — Bark — 3.7 ppm. M

Bertholletia excelsa BONPL. — Brazilnut, Brazilnut-Tree, Creamnut, Paranut — Seed — 3.5 ppm. E

Citrus paradisi MacFAD. — Grapefruit — Fruit — 3.3 ppm. E

Carya ovata (MILL.) K. KOCH — Shagbark Hickory — Seed — 3.2 ppm. E

Daucus carota L. — Carrot — Root — 3 ppm. E

Beta vulgaris subsp. vulgaris — Beet, Beetroot, Garden Beet, Sugar Beet — Root — 2.8 ppm. E

Corylus avellana L. — Cobnut, English Filbert, European Filbert, European Hazel, Hazel — Seed — 2.7 ppm. E

Symphoricarpos orbiculatus MOENCH. — Buckbush — Stem — 2.6 ppm. TM

Quercus alba L. — White Oak — Bark — 2.2 ppm. EM

Carya illinoensis (WANGENH.) K. KOCH — Pecan — Seed — 1.8 ppm. E

Zea mays L. — Corn — Seed — 1.8 ppm. E

Juglans nigra L. — Black Walnut — Seed — 1.7 ppm. E

Cocos nucifera L. — Coconut, Coconut Palm, Cocotero (Sp.), Copra, Kokospalme (Ger.), Nariyal — Seed — 1.5 ppm. E

Scutellaria lateriflora L. — Mad-Dog, Skullcap, Scullcap — Plant — 1.2 ppm. M

Titanium

Lactuca sativa L. — Lettuce — Leaf — 870 ppm. E

Taraxacum officinale WEBER EX F. H. WIGG. — Dandelion — Plant — 330 ppm. EM

Artemisia vulgaris L. — Mugwort — Plant — 290 ppm. M

Symphoricarpos orbiculatus MOENCH. — Buckbush — Stem — 264 ppm. TM

Boehmeria nivea (L.) GAUDICH. — Ramie — Plant — 230 ppm. M

Brassica oleracea var. capitata L. — Cabbage, Red Cabbage, White Cabbage — Leaf — 203 ppm. E

Petasites japonicus (SIEBOLD & ZUCC.) MAXIM. — Butterbur — Plant — 200 ppm. T

Nyssa sylvatica MARSHALL — Black Gum, Black Tupelo — Leaf — 182 ppm. EM

Asparagus officinalis L. — Asparagus — Shoot — 180 ppm. E

Diospyros virginiana L. — American Persimmon — Stem — 162 ppm. EM

Prunus serotina subsp. serotina — Black Cherry, Wild Cherry — Leaf — 144 ppm. TEM

Rhus copallina L. — Dwarf Sumac, Winged Sumac — Leaf — 144 ppm. EM

Lycopersicon esculentum MILLER — Tomato — Fruit — 140 ppm. TEM

Juniperus virginiana L. — Red Cedar — Shoot — 128 ppm. TEM

Polystichum polyblepharum (ROEM.) PRESL — Chinese Polystichum — Plant — 121 ppm. T

Carya glabra (MILLER) SWEET — Pignut Hickory — Shoot — 110 ppm. E

Phaseolus vulgaris var. vulgaris — Black Bean, Dwarf Bean, Field Bean, Flageolet Bean, French Bean, Garden Bean, Green Bean, Haricot, Haricot Bean, Haricot Vert, Kidney Bean, Navy Bean, Pop Bean, Popping Bean, Snap Bean, String Bean, Wax Bean — Fruit — 105 ppm. E

Sassafras albidum (NUTT.) NEES — Sassafras — Leaf — 102 ppm. TEM

Momordica charantia L. — Bitter Melon, Sorosi — Fruit — 100 ppm. E

Peucedanum decursivum (MIQ.) MAX. — Qian Hu — Plant — 100 ppm. M

Rhus glabra L. — Smooth Sumac — Stem — 100 ppm. EM

Polygonum cuspidatum SIEBOLD & ZUCC. — Giant Knotweed, Hu-Zhang, Japanese Knotweed, Mexican Bamboo — Plant — 90 ppm. TEM

Pinus echinata MILLER — Shortleaf Pine — Shoot— 84 ppm. M

Vigna unguiculata subsp. sesquipedalis (L.) VERDC. — Asparagus Bean, Pea Bean, Yardlong Bean — Seed — 84 ppm. E

Quercus alba L. — White Oak — Stem — 76 ppm. EM

Sassafras albidum (NUTT.) NEES — Sassafras — Stem — 74 ppm. TEM

Zea mays L. — Corn — Seed — 63 ppm. E

Cinnamomum sieboldii — Japanese Cinnamon — Root — Bark — 60 ppm. TEM

Liquidambar styraciflua L. — American Styrax, Sweetgum — Leaf — 57 ppm. EM

Cinnamomum aromaticum NEES — Canela de la China (Sp.), Canelero chino (Sp.), Canelle de Cochinchine (Fr.), Cannelier Casse (Fr.), Cannelier de Chine (Fr.), Cassia, Cassia Bark, Cassia Lignea, China Junk Cassia, Chinazimt (Ger.), Chinese Cassia, Chinese Cinnamon, Chinesischer Zimtbaum (Ger.), Kashia-Keihi (Jap.), Saigon Cinnamon, Zimtcassie (Ger.) — Bark — 50 ppm. TEM

Diospyros virginiana L. — American Persimmon — Leaf — 50 ppm. EM

Glechoma hederacea L. — Alehoof — Plant — 50 ppm. M

Carya ovata (MILL.) K. KOCH — Shagbark Hickory — Shoot— 45 ppm. E

Rhus copallina L. — Dwarf Sumac, Winged Sumac — Stem — 43 ppm. EM

Quercus phellos L. — Willow Oak — Stem — 42 ppm. EM

Quercus stellata WANGENH. — Post Oak — Stem — 42 ppm. EM

Cinnamomum verum J. PRESL — Ceylon Cinnamon, Cinnamon — Bark — 40 ppm. TEM

Prunus serotina subsp. serotina — Black Cherry, Wild Cherry — Stem— 38 ppm. TEM

Liquidambar styraciflua L. — American Styrax, Sweetgum — Stem — 36 ppm. EM

Nyssa sylvatica MARSHALL — Black Gum, Black Tupelo — Stem — 30.8 ppm. EM

Cinnamomum burmannii (NEES) BLUME — Java Cinnamon, Padang Cassia — Bark — 30 ppm. TEM

Cinnamomum sieboldii — Japanese Cinnamon — Bark — 30 ppm. TEM

Daucus carota L. — Carrot — Root — 30 ppm. E

Prunus persica (L.) BATSCH — Peach — Fruit — 30 ppm. TEM

Prunus domestica L. — Plum — Fruit — 25.5 ppm. TEM

Phaseolus lunatus L. — Butter Bean, Lima Bean — Seed — 20 ppm. E

Quercus rubra L. — Northern Red Oak — Stem — 20 ppm. EM

Cucumis sativus L. — Cucumber — Fruit — 18 ppm. E

Solanum tuberosum L. — Potato — Tuber — 17 ppm. E

Capsicum annuum L. — Bell Pepper, Cherry Pepper, Cone Pepper, Green Pepper, Paprika, Sweet Pepper — Fruit — 16 ppm. E

Glycine max (L.) MERR. — Soybean — Seed— 12 ppm. E

Quercus velutina LAM. — Black Oak — Stem — 12 ppm. EM

Allium cepa L. — Onion, Shallot — Bulb — 11 ppm. E

Beta vulgaris subsp. vulgaris — Beet, Beetroot, Garden Beet, Sugar Beet — Root — 9.8 ppm. E

Citrus paradisi MacFAD. — Grapefruit — Fruit — 7.7 ppm. E

Vitis vinifera L. — European Grape, Grape, Grapevine, Parra (Sp.), Vid (Sp.), Vigne Vinifere (Fr.), Weinrebe (Ger.), Wine Grape — Fruit — 7.7 ppm. EM

Phaseolus vulgaris var. vulgaris — Black Bean, Dwarf Bean, Field Bean, Flageolet Bean, French Bean, Garden Bean, Green Bean, Haricot, Haricot Bean, Haricot Vert, Kidney Bean, Navy Bean, Pop Bean, Popping Bean, Snap Bean, String Bean, Wax Bean — Seed — 7.4 ppm. E

Pyrus communis L. — Pear — Fruit — 7.4 ppm. E

Bertholletia excelsa BONPL. — Brazilnut, Brazilnut-Tree, Creamnut, Paranut — Seed — 6.1 ppm. E

Cocos nucifera L. — Coconut, Coconut Palm, Cocotero (Sp.), Copra, Kokospalme (Ger.), Nariyal — Seed — 5.6 ppm. E

Carya ovata (MILL.) K. KOCH — Shagbark Hickory — Seed — 4.3 ppm. E

Citrus sinensis (L.) OSBECK — Orange — Fruit — 3.85 ppm. E

Prunus dulcis (MILLER) D. A. WEBB — Almond — Seed — 3.5 ppm. TEM

Quercus rubra L. — Northern Red Oak — Seed — 3.2 ppm. EM

Pistacia vera L. — Pistachio — Seed — 3.1 ppm. E

Malus domestica BORKH. — Apple — Fruit — 3 ppm. E

Juglans nigra L. — Black Walnut — Seed — 2.9 ppm. E

Carya illinoensis (WANGENH.) K. KOCH — Pecan — Seed — 2.8 ppm. E

Juglans cinerea L. — Butternut — Seed — 2.7 ppm. E

Anacardium occidentale L. — Cashew — Seed — 2.4 ppm. E

Corylus avellana L. — Cobnut, English Filbert, European Filbert, European Hazel, Hazel — Seed — 2.3 ppm. E

Cucumis melo var. cantalupensis NAUDIN — Cantaloupe, Melon, Muskmelon, Netted Melon, Nutmeg Melon, Persian Melon — Fruit — 2.2 ppm. E

Petroselinum crispum (MILLER) NYMAN EX A. W. HILLL — Parsley — Plant — 2 ppm. E

Cichorium endivia L. — Endive, Escarole — Leaf — 1.2 ppm. E

Brassica pekinensis (LOUR.) RUPR. — Chinese Cabbage— Leaf — 1.05 ppm. E

Solanum melongena L. — Aubergine, Eggplant — Fruit. E

Tungsten

Liquidambar styraciflua L. — American Styrax, Sweetgum — Leaf — 5.7 ppm — Stem — 3.6 ppm. EM

Sassafras albidum (NUTT.) NEES — Sassafras — Leaf — 3.4 ppm. TEM

Cocos nucifera L. — Coconut, Coconut Palm, Cocotero (Sp.), Copra, Kokospalme (Ger.), Nariyal — Seed. E

Anacardium occidentale L. — Cashew — Seed. E

Bertholletia excelsa BONPL. — Brazilnut, Brazilnut-Tree, Creamnut, Paranut — Seed. E

Juglans nigra L. — Black Walnut — Seed. E

Pistacia vera L. — Pistachio — Seed. E

Prunus dulcis (MILLER) D. A. WEBB — Almond — Seed. TEM

Quercus rubra L. — Northern Red Oak — Seed. EM

Juglans cinerea L. — Butternut — Seed. E

Carya illinoensis (WANGENH.) K. KOCH — Pecan — Seed. E

Carya ovata (MILL.) K. KOCH — Shagbark Hickory — Seed. E

Corylus avellana L. — Cobnut, English Filbert, European Filbert, European Hazel, Hazel — Seed. E

Vanadium

Phaseolus vulgaris var. vulgaris — Black Bean, Dwarf Bean, Field Bean, Flageolet Bean, French Bean, Garden Bean, Green Bean, Haricot, Haricot Bean, Haricot Vert, Kidney Bean, Navy Bean, Pop Bean, Popping Bean, Snap Bean, String Bean, Wax Bean — Fruit — 105 ppm. E

Lactuca sativa L. — Lettuce — Leaf — 20.3 ppm. E

Brassica oleracea var. capitata L. — Cabbage, Red Cabbage, White Cabbage — Leaf — 14.5 ppm. E

Lycopersicon esculentum MILLER — Tomato — Fruit — 6 ppm. TEM

Prunus serotina subsp. serotina — Black Cherry, Wild Cherry — Leaf — 4.8 ppm. TEM

Rhus copallina L. — Dwarf Sumac, Winged Sumac — Leaf — 4.8 ppm. EM

Nyssa sylvatica MARSHALL — Black Gum, Black Tupelo — Leaf — 4.55 ppm. EM

Symphoricarpos orbiculatus MOENCH. — Buckbush — Stem — 4.4 ppm. TM

Sassafras albidum (NUTT.) NEES — Sassafras — Leaf — 3.4 ppm. TEM

Phaseolus lunatus L. — Butter Bean, Lima Bean — Seed — 3 ppm. E

Juniperus virginiana L. — Red Cedar — Shoot — 2.64 ppm. TEM

Sassafras albidum (NUTT.) NEES — Sassafras — Stem — 2.59 ppm. TEM

Liquidambar styraciflua L. — American Styrax, Sweetgum — Leaf — 2.46 ppm. — Stem — 2.4 ppm. EM

Vigna unguiculata subsp. sesquipedalis (L.) VERDC. — Asparagus Bean, Pea Bean, Yardlong Bean — Seed — 2.4 ppm. E

Asparagus officinalis L. — Asparagus — Shoot — 2 ppm. E

Rhus copallina L. — Dwarf Sumac, Winged Sumac — Stem — 1.83 ppm. EM

Prunus serotina subsp. serotina — Black Cherry, Wild Cherry — Stem — 1.6 ppm. TEM

Quercus alba L. — White Oak — Stem — 1.52 ppm. EM

Diospyros virginiana L. — American Persimmon — Leaf — 1.5 ppm. EM

Zea mays L. — Corn — Seed — 1.35 ppm. E

Nyssa sylvatica MARSHALL — Black Gum, Black Tupelo — Stem — 1.32 ppm. EM

Quercus rubra L. — Northern Red Oak — Stem — 1.32 ppm. EM

Pinus echinata MILLER — Shortleaf Pine — Shoot — 1.26 ppm. M

Carya glabra (MILLER) SWEET — Pignut Hickory — Shoot — 1.1 ppm. E

Diospyros virginiana L. — American Persimmon — Stem — 1.08 ppm. EM

Quercus velutina LAM. — Black Oak — Stem. EM

Pyrus communis L. — Pear — Fruit. E

Pimenta dioica (L.) MERR. — Allspice, Clover-Pepper, Jamaica-Pepper, Pimenta, Pimento — Plant. E

Juglans nigra L. — Black Walnut — Seed. E

Anacardium occidentale L. — Cashew — Seed. E

Juglans cinerea L. — Butternut — Seed. E

Panax quinquefolius L. — American Ginseng, Ginseng — Plant. M

Prunus dulcis (MILLER) D. A. WEBB — Almond — Seed. TEM

Quercus rubra L. — Northern Red Oak — Seed. EM

Bertholletia excelsa BONPL. — Brazilnut, Brazilnut-Tree, Creamnut, Paranut — Seed. E

Carya illinoensis (WANGENH.) K. KOCH — Pecan — Seed. E

Carya ovata (MILL.) K. KOCH — Shagbark Hickory — Seed. E

Corylus avellana L. — Cobnut, English Filbert, European Filbert, European Hazel, Hazel — Seed. E

Pistacia vera L. — Pistachio — Seed. E

Cocos nucifera L. — Coconut, Coconut Palm, Cocotero (Sp.), Copra, Kokospalme (Ger.), Nariyal — Seed. E

Yttrium

Carya glabra (MILLER) SWEET — Pignut Hickory — Shoot — 55 ppm. E

Brassica oleracea var. capitata L. — Cabbage, Red Cabbage, White Cabbage — Leaf — 29 ppm. E

Liquidambar styraciflua L. — American Styrax, Sweetgum — Leaf — 24.6 ppm. — Stem — 18 ppm. EM

Diospyros virginiana L. — American Persimmon — Stem — 16.2 ppm — Leaf — 15 ppm. EM

Prunus serotina subsp. serotina — Black Cherry, Wild Cherry — Leaf — 14.4 ppm. TEM

Rhus copallina L. — Dwarf Sumac, Winged Sumac — Leaf — 14.4 ppm. EM

Carya ovata (MILL.) K. KOCH — Shagbark Hickory — Shoot — 13.5 ppm. E

Lactuca sativa L. — Lettuce — Leaf — 8.7 ppm. E

Quercus rubra L. — Northern Red Oak — Stem — 6.6 ppm. EM

Nyssa sylvatica MARSHALL — Black Gum, Black Tupelo — Leaf — 6.37 ppm. EM

Lycopersicon esculentum MILLER — Tomato — Fruit — 6 ppm. TEM

Symphoricarpos orbiculatus MOENCH. — Buckbush — Stem — 4.4 ppm. TM

Rhus copallina L. — Dwarf Sumac, Winged Sumac — Stem — 4.27 ppm. EM

Quercus alba L. — White Oak — Stem — 4.1 ppm. EM

Prunus serotina subsp. serotina — Black Cherry, Wild Cherry — Stem — 3.78 ppm. TEM

Nyssa sylvatica MARSHALL — Black Gum, Black Tupelo — Stem — 3.08 ppm. EM

Quercus velutina LAM. — Black Oak — Stem — 2.5 ppm. EM

Vigna unguiculata subsp. sesquipedalis (L.) VERDC. — Asparagus Bean, Pea Bean, Yardlong Bean — Seed — 2.4 ppm. E

Zinc

Prunus serotina subsp. serotina — Black Cherry, Wild Cherry — Stem — 378 ppm. TEM

Liquidambar styraciflua L. — American Styrax, Sweetgum — Stem — 360 ppm. EM

Nyssa sylvatica MARSHALL — Black Gum, Black Tupelo — Leaf — 182 ppm. EM

Liquidambar styraciflua L. — American Styrax, Sweetgum — Leaf — 164 ppm. EM

Symphoricarpos orbiculatus MOENCH. — Buckbush — Stem — 132 ppm. TM

Diospyros virginiana L. — American Persimmon — Stem — 108 ppm. EM

Sassafras albidum (NUTT.) NEES — Sassafras — Leaf — 102 ppm. TEM

Lycopersicon esculentum MILLER — Tomato — Fruit — 100 ppm. TEM

Brassica oleracea var. capitata L. — Cabbage, Red Cabbage, White Cabbage — Leaf — 87 ppm. E

Corylus avellana L. — Cobnut, English Filbert, European Filbert, European Hazel, Hazel — Seed — 82 ppm. E

Sassafras albidum (NUTT.) NEES — Sassafras — Stem — 56 ppm. TEM

Sesamum indicum L. — Ajonjoli (Sp.), Beni, Benneseed, Sesame, Sesamo (Sp.) — Plant — 56 ppm. EM

Carya glabra (MILLER) SWEET — Pignut Hickory — Shoot — 55 ppm. E

Brassica oleracea var. botrytis L. — Cauliflower — Leaf — 52 ppm. E

Carya ovata (MILL.) K. KOCH — Shagbark Hickory — Shoot — 45 ppm. E

Phaseolus vulgaris var. vulgaris — Black Bean, Dwarf Bean, Field Bean, Flageolet Bean, French Bean, Garden Bean, Green Bean, Haricot, Haricot Bean, Haricot Vert, Kidney Bean, Navy Bean, Pop Bean, Popping Bean, Snap Bean, String Bean, Wax Bean — Fruit — 45 ppm. E

Brassica oleracea var. viridis l. L. — Collards, Cow Cabbage, Spring-Heading Cabbage, Tall Kale, Tree Kale — Leaf — 43 ppm. E

Cucumis sativus L. — Cucumber — Fruit — 42 ppm. E

Quercus stellata WANGENH. — Post Oak — Stem — 42 ppm. EM

Anacardium occidentale L. — Cashew — Seed — 37 ppm. E

Rosa canina L. — Dog Rose, Dogbrier, Rose — Fruit — 36 ppm. EM

Rhizophora mangle L. — Red Mangrove — Leaf — 35 ppm. M

Prunus domestica L. — Plum — Fruit — 34 ppm. TEM

Cocos nucifera L. — Coconut, Coconut Palm, Cocotero (Sp.), Copra, Kokospalme (Ger.), Nariyal — Seed — 33 ppm. E

Pistacia vera L. — Pistachio — Seed — 33 ppm. E

Psophocarpus tetragonolobus (L.) DC. — Asparagus Pea, Goa Bean, Winged Bean — Seed — 33 ppm. E

Senna obtusifolia (L.) H.IRWIN & BARNE-BY — Sicklepod — Seed — 32 ppm. TE

Nyssa sylvatica MARSHALL — Black Gum, Black Tupelo — Stem — 31 ppm. EM

Quercus velutina LAM. — Black Oak — Stem — 31 ppm. EM

Cucurbita maxima DUCH. — Pumpkin — Leaf — 30 ppm. E

Helianthus tuberosus L. — Jerusalem Artichoke — Plant — 30 ppm. E

Momordica charantia L. — Bitter Melon, Sorosi — Fruit — 30 ppm. E

Prunus persica (L.) BATSCH — Peach — Fruit — 30 ppm. TEM

Rhus copallina L. — Dwarf Sumac, Winged Sumac — Stem — 30 ppm. EM

Rumex acetosa L. — Garden Sorrel — Leaf — 30 ppm. TEM

Arctium lappa L. — Burdock, Gobo, Great Burdock — Root — 29 ppm. EM

Lactuca sativa L. — Lettuce — Leaf — 29 ppm. E

Prunus serotina subsp. serotina — Black Cherry, Wild Cherry — Leaf — 29 ppm. TEM

Quercus phellos L. — Willow Oak — Stem — 29 ppm. EM

Carthamus tinctorius L. — Safflower — Flower — 26 ppm. M

Houttuynia cordata THUNB. — Dokudami, Fishwort, Yu Xing Cao — Plant — 26 ppm. EM

Hyoscyamus niger L. — Henbane — Seed — 26 ppm. T

Avena sativa L. — Oats — Seed — 25.7 ppm. EM

Myristica fragrans HOUTT. — Mace, Muskatnussbaum (Ger.), Nutmeg, nogal moscado (Sp.), nuez moscada (Sp.) — Aril — 25 ppm. E

Pachyrhizus erosus RICH. ex DC. — Yam-bean. Jicama — Tuber — 25 ppm. E

Asparagus officinalis L. — Asparagus — Shoot — 24 ppm. E

Chaenomeles lagenaria KOIDZ. — Chinese Quince, Mu-Kua — Fruit — 24 ppm. E

Cynara cardunculus subsp. cardunculus — Artichoke — Flower — 24 ppm. E

Foeniculum vulgare MILLER — Fennel — Fruit — 24 ppm. M

Spinacia oleracea L. — Spinach — Plant — 24 ppm. E

Theobroma cacao L. — Cacao, Chocolate — Seed — 24 ppm. E

Geranium thunbergii SIEB. & ZUCC — Gennoshiouko, Oriental Geranium — Plant — 23 ppm. EM

Papaver somniferum L. — Opium Poppy, Poppyseed Poppy — Seed — 23 ppm. E

Schizonepeta tenuifolia BRIQ. — Ching-Chieh, Jing-Jie — Plant — 23 ppm. M

Vigna radata (L.) WILCZEK — Green Gram, Mungbean — Sprout — Seedling — 23 ppm. E

Abelmoschus manihot (L.) MEDIK. — Manioc Hibiscus — Leaf — 21.5 ppm. EM

Myristica fragrans HOUTT. — Mace, Muskatnussbaum (Ger.), Nutmeg, nogal moscado (Sp.), nuez moscada (Sp.) — Seed — 21 ppm. E

Tamarindus indica L. — Indian Tamarind, Kilytree, Tamarind — Leaf — 21 ppm. M

Artemisia vulgaris L. — Mugwort — Plant — 20 ppm. M

Brassica oleracea var. acephala DC — Curly Kale, Kale, Kitchen Kale, Scotch Kale — Leaf — 20 ppm. E

Camellia sinensis (L.) KUNTZE — Tea — Leaf — 20 ppm. E

Capsicum annuum L. — Bell Pepper, Cherry Pepper, Cone Pepper, Green Pepper, Paprika, Sweet Pepper — Fruit — 20 ppm. E

Hordeum vulgare L. — Barley, Barleygrass — Seed — 20 ppm. EM

Mentha arvensis var. piperascens MALINV. EX L. H. BAILEY — Cornmint, Field Mint, Japanese Mint — Plant — 20 ppm. TEM

Piper nigrum L. — Black Pepper, Pepper, White Pepper — Fruit — 20 ppm. EM

Rhus glabra L. — Smooth Sumac — Stem — 20 ppm. EM

Solanum melongena L. — Aubergine, Egg-plant — Fruit — 20 ppm. E

Trichosanthes anguina L. — Snakegourd — Fruit — 20 ppm. E

Zinc, cont.

Tussilago farfara L. — Coltsfoot — Flower — 20 ppm. TM

Zea mays L. — Corn — Fruit — 20 ppm. E

Amaranthus sp. — Pigweed — Leaf — 19 ppm. EM

Forsythia suspensa VAHL — Lian-Jiao, Lien-Chiao — Fruit — 19 ppm. M

Helianthus annuus L. — Girasol, Sunflower — Seed — 19 ppm. E

Ipomoea aquatica FORSSKAL — Swamp Cabbage, Water Spinach — Leaf — 19 ppm. E

Juglans nigra L. — Black Walnut — Seed — 19 ppm. E

Portulaca oleracea L. — Purslane, Verdolaga — Plant — 19 ppm. E

Rhus copallina L. — Dwarf Sumac, Winged Sumac — Leaf — 19 ppm. EM

Taraxacum mongolicum HAND.-MAZZ. — Mongoloid Dandelion — Plant — 19 ppm. EM

Allium cepa L. — Onion, Shallot — Seed — 18.2 ppm. E

Atractylodes ovata DC. — Bai-Zhu, Pai-Chu — Rhizome — 18 ppm. M

Bertholletia excelsa BONPL. — Brazilnut, Brazilnut-Tree, Creamnut, Paranut — Seed — 18 ppm. E

Coriandrum sativum L. — Chinese Parsley, Cilantro, Coriander — Leaf — 18 ppm. E

Daucus carota L. — Carrot — Root — 18 ppm. E

Gentiana scabra BUNGE — Japanese Gentian — Root — 18 ppm. M

Glycine max (L.) MERR. — Soybean — Seed — 18 ppm. E

Scutellaria baicalensis GEORGI — Baikal Skullcap, Chinese Skullcap, Huang Qin — Root — 18 ppm. M

Trifolium pratense L. — Cowgrass, Peavine Clover, Purple Clover, Red Clover — Hay — 18 ppm. EM

Juniperus virginiana L. — Red Cedar — Shoot — 17.6 ppm. TEM

Eupatorium odoratum L. — Christmas bush — Leaf — 0-35 ppm. M

Anethum graveolens L. — Dill, Garden Dill — Plant — 17 ppm. E

Beta vulgaris subsp. vulgaris — Beet, Beet-root, Garden Beet, Sugar Beet — Root — 17 ppm. E

Coptis chinensis FRANCH. — Chinese Goldthread, Huang-Lian, Huang-Lien — Rhizome — 17 ppm. M

Coptis japonica (THUNB.) MAKINO — Huang-Lia, Huang-Lian, Huang-Lien, Japanese Goldthread — Rhizome — 17 ppm. M

Coptis spp. — Generic Goldthread — Rhizome — 17 ppm. M

Curcuma longa L. — Indian Saffron, Turmeric — Rhizome — 17 ppm. E

Fragaria spp. — Strawberry — Fruit — 17 ppm. E

Lycium chinense MILL. — Chinese Boxthorn, Chinese Matrimony Vine, Chinese Wolfberry, Chinesischer Bocksdorn (Ger.), Daun Koki (Indones.), Gou Qi (Chin.), Kaukichai (Malays.), Kuko (Jap.), Lyciet de Chine (Fr.), Spina Santa Cinese (Ital.), Wolfberry — Root — Bark — 17 ppm. EM

Nelumbo nucifera L. — Water Lotus — Seed — 17 ppm. EM

Panax ginseng C. A. MEYER — Chinese Ginseng, Ginseng, Korean Ginseng, Oriental Ginseng — Root — 17 ppm. M

Perilla frutescens (L.) BRITTON — Perilla — Plant — 17 ppm. TEM

Cichorium endivia L. — Endive, Escarole — Leaf — 16.8 ppm. E

Triticum aestivum L. — Wheat — Seed — 16.7 ppm. EM

Mangifera indica L. — Mango — Fruit — 16.6 ppm. EM

Bupleurum chinense DC. — Chai-Hu — Root — 16 ppm. M

Cuminum cyminum L. — Cumin — Fruit — 16 ppm. EM

Euodia rutaecarpa BENTH. — Wou Chou Yu — Fruit — 16 ppm.

Lablab purpureus (L.) SWEET — Bonavist Bean, Hyacinth Bean, Lablab Bean — Seed — 16 ppm. TEM

Magnolia denudata DESR. — Hsin-I, Xin-Yi — Flower — 16 ppm. EM

Magnolia fargesii CHENG — Hsin-I, Xin-Yi — Flower — 16 ppm. EM

Magnolia kobus DC. — Hsin-I, Xin-Yi — Flower — 16 ppm. EM

Petasites japonicus (SIEBOLD & ZUCC.) MAXIM. — Butterbur — Plant — 16 ppm. T

Physalis ixocarpa BROT. — Tomatillo — Fruit — 16 ppm. E

Prunus armeniaca L. — Apricot — Seed — 16 ppm. TEM

Sinomenium acutum (THUNB.) REHD. & WILS. — Ching-Feng-Teng — Rhizome — 16 ppm. EM

Zingiber officinale ROSCOE — Ginger — Rhizome — 16 ppm. EM

Elettaria cardamomum (L.) MATON — Cardamom — Fruit — 15.4 ppm. EM

Quercus alba L. — White Oak — Stem — 15.2 ppm. EM

Alisma plantago-aquatica L. — Mud Plantain, Tse-Hsieh, Water Plantain, Ze-Xie — Rhizome — 15 ppm. M

Areca catechu L. — Betel Nut, Pin-Lang — Seed — 15 ppm. EM

Carya illinoensis (WANGENH.) K. KOCH — Pecan — Seed — 15 ppm. E

Cucurbita pepo L. — Pumpkin — Seed — 15 ppm. E

Firmiana simplex (L.) W. F. WIGHT — Chinese Parasol — Seed — 15 ppm. EM

Glehnia littoralis F. SCHMIDT & MIQUEL — Bei Sha Shen — Root — 15 ppm. EM

Jussiaea repens L. — Jussiaeae Herba, Pond Dragon — Plant — 15 ppm. M

Lycium chinense MILL. — Chinese Boxthorn, Chinese Matrimony Vine, Chinese Wolfberry, Chinesischer Bocksdorn (Ger.), Daun Koki (Indones.), Gou Qi (Chin.), Kaukichai (Malays.), Kuko (Jap.), Lyciet de Chine (Fr.), Spina Santa Cinese (Ital.), Wolfberry — Fruit — 15 ppm. EM

Phaseolus lunatus L. — Butter Bean, Lima Bean — Seed — 15 ppm. E

Phaseolus vulgaris var. vulgaris — Black Bean, Dwarf Bean, Field Bean, Flageolet Bean, French Bean, Garden Bean, Green Bean, Haricot, Haricot Bean, Haricot Vert, Kidney Bean, Navy Bean, Pop Bean, Popping Bean, Snap Bean, String Bean, Wax Bean — Seed — 15 ppm. E

Rubia cordifolia L. — Madder — Root — 15 ppm. M

Senna occidentalis (L.) H. IRWIN & BARNEBY — Coffee Senna — Seed — 15 ppm. TE

Urtica dioica L. — European Nettle, Stinging Nettle — Leaf — 15 ppm. EM

Acanthopanax gracilistylis W.W.SMITH — Wu Chia Pi — Root — Bark — 14 ppm. M

Apium graveolens L. — Celery — Seed — 14 ppm. E

Aristolochia debilis SIEB. & ZUCC. — Chinese Birthwort — Fruit — 14 ppm. TEM

Artemisia herba-alba ASSO. — Desert Wormwood — Plant — 14 ppm. M

Asarum heterotropoides MAEK. — Asian Wild Ginger — Root — 14 ppm. M

Asarum sieboldii (MIQ.) MAEK. — Siebold's Wild Ginger — Root — 14 ppm. M

Brassica juncea (L.) CZERNJ. & COSSON — Mustard Greens — Leaf — 14 ppm. E

Capsicum frutescens L. — Cayenne, Chili, Hot Pepper, Red Chili, Spur Pepper, Tabasco — Fruit — 14 ppm. E

Glycyrrhiza uralensis FISCH. EX DC. — Chinese Licorice, Gan-Cao, Kan-Tsao — Root — 14 ppm. M

Ocimum basilicum L. — Basil, Cuban Basil, Sweet Basil — Leaf — 14 ppm. E

Phyllanthus emblica L. — Emblic, Myrobalan — Fruit — 14 ppm. E

Plantago asiatica L. — Asian Plantain — Plant — 14 ppm. EM

Solanum tuberosum L. — Potato — Tuber — 14 ppm. E

Xanthosoma sagittifolium (L.) SCHOTT — Malanga, Tannia, Yautia — Root — 14 ppm. E

Carum carvi L. — Caraway, Carum, Comino (Sp.), Comino de prado (Sp.), Kummel (Ger.) — Fruit — 13.8 ppm. E

Quercus rubra L. — Northern Red Oak — Stem — 13.2 ppm. EM

Boehmeria nivea (L.) GAUDICH. — Ramie — Plant — 13 ppm. M

Coriandrum sativum L. — Chinese Parsley, Cilantro, Coriander — Fruit — 13 ppm. E

Erythroxylum coca var. coca — Coca — Leaf — 13 ppm. EM

Zinc, cont.

Gardenia jasminoides J. ELLIS — Cape Jasmine, Gardenia, Jasmin, Shan-Chih-Tzu, Shan-Zhi-Zi, Zhi Zi — Fruit — 13 ppm. M

Lonicera japonica THUNB. — Japanese Honeysuckle — Flower — 13 ppm. M

Lygodium japonicum (THUNB.) SW. — Climbing Fern — Pollen or Spore — 13 ppm. M

Oenothera biennis L. — Evening-Primrose — Seed — 13 ppm. EM

Panax quinquefolius L. — American Ginseng, Ginseng — Plant — 13 ppm. M

Pueraria pseudohirsuta TANG & WANG — Chinese Kudzu — Root — 13 ppm. EM

Quisqualis indica L. — Rangoon Creeper — Fruit — 13 ppm. TE

Vigna angularis (WILLD.) OHWI & H. OHASHI — Adzuki Bean — Seed — 13 ppm. E

Vigna radata (L.) WILCZEK — Green Gram, Mungbean — Seed — 13 ppm. E

Aconitum carmichaelii DEBX. — Aconite, Fu-Tsu — Tuber — 12 ppm. TM

Atractylodes lancea DC. — Cang Zhu — Rhizome — 12 ppm. M

Bletilla striata (THUNB.) REICHB. f. — Bletilla, Chinese Ground Orchid, Dai Chi (Chin.), Hardy Orchid, Hyacinth Bletilla, Hyacinth Orchid, Shiran (Jap.) — Tuber — 12 ppm. M

Broussonetia papyrifera (L.) VENT — Paper Mulberry — Fruit — 12 ppm. EM

Cajanus cajan (L.) HUTH — Pigeonpea — Seed — 12 ppm. E

Cucurbita spp. — Summer Squash — Fruit — 12 ppm. E

Cynanchum atratum BUNGE — Bai-Wei, Pai-Wei — Root — 12 ppm. EM

Fritillaria thunbergii MIQ. — Bei-Mu, Fritillary — Bulb — 12 ppm. EM

Lens culinaris MEDIK. — Lentil — Sprout — Seedling — 12 ppm. E

Ligustrum japonicum THUNB. — Japanese Privet, Ligustri Fructus — Fruit — 12 ppm. M

Ligustrum lucidum W. T. AITON — Chinese Privet, Glossy Privet, Ligustri Fructus, Privet, White Waxtree — Fruit — 12 ppm. M

Lupinus albus L. — White Lupine — Seed — 12 ppm. TE

Pastinaca sativa L. — Parsnip — Root — 12 ppm. E

Petroselinum crispum (MILLER) NYMAN EX A. W. HILLL — Parsley — Plant — 12 ppm. E

Rubus chingii HU — Chinese Raspberry — Fruit — 12 ppm. EM

Taraxacum officinale WEBER EX F. H. WIGG. — Dandelion — Leaf — 12 ppm. EM

Vitis vinifera L. — European Grape, Grape, Grapevine, Parra (Sp.), Vid (Sp.), Vigne Vinifere (Fr.), Weinrebe (Ger.), Wine Grape — Fruit — 11.6 ppm. EM

Chamissoa altissima (JACQ.) HBK — Guanique — Leaf — 2-23 ppm. M

Brassica nigra (L.) W. D. J. KOCH — Black Mustard — Leaf — 11.2 ppm. E

Tephrosia candida (ROXB.) DC. — White Tephrosia — Plant — 11.2 ppm. TM

Pyrus communis L. — Pear — Fruit — 11.1 ppm. E

Achyranthes bidentata BLUME — Chaff Flower — Root — 11 ppm. M

Allium cepa L. — Onion, Shallot — Bulb — 11 ppm. E

Apium graveolens L. — Celery — Root — 11 ppm. E

Arachis hypogaea L. — Groundnut, Peanut — Seed — 11 ppm. EM

Glechoma hederacea L. — Alehoof — Plant — 11 ppm. M

Origanum majorana L. — Marjoram, Sweet Marjoram — Plant — 11 ppm. E

Persea americana MILLER — Avocado — Fruit — 11 ppm. E

Physalis peruviana L. — Cape Gooseberry, Ground Cherry — Fruit — 11 ppm. E

Prunus dulcis (MILLER) D. A. WEBB — Almond — Seed — 11 ppm. TEM

Schisandra chinensis (TURCZ.) BAILL. — Chinese Magnolia Vine, Five-Flavor-Fruit, Magnolia Vine, Schizandra, Wu Wei Zi, Wu Wei Zu — Fruit — 11 ppm. M

Trigonella foenum-graecum L. — Alholva (Sp.), Bockshornklee (Ger.), Fenugreek, Greek Clover, Greek Hay — Seed — 11 ppm. EM

Cinnamomum verum J. PRESL — Ceylon Cinnamon, Cinnamon — Leaf — 10.9 ppm. TEM

Dioscorea alata L. — Greater Yam, Winged Yam — Root — 10.7 ppm. E

Amphicarpaea bracteata (L.) FERNALD — Hog Peanut — Shoot — 0-20 ppm. EM

Angelica dahurica BENTH & HOOK. — Bai Zhi — Root — 10 ppm. M

Cassia tora L. — Sickle Senna — Seed — 10 ppm. M

Cicer arietinum L. — Chickpea, Garbanzo — Seed — 10 ppm. E

Cinnamomum aromaticum NEES — Canela de la China (Sp.), Canelero chino (Sp.), Canelle de Cochinchine (Fr.), Cannelier Casse (Fr.), Cannelier de Chine (Fr.), Cassia, Cassia Bark, Cassia Lignea, China Junk Cassia, Chinazimt (Ger.), Chinese Cassia, Chinese Cinnamon, Chinesischer Zimtbaum (Ger.), Kashia-Keihi (Jap.), Saigon Cinnamon, Zimtcassie (Ger.) — Bark — 10 ppm. TEM

Citrus aurantium L. — Bitter Orange, Petitgrain — Fruit — 10 ppm. E

Cyperus rotundus L. — Nutsedge — Rhizome — 10 ppm. EM

Drynaria fortunei (KUNZE) J. SMITH — Fortune's Fern — Rhizome — 10 ppm. M

Isatis tinctoria L. — Dyer's Woad — Root — 10 ppm. M

Nardostachys chinensis BATALIN — Chinese Spikenard — Rhizome — 10 ppm. M

Peucedanum decursivum (MIQ.) MAX. — Qian Hu — Plant — 10 ppm. M

Pimenta dioica (L.) MERR. — Allspice, Clover-Pepper, Jamaica-Pepper, Pimenta, Pimento — Bud — 10 ppm. E

Pisum sativum L. — Pea — Seed — 10 ppm. E

Platycodon grandiflorum (JACQ.) A.DC. — Balloon Flower, Chieh-Keng, Jie-Geng — Root — 10 ppm. TEM

Polygonum cuspidatum SIEBOLD & ZUCC. — Giant Knotweed, Hu-Zhang, Japanese Knotweed, Mexican Bamboo — Plant — 10 ppm. TEM

Polystichum polyblepharum (ROEM.) PRESL — Chinese Polystichum — Plant — 10 ppm. T

Prunus persica (L.) BATSCH — Peach — Seed — 10 ppm. TEM

Rheum palmatum L. — Chinese Rhubarb — Rhizome — 10 ppm. E

Sechium edule (JACQ.) SW. — Chayote — Leaf — 10 ppm. EM

Siegesbeckia orientalis L. — Hsi Chien, Saint Paul's Wort — Plant — 10 ppm. M

Simmondsia chinensis (LINK) C. SCHNEID. — Jojoba — Seed — 10 ppm.

Sophora angustifolia AIT. — Narrowleaf Sophora — Root — 10 ppm. TM

Vigna unguiculata subsp. sesquipedalis (L.) VERDC. — Asparagus Bean, Pea Bean, Yardlong Bean — Seed — 10 ppm. E

Allium sativum var. sativum L. — Garlic — Bulb — 9.7 ppm. E

Trachyspermum ammi (L.) SPRAGUE ex TURRILL — Ajwan — Fruit — 9.1 ppm. EM

Abelmoschus esculentus (L.) MOENCH — Okra — Fruit — 9 ppm. EM

Anemarrhena asphodeloides BUNGE — Chih-Mu, Zhi-Mu — Rhizome — 9 ppm. M

Angelica laxiflora DIELS — Tu Huo — Root — 9 ppm. M

Armoracia rusticana GAERTN. ET AL. — Horseradish — Root — 9 ppm. E

Celosia cristata L. — Cockscomb — Flower — 9 ppm. M

Cinnamomum sieboldii — Japanese Cinnamon — Root — Bark — 9 ppm. TEM

Cinnamomum verum J. PRESL — Ceylon Cinnamon, Cinnamon — Bark — 9 ppm. TEM

Citrus medica L. — Citron — Fruit — 9 ppm. E

Cnidium officinale MAKINO — Jih-Chiung — Rhizome — 9 ppm. EM

Dendrobium nobile LINDL. — Noble Dendrobium — Stem — 9 ppm. M

Eriocaulon sp — Oriental Pipewort — Leaf — 9 ppm. M

Lens culinaris MEDIK. — Lentil — Seed — 9 ppm. E

Lophatherum gracile BROGN. — Dan Zhu Ye — Plant — 9 ppm. M

Origanum vulgare L. — Common Turkish Oregano, European Oregano, Oregano, Pot Marjoram, Wild Marjoram, Wild Oregano — Plant — 9 ppm. E

Peganum harmala L. — Harmel, Syrian Rue — Plant — 9 ppm. TEM

Pimpinella anisum L. — Anise, Sweet Cumin — Seed — 9 ppm. EM

Polygala tenuifolia WILLD. — Chinese Senega — Root — 9 ppm. M

Psidium guajava L. — Guava — Fruit — 9 ppm. E

Pulsatilla chinensis (BUNGE) REGEL — Chinese Anemone — Root — 9 ppm. M

Rosa laevigata MICHX. — Cherokee Rose — Fruit — 9 ppm. EM

Satureja hortensis L. — Summer Savory — Leaf — 9 ppm. E

Satureja montana L. — Savory, Winter Savory — Leaf — 9 ppm. E

Syzygium aromaticum (L.) MERR. & L. M. PERRY — Clove, Clovetree — Flower — 9 ppm. E

Thymus vulgaris L. — Common Thyme, Garden Thyme, Thyme — Plant — 9 ppm. EM

Vigna aconitifolia (JACQ.) MARECHAL — Mat Bean, Moth Bean — Seed — 9 ppm. E

Ananas comosus (L.) MERR. — Pineapple — Fruit — 8.8 ppm. E

Juglans cinerea L. — Butternut — Seed — 8.4 ppm. E

Amomum xanthioides WALL. — Bastard Cardamom, Chin Kousha, Malabar Cardamom, Tavoy Cardamom — Seed — 8 ppm. E

Amorphophallus campanulatus BLUME — Elephant-Foot Yam — Root — 8 ppm. TEM

Anethum graveolens L. — Dill, Garden Dill — Fruit — 8 ppm. E

Artemisia capillaris THUNB. — Capillary Wormwood — Plant — 8 ppm. M

Blechnum orientale L. — Kuan Chung, Shield Fern — Rhizome — 8 ppm. TEM

Brassica oleracea var. botrytis L. — Cauliflower — Flower — 8 ppm. E

Canavalia ensiformis (L.) DC. — Jack Bean — Seed — 8 ppm. E

Cimicifuga dahurica (TURCZ. EX FISCH. & C. A. MEY.) MAXIM. — Sheng Ma — Rhizome — 8 ppm. M

Cistanche salsa (C.A.MEYER) G. BECK — Broomrape, Cistanchis Herba, Jou Tsung Jung — Plant — 8 ppm. M

Colocasia esculenta (L.) SCHOTT — Taro — Root — 8 ppm. E

Crataegus cuneata SIEB. & ZUCC. — Hawthorn — Fruit — 8 ppm. M

Dioscorea bulbifera L. — Air Potato, Potato Yam — Rhizome — 8 ppm. E

Hordeum vulgare L. — Barley, Barleygrass — Sprout Seedling — 8 ppm. EM

Juncus effusus L. — Rush — Pith — 8 ppm. TEM

Lycopodium clavatum L. — Antler Herb, Clubmoss — Plant — 8 ppm. TM

Magnolia officinalis REHDER & E. H. WILSON — Chinese Magnolia, Hou Pu, Magnolia-Bark — Bark — 8 ppm. EM

Prunella vulgaris L. — Heal-All, Self-Heal — Flower — 8 ppm.

Raphanus sativus L. — Radish — Root — 8 ppm. E

Salvia miltiorrhiza BUNGE — Dan-Shen, Red Sage, Tan-Shen — Root — 8 ppm. EM

Salvia officinalis L. — Sage — Leaf — 8 ppm. EM

Sinapis alba L. — White Mustard — Seed — 8 ppm. TEM

Tetrapanax papyrifera (HOOK.) K.KOCH — Rice Paper Tree, Tong-Cao, Tung-Tsao — Pith — 8 ppm. M

Vigna mungo (L.) HEPPER — Black Gram — Seed — 8 ppm. E

Carya ovata (MILL.) K. KOCH — Shagbark Hickory — Seed — 7.8 ppm. E

Citrus paradisi MacFAD. — Grapefruit — Fruit — 7.7 ppm. E

Cucumis melo var. cantalupensis NAUDIN — Cantaloupe, Melon, Muskmelon, Netted Melon, Nutmeg Melon, Persian Melon — Fruit — 7.7 ppm. E

Artocarpus altilis (PARKINS.) FOSBERG — Breadfruit — Fruit — 7.5 ppm. E

Averrhoa carambola L. — Carambola, Star Fruit — Fruit — 1-15 ppm. E

Diospyros virginiana L. — American Persimmon — Leaf — 7.5 ppm. EM

Akebia quinata (THUNB.) DECNE — Chocolate Vine — Stem — 7 ppm. M

Apium graveolens L. — Celery — Plant — 7 ppm. E

Arisaema consanguineum SCHOTT — Chinese Jack-In-The-Pulpit — Rhizome — 7 ppm. TEM

Artemisia dracunculus L. — Tarragon — Plant — 7 ppm. M

Artocarpus heterophyllus LAM. — Jackfruit — Fruit — 7 ppm. E

Castanea dentata (MARSHALL) BORKH. — American Chestnut — Seed — 7 ppm. EM

Cinnamomum sieboldii — Japanese Cinnamon — Bark — 7 ppm. TEM

Eriobotrya japonica (THUNB.) LINDL. — Loquat — Leaf — 7 ppm. E

Ipomoea batatas (L.) LAM — Sweet Potato — Root — 7 ppm. E

Morinda sp — Morinda — Root — 7 ppm. M

Musa x paradisiaca L. — Banana, Plantain — Fruit — 7 ppm. E

Notopterygium incisum TING. — Qiang Huo — Rhizome — 7 ppm. M

Quercus rubra L. — Northern Red Oak — Seed — 7 ppm. EM

Ribes nigrum L. — Black Currant — Fruit — 7 ppm. E

Ribes rubrum L. — Red Currant, White Currant — Fruit — 7 ppm. E

Syzygium cumini SKEELS — Aceituna Dulce, Jambolan, Java Plum — Fruit — 2.3-14 ppm. E

Zizyphus jujuba MILL. — Da-Zao, Jujube, Ta-Tsao — Fruit — 7 ppm. EM

Valerianella locusta (L.) LATERRADE — Corn Salad, Lamb's Lettuce — Plant — 13-13.2 ppm. E

Elaeagnus angustifolia — Russian Olive — Fruit — 2-13 ppm. EM

Vaccinium myrtillus L. — Bilberry, Dwarf Bilberry, Whortleberry — Fruit — 6.3 ppm. E

Albizia julibrissin DURAZZ. — Mimosa — Bark — 6 ppm. EM

Belamcanda chinensis (L.) DC. — Blackberry Lily, Iris Tigre (Fr.), Leopard Lily, Leopardenblume (Ger.), Maravilla (Sp.), Mariposa (Sp.), Shenan — Rhizome — 6 ppm. M

Brassica rapa L. — Sarson — Seed — 6 ppm. E

Castanea mollisima BLUME — Chinese Chestnut — Seed — 6 ppm. EM

Citrus aurantiifolia (CHRISTM.) SWINGLE — Lime — Fruit — 6 ppm. E

Cornus officinalis SIEB. & ZUCC. — Chinese Dogwood — Fruit — 6 ppm. EM

Fraxinus rhynchophylla HANCE — Chinese Ash — Bark — 6 ppm. M

Ginkgo biloba L. — Ginkgo, Maidenhair — Tree — Seed — 6 ppm. TEM

Morus alba L. — Sang-Pai-Pi, White Mulberry — Root — Bark — 6 ppm. EM

Murraya sp. — Curry Leaf — Fruit — 6 ppm. EM

Paeonia lactiflora PALL. — Bai Shao (Chinese), Chih-Shao, Common Garden Peony, Peony, White Peony — Root — 6 ppm. M

Paeonia suffruticosa ANDREWS — Moutan, Moutan Peony, Tree Peony — Root — Bark — 6 ppm. M

Panax japonicus C.A.MEYER — Japanese Ginseng — Rhizome — 6 ppm. M

Phellodendron amurense RUPR. — Amur Cork Tree, Huang Bai, Huang Po, Po Mu — Bark — 6 ppm. M

Pinus edulis ENGELM — Pinyon Pine — Seed — 10-12 ppm. EM

Raphanus sativus L. — Radish — Seed — 6 ppm. E

Ribes uva-crispa L. — Gooseberry — Fruit — 6 ppm. E

Rosmarinus officinalis L. — Rosemary — Plant — 6 ppm. EM

Scrophularia buergeriana MIQ. — Hsuan-Shen, Yuan-Shen — Root — 6 ppm. M

Citation of sources does not imply that nature supervises equal uptake in all plants of the same species. The *Journal of the American College of Nutrition* has now made available new findings out of the University of Texas revealing diminished levels of nutrients in vegetables and fruits under circumstances of certain salt fertilization, the presence of toxic rescue chemistry, genetic modification and hybridization. Specific details identify a decline in levels of calcium, riboflavin, vitamin C, iron, potassium and protein over the last decade or more. Selective breeding and genetic modification stand indicted, the modest benefits of cosmetic beauty being outweighed by nutrient deficiency.

Plants in the wild also bear the marks of environmental degradation, much of it manmade, the worst case scenario being atomic fallout. Withal, it is the transformation of botanicals from food to commodity status that has robbed plants of therapeutic integrity and human beings of mental acuity.

Nevertheless, knowledge of sources becomes vital as international frustration economics brings currently readily available health food supplements under pharmaceutical control.

The Terminal Word

I have agonized over whether to add further to an already detailed book. In fact I have little that is new to add. The results of this story have been made a matter of record in the public prints in books that give us a day-by-day diary of government malfeasance and crime in clinical reports that detail the slow but steady slide of the population into ill health and medical hopelessness. Post World War II reports tell us of Ishii Shiro, a Japanese doctor, who ran the bio-weapons program for Nippon. At war's end he was offered a job with the United States, this or execution as a war criminal.

Reports have it that the Japanese introduced the disease kuru to New Guinea.

My own recollection of story elements goes back to the end of World War II when it was revealed that the notorious prison camp 731 in Manchuria was using malaria to test biological weapons on servicemen who had otherwise outlived Japanese brutality. The story trailed off into New Guinea to the Fore Tribe and the scourge of kuru, or wasting disease. Richard Rhodes wrote a near famous book about kuru, *The Deadly Feast*. It reported the conventional story about cannibalism as it emerged from the work of Nobel Prize winner Carleton Gajdusek.

The fragments continued to stack up. Finally the mother lode exploded in the magazine *Nexus*, replete with documentation and awesome details that call into question America's most cherished principles.

In earlier pages I have detailed the work of Ira Allison as related to brucellosis, a nutritional disease of cattle that once upon a time was the scourge of the countryside with varieties that seemed to answer only to magnesium, manganese, cobalt, zinc, copper and iodine. During World War II, scientists discerned that the natural virus of the brucellosis organism could be manipulated by technology faintly related to the technology that would one day emerge as genetic engineering.

At this point it becomes necessary to add a word or two to your vocabulary. The word is mycoplasma. Physicians do not understand the agent because they are too harried to read much of the medical literature or because what they encounter comes in fragments that elude the dots coming together.

The mechanism for health destruction is simple in the extreme. Mycoplasma simply kills the cell. When the cell ruptures the resultant material is deposited into the bloodstream.

Mycoplasma is a product of the laboratory. The agent was created because the elimination of war gases seemed to call for biological weapons. It is a matter of record that the U.S. military incubated the agent and tested it on unsuspecting populations, extrapolating the likely kill or disabling value when released full strength.

Most Americans alive today have no memory of the Great War and its hungry hunt for more deadly weapons. Hearings before congressional committees now validate the claim that Canada, Britain and the United States initiated a secret agreement to evaluate two types of biological weapons, one to kill and one to disable.

Japan and Germany also were doing similar weapons testing. It thus came to pass that the Brucella bacterium became weaponized.

All the powerful agencies of government participated, notably Centers for Disease Control and National Institute of Health. *Weaponize* is a term I use purposefully.

There was a special virus cancer program under the auspices of CIA and NIH, a program fine-tuned to finding agents for which no moral definition existed.

Nexus reports that AIDS was disguised as a war on cancer, but was really a part of a war program. Most of these programs proceeded without congressional oversight or awareness. When the time came to order up the document of a special virus-cancer program, a Senate committee had to retrieve it from a foreign source. We are told that some 200 species of mycoplasma now exist. Most have proved to be a failure for the purpose intended. Not so with the Brucella bacterium. We say bacterium, but the agent enzymes that effect it are not a bacteria or a virus. It is a mutated form combined with a virus from which the mycoplasma is exuded. What was once a fairly innocuous rural animal disease problem has now become as lethal as nuclear fallout.

Scientists have explained that the Brucella has been engineered into a crystalline form. This much accomplished, the weapon was then tested on populations in North America. Scientist Maurice Hillman has stated that the disease agent is now carried by everyone in North America, possibly by most of the world's population. This may well be the reason for a general increase in all neuro-systematic degenerative diseases since World War II. That statement can be amplified to include since 1972, the date when previously unheard of diseases declared their presence, namely chronic disease syndrome and AIDS.

Shy-Ching Lo, a researcher at the Armed Forces Institute of Pathology testified that the disease agent causes cancer, chronic fatigue syndrome, Crohn's disease, colitis, type-1 diabetes, multiple sclerosis, Parkinson's disease, Legionnaire's disease, and vascular disorders such as clogged carotid arteries, as well as Alzheimer's disease. Further, researcher Charles Engel with the National Institute of Health, Bethesda, Maryland, is on record telling an NIH meeting February 7, 2000, "I am now of the view that the probable cause of chronic fatigue syndrome is the mycoplasma."

From peer reviewed articles in medical literature, *New England Journal of Medicine* and of the *American Medical Association Journal* we now learn how mycoplasma works much as we learn how the Olree Standard Genetic Chart holds promise for negating the worst effects.

Mycoplasma has its own marching orders. It enters into the individual cells of the body as governed by genetics. If cells of the brain are mutated, neurological disease conditions result. If the pathogen invades the intestines, Crohn's or colitis is the consequence. Cell biologists tell us that mycoplasma can lie dormant for decades. If, however, trauma or stress occurs or a vaccination challenges the system, the damaged cell asserts its programmed mischief.

A Brucella toxin in crystalline form competes with the madness of war. It turns out created diseases enable the creation of drug remedies for those same diseases. The crystalline form could be stored, transported, and be ready for battle much like mortar or a rocket shell. Instead of guns, insect vectors could be used to retail the disease. The food chain suggests itself as a transport mechanism.

Testing of mycoplasma at less than battle strength has forced the military to evaluate the casualties under extreme conditions. Moved up in strength, the bio-weapon can be called on to kill in about any time frame, or simply disable and order up a lingering death. The weapon calculates on bypassing protective nutrition as suggested by the minerals that are the subject of this book.

In theory, a salt shaker full of the crystalline brucellosis form could sicken an entire country. Medical doctors who are used to reading symptoms via the blood test seem helpless when confronted with mycoplasma. Its permission to attack and destroy is best regulated by a pH of 8.1. Blood usually has a pH of 7.4. The physician runs his eyes over the figures and dismisses the patient.

The vaccination program President Gerald Ford loosed on the nation to combat a non-existent swine flu left its legacy, countless cases of Gillian-Barre. Personnel knew high speed crystalline brucellosis had been connected with multiple sclerosis, but not made known to the public. When Brucella settles in the brain, the sclerosis connection becomes imminent.

The history of our times is chock full of case reports making bio-weapon works. It also chronicles tests on populations, for which reason pandemics have resulted. These tests would have wiped out populations had they been conducted full strength.

These statements are not mere hyperbole. Chapter and verse tell of mosquitoes used as vectors, wholesale swarms of the little critters being detailed to distribute the disease in Punta Gorda, Florida, this according to the *New England Journal of Medicine.* The resultant chronic fatigue syndrome pleased the weapon's creators. Queen's University of Canada readied the mosquitoes for the trial work.

According to the footnotes that adorn a Punta Gorda, Florida release, 450 diseases cases developed. Infect the mosquitoes at Queen's University, release them half a continent away, and then issue statements of plausible denial to the press — that has been the *modus operandi.* Similar tests have been run in the St. Lawrence Valley. This was in 1984 where some 700 people developed encephalitis or chronic disease syndrome.

When people came to the clinics, their cases were added to the database. A Princeton press conference in 1997 confirmed the test, which Canada simply denied via storytelling. At full strength, 33% of the population would have developed cancer in five years. This much stated, it now becomes necessary to retreat to the Olree Standard Genetic Chart, starting with the minerals best calculated to neutralize the agents mentioned here.

We know that boron challenges and defeats radiation. Yttrium stands as a stone-faced guard against errant pathways in the digestion. Selenium is a foe to cancer and other degenerative metabolic diseases. The full pantheon of minerals reflected in the Olree Standard Genetic Chart joins the Sources section of this book which centers on crops, botanicals, forbs, and trees that provide the materials human metabolism yearns for.

294 Minerals for the Genetic Code

Acknowledgments

This book is an exposition and analysis of Dr. Richard Olree's Standard Genetic Chart as it relates to the life and works of Walter Russell. Russell, it will be remembered, hypothesized the existence of 22 subatomic particles in 1926. A full ten years later Richard Olree stumbled across another extraordinary book that was again enormously influential in the comprehension of the dynamics of the study of genetics. This phenomenal book, *DNA and the I Ching*, by Johnson F. Yan, created the melting point between Walter Russell's mineral chart and the *I Ching* through Dr. Yan's work.

Chaim T. Horovitz's book *Biochemistry of Scandium and Yttrium* provided Olree considerable insight into what will be a new frontier in human longevity as it pertains to the mineral yttrium. Horovitz's book inspired Olree to recognize the overwhelming role yttrium and scandium play in the maintenance of human health.

Finally, without the help of the following people, Olree would not have been able to finish what has been his life work: Betty Jo Bruder has been a patient and loving partner who has allowed him the time and space to follow his passion for this project. His son and daughter, Richard N. Olree III, and Abby Avalon Olree have been important contributors in developing the Sourcing the Elements chapter in this book. Olree's secretary, Melissa Wilkins, has furnished much of the inspiration required for the completion of this ever-growing work. Finally, without the encouragement and support of Olree's parents, Richard and Marilyn Olree, he could not have pursued his profession or the study of genetics reported here.

Bryan Kight must be thanked for painstakingly turning raw text into a well-designed book. And special thanks to Richard Simmers, Ph.D., for help with the second proofreading.

As has been the custom in books by this author, sources and books consulted are generally acknowledged in the text — all are easily located in the index.

Index

abortion, spontaneous, 117, 176
abscesses, 126, 135
aches and pains, 127
acidosis, 131, 135
acne, 122, 143, 169
Acupuncture Meridian, 81, 91
ADD/ADHD, 146
adenosine triphosphate, 159
adenoids, 168
AIDS virus, 97, 98
alanine, 105, 111, 138, 164
alberton, 171
Albrecht, Professor William A.,
    18-19
alcohol cravings, 148
allergies, 121, 131, 147, 170
alphanon, 169
aluminum, 8-9, 110, 114, 134, 136-137
aluminum toxicity, 98
Alzheimer's disease, 79, 111, 134, 136,
    177
amino acids, 34
amnesia, 171
anemia, 121, 155
angina, 122
anion, 16-17
anorexia, 121
antibiotic-resistant genes, 54
antimony, 106

anxiety, 121, 127
apoptosis, 80, 116, 143
appendicitis, 131, 135
arginine, 97, 115, 128, 144, 145, 149
argon, 128
arsenic, 117-118
arteriosclerosis, 120, 126
arthritis, 121, 131, 146, 155
asparagine, 99, 100, 132, 154, 166
aspartame, 7
aspirin, 137
asthma, 121, 122, 139, 161
athenon, 166
atomic energy, 152
atomic fallout, 35
awkwardness, 104

back spasms, 125
backaches, 128
bacteria, 54, 58
Banik, Dr. Allen E., 18
barium, 97-98
barnordon, 165
Beauchamp, Antoine, 3-4
bebegen, 154
beet, red, 80-81
beet, sugar, 46-47
behavioral problems, 148
benzene, 79

berylliosis, 147
beryllium, 147
betaanon, 163
Bifidobacterium bifidum, 110
Bifidobacterium longum, 110
bindweed, 3
blackstrap molasses, 120
blackton, 170
blindness, 170
body odor, 122
body weight, excess, 120
boils, 143
bone cells, 111
bone density loss, 133
bone metabolism, 121
bone softening, 126
boron, 62, 146, 181
boston, 170
brain softening, 133
brittle nails, 121
bromine, 114
bronchitis, 158
Brookside Laboratories, 19-20
brucellosis, 2
Brucella bacterium, 290-292
bursitis, 163
buzzeon, 158

caffeine addiction, 102
Calabar bean, 24
calcium, xv, 21, 125-126, 138
calcium and magnesium in urine, 146
calcium metabolism, 123
cancer, 3, 55, 70, 99, 107, 116, 122, 144
carbogenn, 156
carbon, 27, 145
cardiac insufficiency, 122
cardiovascular disease, 131
carpal tunnel syndrome, 121
catarrh, 126, 168
cation, 16-17
cation exchange capacity (CEC), 17
cell osmosis, 99
cellular damage, 37
cervical 1 bone, 171
cervical 2 bone, 170
cervical 2 disc, 170
cervical 3 bone, 169
cervical 3 disc, 168

cervical 4 bone, 168
cervical 4 disc, 167
cervical 5 bone, 166
cervical 5 disc, 165
cervical 6 bone, 164
cervical 6 disc, 163
cervical 7 bone, 163
cervical 7 disc, 162
cesium, 99
chest pains, 160
childlike behavior, 104
chlorine, 129
chlorophyll, 179
cholesterol, 120, 127, 131
chromium, 120
chromosomes, 37
chronic tiredness, 145, 171
Chronic Wasting Disease, 120
cigarette smoke, 105
circulatory problems, 131
cirrhosis, 122
cobalt, 93-94, 119-121
coccyx 1 bone, 105
coccyx 1 disc, 102
coccyx 2 bone, 100
coccyx 2 disc, 99
coccyx 3 bone, 97
coccyx 3 disc, 95
coccyx 4 bone, 93
colas, 132
cold feet, 126
colds, 163
colitis, 139
colorectal cancers, 115
confusion, 121
congestion, 158
constipation, 121, 139
convulsions, 121
copper, 121
cotton, 48
cough, 161
cracking joints, 121, 131
cramps, 126, 131, 135, 139
cretinism, 102, 104
Crohn's disease, 122
crossed eyes, 170
croup, 164
cysteine, 117, 147

DDT, 25, 29
deafness, 170
delphanon, 164
deodorant, aluminum-based, 136
depression, 120, 121, 122, 134, 139, 148
deuterium, 151
diabetes, 120, 122, 131, 151
diarrhea, 139
difficult breathing, 131, 135, 161
digestive disorders, 126
diuretics, 138, 180
dizziness, 121, 171
DNA, 36, 95
drooling, 104
dysentery, 139
dyspepsia, 153

earaches, 170
eczema, 143, 169
Electron Valence of Mineral, 92
electron valences, xii, 75
elements, 26
energy, lack of, 159
enzymes, 36, 46, 67
erneston, 168
erysipelas, 170
ethlogen, 155
eye matter, 103
eye troubles, 170
eyelids twitching, 125
eykaon, 167

Fagan, John, 44-45
Fagan, John, interview, 45-52
fainting, 139
fainting spells, 170
fatigue, 121, 126, 133, 135, 146
feet cramps, 125
Fenzau, C.J., 21
fevers, 155
fibrocystic tumor, 102
flabby skin, 104
FlavrSavr, 47
fluoridation, xiii-xiv
fluoride, xi, xiii
fluorine, xv, 142
folic acid, 1
food coloring, 136

fragile bone, 121
free radicals, 70

gall bladder conditions, 156
gammanon, 156
gas pain, 141
gastritis, 151
gene therapy, 55
genetic alteration, 52
genetic engineering, 46
genetic information, 45-46
genetic surgery, 46
genetically modified organisms (GMOs), 5
genetically modified potatoes, 56-57
germanium, 122
glucose oxidation, 120
glutamate, 157
glutamine, 102, 167
glycine, 129, 143, 161, 171
GM food, 56
goiter, 104, 163
golden rice, 58-59
gout, 121, 134
growth failure, 139

hair, falling, 134
hair loss, 122
hair, white, 121
halanon, 151
Hale, Stephen, 12
hard of hearing, 168
hardening of the arteries, 145
hay fever, 168
H-bomb, 34-35
head colds, 171
headaches, 125, 171
"Healthy Hunzas: A Climax Crop, The," 18
heart, 180, 181
heart conditions, 160
heart palpitations, 125
heartburn, 129, 153
helenine, 157
helionon, 150
helium, 149
hemorrhaging, 126
hemorrhoids, 106
hernia, 121, 139

heroin, 106
hiccoughs, 149
high blood pressure, 171
histidine, 148, 169
Hitler, xvi
hives, 147
Ho, Mae-Wan, 52
Ho, Mae-Wan, interview, 54-56
hoarseness, 166
homocystein, 112
human spine, 74
hydrocarbons, 26-27, 29
hydrogen, 153
hydroxyl group, xvi
hyperinsulinemia, 131
hypertension, 122, 123, 127
hyperthyroidism, 120, 121
hypoglycemia, 120, 131
hypotension, 122, 127
hypothyroidism, 120, 121

I Ching, 173
immune system, 116
immune system, compromised, 99
impatience, 121
impotency, 148
impulsiveness, 131
inability to heal, 134
indigestion, 153
infant mortality, 131
infections, 122
infertility, 121, 122, 131
inflammatory reactions, 116
influenza, 158
Ingenhousz, Jan, 13
initiation codon, 69
innate intelligence, 78
insomnia, 171
insulin, 120
iodine, 102-103, 127
ionization, 33-34
iron storage disease, 121
iron, 121
irritability 121
isoleucine, 113, 136, 160
itching, 106

jamearnon, 168
jaundice, 156

junk DNA, 63, 95

kidney dialysis, 62
kidney function, 140
kidney stones, 125
kidney troubles, 145
kidneys, 181
killer cells, 116
krypton, 113
Kuck, E.R., 19-20

lanthanum, 5, 62-63, 95
laryngitis, 166
leg cramps, 125, 126
leucine, 106, 119, 125, 140, 141, 158
leukemia, 117-118, 122
libido, loss of, 121
ligament weakness, 134
lithium, 148
liver, 156
liver cirrhosis, 121
liver conditions, 155
living soil, 16
Location of Spinal Segments, 91
Lou Gehrig's disease, 177
low blood pressure, 155
low body temperature, 135
low energy levels, 127
lower resistance, 149
lumbago, 128
lumbar 1 bone, 138
lumbar 1 disc, 136
lumbar 2 bone, 134
lumbar 2 disc, 132
lumbar 3 bone, 130
lumbar 3 disc, 129
lumbar 4 bone, 128
lumbar 4 disc, 127
lumbar 5 bone, 125
lumbar 5 disc, 123
luminon, 152
lunchmeats, 105, 144
lung, 115
lung cancer, 178
lutetium, 93-94
lymph system, 179
lysine, 156, 170
magnesium, 21, 125-126, 138-139,
    179-180

magnetic energy, 113
male fertility, 116
malnutrition, 39
mandatory valence, 75
manganese, 120-121
manic depression, 148
marconium, 162
Mendeleyev, Dmitri, 14, 26, 77
mental conditions, 171
mental confusion, 121
mental illness, 127
messenger RNA, 90
metabolism of fats, 103
methionine, 69-70, 112
migraine headaches, 171
migraines, menstrual, 139
milk, 41
milliequivalents (ME), 17
Monsanto, 43
Mosca, Dr. Americo, 33-34
mosquitoes, 292
motor function, decreased, 146
multiple sclerosis, 109
muscle cramps, 131
muscular weakness, 139
mutagenic, xvi
myasthenia gravis, 119
mycoplasm, 290-292

neon, 141
nephritis, 145
nerve damage, 121
nerve sensitivity, 134
nervous breakdowns, 171
nervous stomach, 134, 153
nervousness, 104, 127, 171
neuralgia, 122, 133, 139, 169
neuritis, 169
neutrino, 156
nicotine, 179
nightmares, 121
nitrogen, 22, 144
noble gas, 100
noise sensitivity, 133
NPK, 16, 39
numb fingers, 104
Number of Times in DNA, 91
numbness, 133

obesity, 122, 131
oil industry, 15
Olree Biological Periodic Chart,
    84-85
organ calcification, 139
organic, 39
organophosphates, 23
osteoblasts, 111
osteoporosis, 146, 180
ovarian cyst, 102
over-acidity, 127
oxygen, 143

pain at end of spine, 106
pain in lower arms and hands, 161
pain in upper arm, 164
paranoia, 122, 133
parasites, 121
Parents of Fluoride Poisoned
    Children, 142
Parkinson's syndrome, 107, 114, 176-
    177
Pasteur, Louis, 3
Paul Connett Fluoride Action
    Network, 142
penrynium, 161
peppermint plant, 12
peripheral neuropathy, 120
pernicious anemia, 121
pH, 21
phenylalanine, 95, 155
phosphoric acid, 132, 138
phosphorus, xv, 132-133
photosynthesis, 13
physostigmine, 23
piles, 106
pimples, 143, 169
pine needles, 117
pleurisy, 158
PMS, 122
pneumonia, 158
poisons, 28
poor circulation, 155
poor circulation in legs, 126
potassium, 127
prednisone, 5, 6
pregnancy, 117
Priestley, Joseph, 13
probiotics, 7-8, 109-110

processed foods, 136
proline, 93, 123, 134, 168
promoter, 55
prostate cancer, 115
prostate gland, 120
protium, 152
Prozac, xiii
pruritus, 106
Pusztai, Arpad, 56
pyelitis, 145
pyridostigmine, 23

quarks, 152
quinsy, 166
quinton, 160

radiation, 37, 177, 181
radioactive, 177
radiomimetic, 36
recombination, 54, 55
reduced oxygenation, 127
restlessness, 127
rheumatism, 141
rhodium, 107
rickets, 126
RNA, 64
romanon, 163
rubidium, 112
ruptured disc, 121
ruptures, 139
Russell Number, 90
Russell, Walter, 74-75
Russell, Walter, biographical overview, 76-77
Russian knotweed, 3

sacral 1 bone, 119
sacral 1 disc, 117
sacral 2 bone, 115
sacral 2 disc, 114
sacral 3 bone, 113
sacral 3 disc, 112
sacral 4 bone, 111
sacral 4 disc, 108
sacral 5 bone, 107
sacral 5 disc, 106
sacro-iliac conditions, 113
scandium, 108, 123

schizophrenia, 121
Schroeder, M.D., Henry A., 26
sciatic, 128
selenium, 9, 69-70, 97-98, 115-116, 178
serine, 107, 114, 146, 152, 156, 159
sexual dysfunction, 134
shingles, 156
shortness of breath, 161
short-term memory, decreased, 146
silica, 134
silicon, 134
sinus trouble, 170
skin disorders, 127
sleep, loss of 125
sleepiness, 139
sleeping sickness, 171
slow growth, 131
slow oxidation, 133
sodium, 140
sodium fluoride, xvi-xvii, xviii
softening of brain tissue, 122
soil, 22
soil audit, 18
somites, 74, 91
sore throat, 166
soybeans, 50-51
spinal curvatures, 113
spleen, 113
Splenda, 9, 119-120
St. Vitus dance, 171
Standard Genetic Chart (SGC), 65, 66-67, 68-69
sterility, 141
stiff muscles, 139
stiff neck, 164
stitches, 104
stomach, 170
stomach acid, excess, 131
STOP, 108, 130, 153
strontium, 111
stunted growth, 121
sulfur, 130-131
suppressor cell activity, increased, 148
sweating, 126
swelling joints, 135
swollen ankles, 126

Teflon, 142
tellurium, 105, 274
tender spine, 134
thoracic 1 bone, 161
thoracic 1 disc, 160
thoracic 2 bone, 160
thoracic 2 disc, 159
thoracic 3 bone, 158
thoracic 3 disc, 157
thoracic 4 bone, 156
thoracic 4 disc, 156
thoracic 5 bone, 155
thoracic 5 disc, 154
thoracic 6 bone, 153
thoracic 6 disc, 152
thoracic 7 bone, 151
thoracic 7 disc, 150
thoracic 8 bone, 149
thoracic 8 disc, 148
thoracic 9 bone, 147
thoracic 9 disc, 146
thoracic 10 bone, 145
thoracic 10 disc, 144
thoracic 11 bone, 143
thoracic 11 disc, 142
thoracic 12 bone, 141
thoracic 12 disc, 140
Three Codon Sequence, 90
threonine, 127, 142, 160, 163
thymus, 9, 119-120
thyroid, 150, 162, 163
thyroid disorders, 122
tobacco, 179
tonsillitis, 164
toxic rescue chemistry, 40
toxicity, 178
tracion, 159
transfer of genes, 41

transgenetic, 53
triglycerides, 127, 131
tritium, 150
tryptophan, 49-50, 162
tumor-suppressing gene (p53), 53, 178
tumor-suppressing proteins (p53), 70, 105, 115
turmeric, 79, 111
tyrosine, 150, 170

ulcers, 151
urination, painful and frequent, 128

valine, 151, 163, 165, 168
van Helmont, Jan Baptista, 11-12
vanadium, 120
varicose veins, 131, 135
vertigo, 139, 171
vinton, 160
viruses, 54, 55, 107, 109
vitamin B-12, 93-94
vitamin D, 108
vitamin D metabolism, 123
weak ankles and arches, 126
weakness, 126
whooping cough, 164
www.bruha.com/pfpc, 142
www.eurekalert.com, 10
www.kazusa.org/codon/, 101
www.pubmed.com, 10

xenon, 100

yttrium, 8, 62, 108, 109, 176

zinc, 121-122

Also from Acres U.S.A.

Cancer, Nutrition & Healing (Video)
BY JERRY BRUNETTI

 In this remarkable video presentation, Jerry shares the priceless lessons and wisdom gained through his successful struggle with an aggressive form of lymphoma. You'll never look at cancer — or cancer treatments — in quite the same way after viewing Jerry Brunetti's step-by-step plan for restoring health using fresh foods and natural, holistic, herbal treatments. You will learn about: strengthening immunity; holistic treatment protocols; health-boosting recipes; supplements and detoxification; supplemental conventional therapies; foods to eat; foods to avoid; and much more! *DVD, 85 min. ISBN 0-911311-81-5*

The Non-Toxic Farming Handbook
BY PHILIP A. WHEELER, PH.D. & RONALD B. WARD

 In this readable, easy-to-understand handbook the authors successfully integrate the diverse techniques and technologies of classical organic farming, Albrecht-style soil fertility balancing, Reams-method soil and plant testing and analysis, and other alternative technologies applicable to commercial-scale agriculture. By understanding all of the available non-toxic tools and when they are effective, you will be able to react to your specific situation and growing conditions. Covers fertility inputs, in-the-field testing, foliar feeding, and more. The result of a lifetime of eco-consulting. *Softcover, 236 pages. ISBN 978-0-911311-56-3*

Weeds: Control Without Poisons
BY CHARLES WALTERS

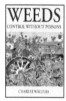 For a thorough understanding of the conditions that produce certain weeds, you simply can't find a better source than this one — certainly not one as entertaining, as full of anecdotes and homespun common sense. It contains a lifetime of collected wisdom that teaches us how to understand and thereby control the growth of countless weed species, as well as why there is an absolute necessity for a more holistic, eco-centered perspective in agriculture today. Contains specifics on a hundred weeds, why they grow, what soil conditions spur them on or stop them, what they say about your soil, and how to control them without the obscene presence of poisons, all cross-referenced by scientific and various common names, and a new pictorial glossary. *Softcover, 352 pages. ISBN 978-0-911311-58-7*

To order call 1-800-355-5313
or order online at www.acresusa.com

Dung Beetles

BY CHARLES WALTERS

Dung beetles have always been nature's greatest recyclers — in a way, they were the first organic farmers. They were also the first casualties of industrial farming. As farmers rediscover the many benefits of grass-based livestock production, dung beetles have a solid shot at reestablishing their rightful place on the farm and ranch. Charles Walters digs deep into modern science and ancient history, traditional folklore and the best practical advice to resurrect the lowly dung beetle, exposing farmers and ranchers — and anyone with a desire to work more closely with nature — to this amazing creature. Meet the world's leading scientists and farmer/researchers who have dedicated years to understanding the roles, actions and value of dung beetles in bringing a grazing operation into compliance with nature's laws, and then harvest the profits. Anyone interested in organic forms of farming will be enchanted by the intriguing tale of the dung beetle. *Softcover, 240 pages. ISBN 978-1-601730-05-3*

Foundations of Natural Farming

BY HAROLD WILLIS, PH.D.

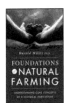

Subtitled *Understanding Core Concepts of Ecological Agriculture.* Join longtime ecological farming author/researcher Harold Willis as he explains the foundation concepts of natural farming and issues the call for cleaner forms of food and fiber production. In this single volume, the author details the interconnections between soil chemistry, microbial life, plants and livestock. He discusses the current problems in agriculture and suggests how lessons from nature provide the roadmap to efficiency, effectiveness and profitability. This book does not stop at providing recipes of what farmers need to do to farm better, but also passes along an understanding of the why of ecological agriculture. This book is certain to become a classic of clean farming and one of the most heavily bookmarked volumes on a farmer's shelf. *Softcover, 384 pages. ISBN 978-1-601730-07-7*

Eco-Farm: An Acres U.S.A. Primer

BY CHARLES WALTERS

In this book, eco-agriculture is explained — from the tiniest molecular building blocks to managing the soil — in terminology that not only makes the subject easy to learn, but vibrantly alive. Sections on NP&K, cation exchange capacity, composting, Brix, soil life, and more! *Eco-Farm* truly delivers a complete education in soils, crops, and weed and insect control. This should be the first book read by everyone beginning in eco-agriculture . . . and the most shop-worn book on the shelf of the most experienced. *Softcover, 476 pages. ISBN 978-0-911311-74-7*

Acres U.S.A. — books are just the beginning!

Farmers and gardeners around the world are learning to grow bountiful crops profitably—without risking their own health and destroying the fertility of the soil. *Acres U.S.A.* can show you how. If you want to be on the cutting edge of organic and sustainable growing technologies, techniques, markets, news, analysis and trends, look to *Acres U.S.A.* For more than 40 years, we've been the independent voice for eco-agriculture. Each monthly issue is packed with practical, hands-on information you can put to work on your farm, bringing solutions to your most pressing problems. Get the advice consultants charge thousands for . . .

- Fertility management
- Non-chemical weed & insect control
- Specialty crops & marketing
- Grazing, composting, natural veterinary care
- Soil's link to human & animal health

CPSIA information can be obtained
at www.ICGtesting.com
Printed in the USA
BVHW030233071222
653538BV00003B/7